ESSEX WINDMILLS, MILLERS AND MILLWRIGHTS

Volume Five

The Publishers of this large work wish to state that it has now been found necessary to issue it in *five* volumes, in order to make them more equal in size and to accommodate extra information which has come to hand during the progress of publication.

ESSEX WINDMILLS, MILLERS AND MILLWRIGHTS

BY KENNETH G. FARRIES

In five volumes:

The reader should note that although this work on Essex windmills and their operators has been divided into several volumes for convenience of handling, it forms an integrated whole, and the illustrative material is not evenly distributed between the volumes. Thus over 180 of the 300 or so photographs are to be found in Volumes III, IV and V in association with the gazetteer of individual mill histories under parishes, while the majority of the drawings illustrating mill structures and working parts are in Volume II. Certain mills, as for instance Moreton post mill, are described historically in one volume and technically in another; it is hoped that the arrangement adopted will be equally acceptable to the casual reader and to the specialist.

The index to the whole work appears in Vol. V, which also includes Addenda to *Windmills of Surrey and Inner London*, of which Kenneth G. Farries was co-author.

221a *Terling Mill, 1938. the last active windmill in Essex: stopped working by wind c 1949. Converted into a residence*

ESSEX WINDMILLS MILLERS & MILLWRIGHTS

VOLUME FIVE

A Review by Parishes, S-Z

Kenneth G. Farries

*

CHARLES SKILTON LTD
Publishers

© The Executors of
Kenneth G. Farries 1988

Made and printed in
Great Britain by
Anchor Press Ltd,
Tiptree, Essex

Published by
CHARLES SKILTON LTD
Banwell Castle
Weston-super-Mare
Avon

ISBN 0284 98821 9

CONTENTS

[Contd.

LIST OF ILLUSTRATIONS

ACKNOWLEDGEMENTS

Because of the death of the Author, it has not been possible to provide such comprehensive acknowledgements as Kenneth Farries would undoubtedly have liked, and any omissions are regretted. However, from manuscript jottings it is evident that he would have wished to thank the following:

Mr P. R. Gifford, until 1984 Librarian, Local Studies, Colchester, for much help of a general nature.

Dr F. G. Emmison, who contributed many items to the Addenda of this Volume, as has Mr Adrian Corder-Birch. (Dr Emmison was proposing Mr Farries' election to Fellowship of the Society of Antiquaries and to the Royal Historical Society when the Author's passing supervened.)

The Appendix H list of Essex watermill sites, an important ancillary to this book, was prepared by Mr R. Hawksley after considerable research.

Miss J. M. Winmill contributed notes on Henham windmill.

The Harwich Town Council kindly gave permission to reproduce the photograph, taken by the late Mr Michael Organ, of the oil painting in the Guildhall (see Vol. III, p. 124).

The Publisher would like to thank Mr Roland W. Smith, who has contributed so many exceptional line drawings to the set, for his prompt help, in conjunction with Mr Farries' family, in locating the remaining material prepared for this Volume by the Author.

Grateful acknowledgement is also given to Mr Martin Watts for contributing the explanatory drawings which do so much to enhance the Glossary. In preparing this invaluable Glossary Mr Farries obviously had the help of a number of experts, which he would have wished publicly to have acknowledged, in particular that of Mr Vincent Pargeter, whose preliminary sketches were of much assistance.

At the proof stage the advice of Mr J. Kenneth Major was enlisted, and his suggestions regarding various text entries of the Glossary were appreciatively adopted.

Mrs Barton McGuire of New Mills, Maryland, provided the Author with a copy of her own Glossary of American milling terms, which he was glad to have the opportunity of comparing.

Mr E. F. Goatcher was already assisting in proof checking during the last months of Mr Farries' life, and he continued with this work on Volume 5 with an assiduity and promptness for which the Publisher is most grateful. Moreover, he very kindly volunteered to complete the Index on which the Author had been working and which was already prepared for the first four Volumes. Without Mr Goatcher's work the final Volume would have been much delayed.

Mr Hawksley's indefatigable help has been of much general assistance: he has also examined the proofs and added widely to the Addenda.

ACKNOWLEDGEMENT OF DRAWINGS

All maps and drawings in this volume were made by Mr Roland W. Smith, of Woodham Ferrers, except for those in the Illustrated Glossary which were made by Mr Martin Watts, of Crowdy Mill, Harbertonford, Devon.

Appreciation is expressed to the following for kind permission to reproduce the photographs in this volume.

SOURCE	PHOTOGRAPH NUMBER
Boston Public Library, U.S.A.	267
Essex Record Office	234, 261
National Buildings Record	227
The Passmore Edwards Museum, Newham	225, 226, 239, 249, 255, 257
Southend Reference Library	238. Also from the Dr Turner Collection: 231, 258, 259
Suffolk Record Office, Ipswich (Cowell Collection, Ref. K400/CC1)	224
Saffron Walden Museum	250
Waltham Abbey Historical Society	254
Walton-on-the-Naze Record Office	256
Mr and Mrs Ambrose, Writtle	265
Sir Edmund C. Bacon, Bt., K.G., K.B.E., T.D., Raveningham, Norfolk (The Sir Hickman Bacon Collection)	229
The late Mr C. Blondel	262
Mr Peter Came, Danbury	246b
The late Rev. F. G. Clarke	233
Mr C. H. Cole, West Tilbury	240
Miss L. M. Cooper, Great Totham	241
Capt. A. J. Coulthard, Piddletrenthide, Dorset	242, 263
The late Mr Stanley Freese	245a, 246a
Mr H. H. Frost, Tolleshunt Major	244
Mrs P. S. Harris, Thorpe-le-Soken	237a
Mr L. D. Jarvis, Stock	232a
Mrs Caroline Mackly, Wickhambrook	268
Mr Bob Malster, Ipswich	228
The late Mr T. J. Mason	252a
Mr Donald W. Muggeridge, San Raphael, California	221a, 222 (Photo: Mr Francis), 230a, 235 (Photo: J. Belsham), 236, 237b, 251 (Photo: James Wright)
Mr B. J. Palmer, Wenden Lofts	260
Mr F. J. Poulton, Great Sampford	223a
Mr Roland W. Smith, Woodham Ferrers	223b, 243, 269
Mr Alan Spencer Green, Wimbish	264
Mr W. E. Springett, Heybridge	247
Mr H. C. Stacey, Saffron Walden	252b (Photo: Adams Coll.)
Miscellaneous (Engravings, picture postcards, etc.)	248
From the Author	223, 230b, 232b, 245b, 253

LIST OF ABBREVIATIONS

Antiq. & Hist. Soc.	Antiquarian and Historical Society	P.R.O.	Public Record Office
B.M.	British Museum, now nominally British Library	R.E. Pol. No.	Royal Exchange Assurance Policy Number
Cal.	Calendar	R.L.	Reference Library
Cambs. Chron.	*Cambridge Chronicle*	S.P.A.B.	Society for the Protection of Ancient Buildings (Windmill and Watermill Section)
C.C.	*Chelmsford Chronicle*		
E.A.T.	*Essex Archaeological Transactions*		
E.C.	*Essex Countryside*	*Suff. Chron.*	*Suffolk Chronicle*
E.R.	*Essex Review*	Sun Pol. No.	Sun Insurance Company Policy Number
E.R.O.	Essex Record Office		
E.S. or E.C.S.	*Essex (County) Standard*	Trans.	Transactions
E.W.N.	*Essex Weekly News*	V.C.H.	*Victoria County History*
I.J.	*Ipswich Journal*	□	This symbol occurs in the parish headings after the national grid references of mills which are illustrated, and is followed by a summary of location. e.g. (□ 125a,b; I 48; II 100) indicates that Plates 125a and 125b are in the present Volume, others being No. 48 in Volume I and No. 100 in Volume II.
Int. Symp.	International Symposium		
K. & E.M.	*Kent and Essex Mercury*		
Lond. Gaz.	*London Gazette*		
MS	Manuscript		
n.d.	Not dated		
O.S.	Ordnance Survey		
P.O.	Post Office		

EXPLANATORY NOTES

Cartographers and map dates

The general policy has been to quote the year of publication in brackets after the names of the cartographers, e.g. Chapman and André (1777), but where greater precision in establishing the existence of a windmill was required, the survey date has been given, e.g. Greenwood (surv. 1824). Invariably for Warburton, Bland and Smyth (c1724) the publication date is given, the survey dates being uncertain, but said to have commenced with 1721. For O.S. maps after 1860, the survey dates are quoted, e.g. revised 2nd O.S. 1in. (1893), not prefaced by 'surv.'. Apparent discrepancies in dates relating to a particular map issue, e.g. of the first O.S. 6in., occur as a result of a wide spread of survey dates (1862-77 in this case). C. & J. Greenwood are abbreviated to Greenwood and are accorded a singular pronoun when referred to; other partnerships, however long, e.g. Warburton, Bland and Smyth, are retained in full.

Floors in tower-type mills

The English convention has been used: the first floor is understood to mean the first floor above the ground floor. Thus, if the stones are stated to be on the second floor, it is apparent that there are two floors below, including the ground. A five-floored mill would be one with a ground floor and four others.

Iron windpumps or wind engines

No attempt has been made to give a census of these machines or to describe their characteristics; bare references will be found under Braintree and Bocking (Other Mills) and under East Tilbury.

Millers' names and dates

For each mill a representative millers' list is given where possible. John Smith (1872, 86) indicates that a John Smith was operating the mill in the two stated years and that the information is taken from trade directories of those dates. While the longest known time span would be quoted, the years given may not have been the first or last of Smith's occupation; neither is it to be assumed that the same John Smith was present throughout. Known continuous occupation is indicated by John Smith (1872-86). Very frequently a son bearing the same name succeeded his father.

Mills of unknown type

The majority of mills described as of unknown type under parish headings must have been post mills. Some are clearly drawn as such on MS maps e.g. Asheldham (1711) and Tilty (1730), at dates when other forms of windmill in Essex were very rare, but in view of known misrepresentations described under The Cartographic Record in Volume I, reliance has not been placed on map symbols alone.

National Grid References

These are not intended to pin-point the mill sites, but to locate them within a unit square of side 1 hectometre (109½ yards approximately). The margin of error from mill site to grid intersection should not exceed 0.7hm or about 75 yards (maxima along bearings at 45° with the main cardinal points).

'Newly-erected'

In old sale notices this description could be used in excess of twenty years after the actual date of building.

Parish headings and boundary changes

Mills have been listed under the parishes in which they contemporarily stood, and therefore basically as demarcated in the period 1800-75. Thus Billericay mills are described under Great Burstead, Tiptree mills under Tolleshunt Knights, and so forth. Occasionally, where expedient, two or more parishes have been taken in combination, e.g. Layer-de-la-Haye and West Mersea, in which the same mill operated, being moved from one to the other. In cases where a mill site now lies in a newly constituted parish, e.g. Eight Ash Green (Fordham windmill), the reader is referred in the Index from the new to the old name and hence to the text headed by the latter. Little Chishill and parts of Kedington and Hadstock, formerly in Essex, are included, also part of Great Chesterford formerly in Ickleton, Cambridgeshire, now in Essex.

Roundhouses

This term was and is loosely used to indicate an enclosure around a post-mill substructure of whatever shape or material. But more confusing, in former usage, was its application to smock and even tower mill bases or ground floors (e.g. Rainsford smock mill, Chelmsford, 1813; Great Dunmow tower mill, 1887). It was also used, it would appear, in reference to lean-to constructions against mill bases (Stansted tower mill, mid-19th century).

Tower-Type Mills

This description is used in the text for smock and tower mills taken together. The reader should note that the current distinction between smock mills as those with a fixed wooden frame over a brick or stone base, and tower mills as built to the curb with brick or stone, was not clearly drawn until comparatively recently. Smock mills were commonly described as tower mills, and occasionally, mainly before 1800, tower mills were named smock mills.

Trade Directory Dates

Kelly's directories providing newly acquired or revised data regarding Essex millers and millwrights appeared in 1845, 1850, 1855, 1859, 1862, 1866, 1870, 1874, 1878, 1882, 1886, 1890, 1894, 1898, 1902, 1906, 1908, 1910, 1912, 1914, 1917, 1922, 1926, 1929, 1933, 1937.

Other dates exist, but were mainly reprints. In attempting to fix critical dates such as the last year in which a positive milling entry was made, the year 1898 would, for instance, be quoted in the text below in preference to 1899, when a reprint was published.

Up to and including 1878 no indication of power in use was given; in 1882 the use of steam or water was noted, but without clarification of the position with respect to wind. In 1886 and after, steam, water and wind are all indicated, often appearing in combination, such as steam and wind at Great Baddow (Galleywood Common) in 1908.

Weights and Measures: Use of Units

The English units have been retained, for they were the measures of the period described, and dimensions are frequently given in sale notices in reference to post-mill body sizes, lengths of sails, diameters of millstones, and so forth. Important equivalents are given in Volume II, Appendix E.

The mill distribution maps by Hundred groupings

These six maps, divided equally between Volumes III and IV, are intended to offer a quick reference to the numbers and types of windmills known to have stood in the parishes after 1700. The totals of the various mill types are summarised — for the area shown — in a bar graph. The watermills are given their approximate location, but no attempt is made to position the windmills on their sites; for close indications of site the reader should refer to the parish headings. In cases where more than one windmill occupied the same site in succession, the last, only, is represented, but where a windmill was moved to a second site, it is shown by an additional symbol if set up in another parish. One may also note that where a map is bounded by a river, a true picture of the density of watermills is to be had only by studying in conjunction the adjoining map area.

Late Additions to the Draft

Important information acquired too late for full assimilation before publication is included in the Addenda in Volume V, or, if possible, in the relevant parish section, the E.R.O. or other references being then quoted in the text. The reader's attention is drawn to the absence of belatedly identified post-1700 windmills from the Hundreds maps and — in one case at least (West Bergholt) — from lists in Volume I where they might have been expected to appear. The number of such additional mills is unlikely to exceed five by the time of completed publication of all five volumes.

KENNETH G. FARRIES AT FROST'S MILL, HALSTEAD

KENNETH GEORGE FARRIES

Photo Phelps & Marchant, Reigate, 1971

AS WORK on this fifth and last volume of *Essex Windmills* was in its final stages, my father, Kenneth Farries, suffered a stroke which was to place him in West Park Hospital, Epsom, where he ended his days.

A quiet, good humoured man of few well-chosen words, he shared a passion for windmills with a love of classical music. He enjoyed a very happy family life and was endeared to his home and garden at Kingswood, Surrey.

My father was born in Southsea, Hampshire, on November 15th, 1916, but when he was four years old his parents moved to Upminster, Essex, and later bought a house backing on to the local windmill from which his interest in windmills developed.

Throughout the 1930s he cycled along the quiet country lanes of Essex photographing windmills and talking to old inhabitants in the villages he visited. When he finally came to write his book he found all this early research invaluable.

He was educated at the Royal Liberty School, Romford, and later at Queen Mary College, University of London, where he was introduced to the delights of the academic life. He started his teaching career at

Pettits Lane School, Romford, and was there when the second world war started.

At first schoolmasters were exempted from military service but later he was called up into the Royal Corps of Signals and served most of his army career abroad, including a three and a half year stint in the Sahara Desert sleeping in the back of a lorry! Typically, my father used any spare time in the army to visit nearby towns and beauty spots, thus enhancing his geographical knowledge, or in studying a number of languages, for he discovered linguistic skills in French, German and Russian.

On demobilisation he returned to Pettits Lane School and was there for several years until in 1950 he was offered a post at Reigate Grammar School in the Geography Department. In the same year he married my mother and set up home in Surrey — firstly in Hooley and for the last twenty years of his life in Kingswood.

During his time at Reigate Grammar School he wrote *Windmills of Surrey and Inner London* in collaboration with the late Martin T. Mason and started his monumental work on *Essex Windmills, Millers and Millwrights.* He retired in 1980 after being head of the Geography Department for ten years and spent his retirement finishing his book and looking after his house and garden.

He leaves behind a widow, two children and four grand-children and countless friends from all walks of life who will all miss him sadly but remember him dearly.

NICHOLAS FARRIES

KENNETH FARRIES' first major foray into the field of windmill research occupied the years 1952-1959, when he collaborated with Martin T. Mason on studies which were to become *The Windmills of Surrey and Inner London*, published by Charles Skilton Ltd in 1966, — a book which set new standards of excellence, both for the quality of the historical research and the attention to detail lavished on every aspect of its production. Rex Wailes described it as "a book that cannot be faulted".

It was early in 1970 that Ken was persuaded to research and write the history of Essex windmills. At that time he was senior geography master at Reigate Grammar School. It was fortunate that the school holidays provided the opportunity for intensive archive research. In this, as in everything, he was exceedingly hard working and thorough. He read everything that might provide a scrap of information and made copious notes that occupied files spanning 6 ft. of shelves in his study. Local enquiries and records of visits to over 300 windmill sites all had to be collated and cross-referenced before each mill history could be written. It was a monumental task, and all done to the highest possible standards, a fact confirmed by the glowing reviews that followed the publication of each of the first four Volumes. It is particularly sad that Ken died before the publication of the fifth and final Volume of his encyclopaedic work.

Kenneth Farries was unquestionably the finest historian to write about windmills. He combined the highest standards of scholarship with an intense interest in the practical problems that faced the millers and millwrights of yesteryear, a combination of talents that made his books outstanding.

Ken was an extremely courteous and good humoured man, who also expressed his enthusiasm for windmills through friendship. He was an active member of the Wind and Watermill Section of The Society for the Protection of Ancient Buildings; also the International Molinological Society, and many others besides, including, of course, The Essex Mills Group. We are all much the poorer for his passing.

ROLAND W. SMITH

THIS IS doubtless the most remarkable book on windmills which will ever be published. A monument of patient research, skilful collation and able prose, it is packed with facts of diverse character from innumerable sources. Most of the compilation was undertaken during the Author's working life, and in the circumstances his industry was amazing.

It is a matter of great regret that Mr Farries was not able to oversee the final stages of the last Volume, though as ever his meticulous attention to detail enabled the Publisher's office to be in full control of the remaining production work. It was unfortunate that the typesetting firm which had so ably undertaken the first four Volumes was not able for arcane reasons to progress the fifth in the way which might have been expected, and this is why the Author was able to read the proofs himself of only the earlier part of this particular Volume.

It is most disappointing too that Kenneth Farries was thus not able to see the completion in printed form of his enormous work, but it was gratifying that the Wind and Watermill Section of The Society for the Protection of Ancient Buildings awarded him their coveted Certificate at a members' meeting in 1985 and Mr Farries, a most modest man, was clearly appreciative of this honour, which had not previously been given to an Author for his written work alone. It was shortly after the 1986 Spring meeting, which he attended, that Mr Farries was taken ill, and although he had the most devoted care of his wife and others he eventually died on August 18th 1986, the funeral being attended by about a hundred mourners from many areas of association. He was 69 years of age.

His interest in windmills and the book had been sustained during his period of illness, and he was kept in touch with progress, and saw proofs of the Glossary and of the accompanying illustrations.

As the Publisher of this work, with which I feel most privileged to be associated, and a great admirer of it, I had earlier drawn the attention of the University of Essex to the book, with the suggestion that an Honorary Degree be awarded to Mr Farries. In spite of support from others more prominent a dusty answer was received from the Vice-Chancellor. I was naïvely not aware that some newer Universities are politically notorious and sometimes seem to award Honorary Degrees less for academic or local research merit than for reasons which appear pleasing enough to the authorities. One can merely echo the withering cannonade of an influential Victorian Editor who remarked on the refusal of the Royal Academy to elect, as Member, James Duffield Harding, a great water-colourist and teacher: "Such a man would have reflected lustre on the Academy as great, if not greater, than the Academy could confer on him."

Finally, may I quote from a letter which Mr Farries wrote to a reviewer who criticised the decision to make the book into five Volumes instead of four, thereby adding to the cost of the set (indeed this last Volume is considerably larger than the others, certainly justifying the decision). This note sets out in the Author's own words our joint attitude to the publication.

> The interval between nominal completion of the work and publication is now a very lengthy one, and I have profited from the time lapse by adding more material as it became available — I hope to the enjoyment of eventual consumers. Mr Skilton has encouraged this activity, and — quite remarkably — has never asked me to prune or reduce the work in any way, despite the great mass of detail included. Where is there another publisher who would have acquiesced in this process, and where is there — where will there ever be? — another mill book of this degree of detail so free from commercial constraints? . . . Of course neither Mr Skilton nor I have had any money-making aim in producing these volumes. The driving force is devotion to mills — one expends time, labour, energy, cash, and one hopes for similar unstinting support from those also interested to make such a publication possible.

Persons engrossed in the history of windmills must be eternally grateful to Kenneth Farries for the enormous amount of time and money he expended in researching and writing this book, an even more extraordinary effort than the earlier work of which he was co-author, and which now fetches such a large sum in the second-hand bookshop. *Si monumentum requiris, circumspice* is Sir Christopher Wren's celebrated tribute in St Paul's Cathedral. It seems appropriate in these pages also.

CHARLES SKILTON, HON.R.W.S., F.S.A.(SCOT.)

Parishes, S-Z

St Osyth

(1) Post mill. Stood in the grounds of 'Colne View' about 100 yards behind the Flag inn. TM 116178

(2) Mill of unknown type. Stood west of the road leading to St Osyth Beach, probably on the rise opposite Brazier's Farm. Shown on the map of Andrews and Dury (1777). No further information. TM 128152

(1) FLAG WINDMILL

This, the Flag windmill, apparently stood already in 1760, when Walter Bevan was miller, later replaced by James Hart (1771-4)[1]. The mill was held in 1789 by Henry Cook, a bankrupt, together with a freehold quay on Flag Creek, off the Colne[2]. In the first decades of the 19th century it was occupied by the Mayhew family, who ran a bakery in Brightlingsea. In 1811 John Mayhew was tenant at the 'low and improvable' rent of £30 per annum[3]. The freehold post mill was built chiefly in oak, had a nearly new bricked roundhouse, two pairs of French stones, a flour mill and a 'clearing-off machine'. In 1818 John Mayhew's effects were auctioned owing to his bankruptcy, but other members of the family filled the breach. In 1823 Barnabas Mayhew was behind the spouts and tackle, and in 1826 was tenant to James Mayhew. In 1840 Mark Mayhew was owner-occuper[4].

The writer of the sale notice in 1811, capitulating subconsciously, perhaps, to the flag-fixation at this site, where Flag Mill on Flag Hill behind Flag Inn overlooked Flag Wharf and the marshes beyond Flag Creek, described the piggeries as paved with flag stone; there was none so naïve as to claim a flagging trade, but such appears to have been the case soon after mid century, when the mill was evidently in decline. The sick proprietor advertised the lease[5] in 1843 and secured H. Derby as miller, the ownership passing to Mrs Mayhew by 1847. From 1847-55 Archer and Grout, already at the tide mill, were in occupation[6], after which the windmill, probably derelict, was in the hands of the owner, F. H. Mayhew, and had disappeared from records by 1858.

The tide mill, using seven pairs of stones in 1858, was then in its prime. At the windmill site today, a solitary millstone lingers on.

NOTES

1 E.R.O. D/P 322/11/1 per R. Hawksley
2 *Lond. Gaz.* March 3-7, 1789, per H.E.S. Simmons; E.R.O. D/DB T1056
3 C.C. 22.2.1811
4 C.C. 3.7.1818 per G. W. Martin; E.R.O. land tax returns 1826; E.R.O. D/CT 305 A (1840)
5 E.S. 28.7.1843
6 E.R.O. D/P 322/4/1 per R. Hawksley

Bardfield Saling

Post mill. Stood at Crow's Green 700 yards south east of the church and immediately south of Mill House. TL 691260 (□ 222; I 36, 37)

THIS mill stood in rustic seclusion, making few and only tardy concessions to the innovators. Steam failed to erupt. The mill was built in 1756, when the lord of the manor of Great Bardfield, Jones Raymond, enclosed a parcel of waste and leased it for 99 years to Moses Matthew, miller, who 'did erect and sett' thereon a windmill[1]. Later, the Rev. B.E. Lampet, then lord, leased the mill to John Hicks, charging a fine of £30 on entry. George Hicks, farmer, of Saling, was disposing of the property in 1797[2]. In a sale notice dated 1823 a roundhouse was mentioned, above which the body was said to measure 16ft. by 10ft. 4in., its ultimate size; one therefore inclines to the view that the addition of a rear bay 3ft. 6in. deep, described by Donald Smith (1932) as occurring 'a hundred years ago', took place in fact in the early 1820s[3]. However, it is possible that a rear platform and porch were original features over the extremities of the sheers, so that a claim to a 16ft. length was always tenable. The sale notice makes reference to only one pair of 4ft. 8in. French stones, having regulating lighters; there were also a flour mill and sack tackle, and a dwelling house and bakery had been newly erected. The going gears of the mill were declared to be 'nearly new, on the most improved plan', breaking 3 loads of wheat per week. Possibly the replacement hollow iron windshaft mentioned by Smith and the iron tail wheel were already in position awaiting the upswing in trade needed to justify the expense of a second pair of stones.

From before 1850 until its last working day the mill had only one change of milling family. Directories return Henry Phillips, corn merchant and parish clerk (1848), Henry Phillips jun. (1874), Henry Phillips (1890, 94), followed by J. W. Francis (1898) and Francis and Sons (wind), (1914). Dr Turner records (c1920) the mill as one of the seven in Essex still working by wind, though at least twice that number were then so working. The shortage of orders in the 1920s brought the sails to a halt c1926, and the hopes of a return to active windmilling still cherished by the last miller ended with the breaking off of a whip and stock from the then surviving pair. The mill owed its prolonged active life in part to transplants from other mills; as Donald Smith entertainingly wrote:

It reminds one of the Irishman's gun, which was the same old gun, although it had had a new lock, a new stock and a new barrel. The automatic fantail and accompanying trolley and gear, mounted on the end of the ladder, was bought thirty-five years ago when the Sisted Post Mill [Cressing, east] was taken down. This tackle, which gears on to both trolley wheels, has affected the stability and balance of the mill. Formerly the ladder, with its iron-shod toes well in the ground, acted as a movable buttress, but now the iron wheels 'side slip' on the rail of York stone. The result is that the mill rocks more and has become 'tail sick' — that is to say, that, lacking the support of the stairs, its structure is inclined backwards. The patent sails were purchased from Mr G. Hasler, of Throws Mill, Little Dunmow, twenty years ago for £25... The stone nut came from the mill at Mill End Green at Great Easton.

The mill stood on through the second world war, slowly succumbing to erosive elements, though the substructure was remarkably sound until the end. With the arrival of a new broom in the guise of lord of the manor, and the menace of a now dangerous hulk shedding sail frames, timbers and stones where children played, the mill was felled and swept away after survey and confirmation of the prohibitive cost of restoration. The task was accomplished on 17th September, 1965, by demolition of the roundhouse and the removal of a brick pier by means of a hawser drawn from a heavy tractor. The main timbers were to be put to further use in restoration work.

222 Bardfield Saling: the mill at work. Undated

As first built, with all or most of the chief members in oak, the mill body would have measured only 12ft. 6in. in length inclusive of the main corner posts, and 9ft. 6in. wide overall. The prow was shallow, barely projecting 1ft. The box-like main frame was about 12ft. high, above which extended the roof rafting with little curvature. Taken from the centre of the crowntree the body was hung fore and aft in the ratio 10:13, with just sufficient room forward to have taken the 4ft. 8in. stones of 1823. As seen and checked in 1965, only the top side rails and sheers ran through the entire 15ft. 6in. length of the body; the latter were doubtless original, first supporting a rear platform, while the former were probably coeval with the rear extension, designed to carry the hindermost part of the roof and give the annexed section greater stability. The original corner posts of this 'four-post' windmill were slight in section — about 7in. square, with no thickening-out at the tops

to carry transverse members, but the added rear corner posts were only 4in. square, representing, probably, a conscious effort to minimise weight, if not also cost.

The crowntree, about 21in. square, carried the side girts, 15in. deep, on shoulders about 2in. deep, no doubt over hidden dovetails. On either side were the customary intermediate upright posts on 27in. centres, of quite small section, from near the feet of which diagonals ran to the side girt extremities as at Mill Green, but, unlike the posts in that contemporary structure, they did not continue through to the top side rails. These girts were devoid of deep mortises or cuts and survived with little deformation until the end. Though angled in to the corner posts at the rear, they appear not to have been so applied forward, where, however, the right post was a replacement in pine, and both it and its opposite oak member had added wooden plates on the inside faces to give extra support to the weather beam. As for the front of the mill body, the prick post, forward sill, meal beam and two pairs of upward converging diagonals followed closely the pattern at Mill Green.

The designer of this mill had a penchant for jowled-out main timbers in the horizontal sense, generously dimensioned at critical points and trimmed down elsewhere. This feature was seen in the crowntree, sheers and crosstrees, and was sometimes concluded with a nicely moulded finish. The crowntree was thickened through some 3-4ft. on its underside over the centre post, the sheers on both undersides and inside faces for 5-6ft., and the crosstrees — on all four faces on the lower member, and on all but the underside on the upper member — over a comparable length to the sheers. This feature also recalls Mill Green in respect of that mill's crosstrees. At Saling the upper crosstree increased from a basic section of 11in. square to 14in. deep by 13in. wide at the abutments to the post, where no wedges were used. Both crosstrees were variously recessed on sides and faces at their intersection within the horns of the main post in the usual manner. Granted that they were original, as doubtless was the case, these members testified to the soundness of the construction for over 200 years, though the crowntree had developed a vertical shake checked by bolts. The quarterbars carried a well-built twin-tenoned collar over which the sheers turned. Whether there was always a roundhouse is not known.

The rear steps and fantail assembly, allegedly from Stisted, were certainly alien to this mill, from which the tail pole had been removed. The pine ladder strings were set wide apart and entered the mill 3ft. over platform level, to be carried on added vertical members inside. To the left of the steps was a simple sack slide and loading platform. The fantail was 8-bladed, driving down through shafting from both ends of the fan shaft through pairs of bevel gears to heavy iron circling wheels or 'travellers' of 9in. face, 27in. D. and with six full-width flat spokes.

The mill offered very cramped working conditions, as the last miller pronounced with feeling, and could not be modified to take two pairs of 4 ft. stones in the breast. The 'nearly new' machinery of 1823 probably included the clasp-arm brake wheel with six cants, which was not a conversion from a compass-arm type. This drove a wooden stone nut and also a skew gear with pulley for dresser drive, while the sack-hoist bollard under the roof ridge was driven by slack belt from a wooden pulley built on the forward side of the brake wheel. The dresser was at floor level behind the tail stones and almost inaccessible; the miller is said to have lain full length to attend to it. The iron mortise wheel on the rear of the windshaft drove the iron nut lately brought from Great Easton.

The front stone nut had probably been in use for a very long time. It was wooden, forming a block 18 in. D. by $9\frac{1}{2}$ in. deep, bound with iron rings, and had 15 wood cogs of $4\frac{1}{2}$ in. face and $3\frac{1}{2}$ in. pitch, with iron pins passing down through the shanks. As recorded by Denis Sanders with his masterly eye for detail, it was secured on the $2\frac{1}{2}$ in. square iron quant by two 12 in. oak wedges channelled upwards through recesses cut in the nave on a pair of adjacent sides. The wedges, $2\frac{1}{2}$ in. wide, tapered from $1\frac{1}{4}$ in. thick below to $\frac{5}{8}$ in. above, and, when driven home, were held at the base by a U-bolt. When re-adjustment of the position of the nut was required as the stones wore thin or were replaced, it could be effected very simply. The front drive was latterly to a 4 ft. 6 in. peak stone over a French burr 2 in. wider; at the rear were two burrs of 4 ft. 6 in. diameter.

The forward bray ran across the front of the mill between the corner posts, carrying the short, heavy, bridgetree pivoted at the rear on a timber depending from the crowntree and braced from it by diagonals; the bray contained wedge adjustments on either side of the bridgetree end to centre the stone spindle, but this became redundant when the more sophisticated bridging box with screw control was introduced. The rear bridgetree also ran fore and aft and was carried on the bray below the bolter. Two conventional lead-ball centrifugal governors were employed, each belt-driven from the stone spindles.

The last working sails were anti-clockwise patents with single shutters 4 ft. by 10 in. as seen on the pair that remained in the 1920s. They were set in a plain canister on an all-iron windshaft, octagonal from the front journal to the rear of the brake wheel, then round. There were seven bays with three shutters in each and the innermost bay with four, all closed by the forward action of the striking rod worked by Y-wheel, rack and pinion over the rear steps. The sole sail remaining in 1960 carried an 8 in. leading board and a 5 in. board on the trailing side of the whip. To the last, the shutters from the sails and vanes from the fantail were stored in the roundhouse as if awaiting the appointed day when man would turn again to the wind as an inexhaustible, ubiquitous, non-polluting form of energy.

1 This section is based principally on information in *English Windmills* Vol. 2. Donald Smith. 1932. pp. 50-1, joint visits by the author and Denis Sanders in 1960 and 1965, and communications from Philip Barrett-Lennard and Donald W. Muggeridge

2 C.C. 29.9.1797

3 C.C. 23.5.1823. Land tax entries (E.R.O.) for 1826 give Samuel Beddall owner, John Hicks occupier

[*See also Addenda:* GREAT SALING]

Great and Little Sampford

(1) Post mill. Stood in Little Sampford south of Mill House on the west side of the Finchingfield road, about 1,000 yards south east of Great Sampford village. TL 652347

(2) Post mill. Stood in Little Sampford parish a few yards west of Mill Farm on the north side of the Thaxted road at a point 1,000 yards directly south west of Great Sampford church. TL 636346

(3) Post mill. Stood in Great Sampford at Moor End on the north side of Sparepenny Lane a few yards west of Hill (formerly Mill) House, and 600 yards north of the parish church as the crow flies. Site in the area known as 'The Mount'. TL 642358

(4) Smock mill. The base has been converted into a cottage in Great Sampford village on the east side of the Radwinter road 140 yards north of the church. TL 643355 (□ 223, 223a, b)

(1) PETTIT'S MILL ON THE FINCHINGFIELD ROAD, LITTLE SAMPFORD

The site of this post mill was occupied by an orchard in 1972 in a well winded position overlooking a sharp drop to the south and a pronounced slope westwards — the only windmill site in the Sampfords to be distinguished by Warburton, Bland and Smyth (c1724) and Chapman and André (1777) on their maps of the county. Isaac Cornell of Little Sampford, miller, had little to show for his services to the community judging by the contents of his will, proved in 1736; he bequeathed 5s. to a brother, 1s. to a grandson, and his debts to his wife, who, however, was to receive the residue of the estate after claims had been met by the sale of 'stones, irons, brasses, cloths and implements' from the windmill[1]. The site bears a symbol on the first O.S. 1 in. map (1805). In December, 1801, the freehold estate, lately held by James Portway, deceased, was advertised for auction[2]. There were two pairs of stones and a bricked roundhouse.

John Pettit was miller in 1826, and also in 1842 under the ownership of Samuel Portway, whose executors auctioned in November, 1843, several local farms and the freehold post mill, as above, capable of stowing 300 quarters of corn[3]. John Pettit paid for it a rental of £30 annually. The Pettits, members of a large family, ran also a mill in Great Sampford village, and were still in occupation at Little Sampford in 1886 when the mill was again for auction, currently worked by George Archer[4]. Mr Graves, a local resident all his life, born in 1882 and hale and hearty in 1973, remembered taking corn to four local mills, but recalled little regarding Pettit's mill. The last reference noted to a miller there is to Caroline Pettit in 1886, and the last map appearance is on the revised second O.S. 1 in. (1893).

(2) STARLING'S OR THAXTED ROAD MILL, MILL FARM, LITTLE SAMPFORD

The space where the mill stood is clearly indicated by a bounding hedge of circular form. The mill appears on the first O.S. 1 in. map of 1799 survey date. It was held with the farm of 34 acres, and in 1796 was insured by Henry Choat senior, farmer, for £80, with an additional £20 cover on the machinery[5]. The thatched tenement then mentioned must be that still existing. In 1803 the mill was insured by Thomas Barker for the trifling sum of £50, being timber built and without roundhouse[6]. In 1801 an inquest was held on the body of Ann Choat 'who it appeared was playing with another child near the windmill belonging to Mr Thomas Barker... when their infant years not giving them sufficient foresight of the danger of approaching too near, they were unfortunately struck by one of the sails, and the above-mentioned received a mortal wound in her head, which terminated its life in about ten minutes after, and the scull (*sic*) of the other was so much fractured, as to admit of 16 or 17 pieces being extracted from it; notwithstanding, the last child is in a fair way of recovery'. The editor of the *Chelmsford Chronicle* took the opportunity to suggest, in view of the frequency of such fatalities, that mill bodies should be so constructed as to free the first ten feet over ground level of the hazard of revolving sails, a matter, in his opinion, calling for parliamentary action[7].

Choat advertised for sale in 1807 the freehold mill property, with the chaseway leading to it and three acres of arable, then leased at £20 annually to Thomas Reynolds, the name also of the owner-occupier in 1842, who had married in 1841[8]. Presumably he was a descendant of the first Thomas. As late as 1866 the mill was held by a James Reynolds, but then passed to Peter Starling, who was in occupation in 1880, when the farm, still containing 34 acres, was to be let, the windmill receiving no more than a bare mention[9]. It lingered on until the turn of the century, at about which time John Stock of Great Bardfield recalled in 1969 having seen it as a post mill in ruins[10]. It did not appear on the third O.S. 1 in. (surv. 1902).

(3) SPAREPENNY LANE MILL, MOOR END, GREAT SAMPFORD

The first appearance of this post mill is on Greenwood (1825), and it was gone by the survey date (1893) of the revised second O.S. 1 in. map. Information on the mill is meagre. William Harrod, owner-occupier in 1830[11], leased the property to John Thomason, who was in occupation in 1842, as also in 1848, five years after Harrod's death[12]. A William Harrod first enters the parish land tax lists in 1803, possibly indicating the date of the windmill's erection.

After 1850 a goodly number of millers came and went at the two village mills; to determine at which mill they severally worked is not simple. George Matthews was operating by wind power at Moor End in 1890, and was evidently the last miller. No sale notice has been identified as relating to Moor End mill, and the assumption that it was a post mill with open trestle rests on the four grey squares by which its site is determined on the first O.S. 1:2500 (surv. 1876).

(4) PETTIT'S, LATTERLY DAY'S MILL, GREAT SAMPFORD VILLAGE

The base of Pettit's mill has become a residence in an attractive garden. There was formerly a blacksmith's shop close by, and the adjoining Mill House is now the scene of a garage business. In 1817, a news report referred to a fire causing damage estimated at £1,000 to outbuildings belonging to one Pettit, who had lately taken a mill at Old Sampford[13]. The O.S. map of 1805 does not mark the mill at site (4), neither does Greenwood (1825). Certainly Richard Pettit owned property in Great Sampford by 1803, and a branch of the family eventually ran a post mill in Waltham Holy Cross[14].

223 *Great Sampford smock base, 1972*

A second codicil added in 1825 to Pettit's long existing will refers to his purchase of an estate in Old Sampford in the occupation of John Turpin and others on part of which he had built a windmill. The date of erection is not given[15]. John Pettit was recorded as owner-occupier of the mill in 1842, when the property was held with Clock House Farm lying beyond his rented post mill in Little Sampford[16].

The only hint as to the working capacity of the village

223a Great Sampford Mill: body removed c 1914

mill comes from a notice to let in October, 1878, when Miss Pettit of Clock House Farm advertised a tower mill driving two pairs of stones[17]. The surviving mill base measures 19ft. across the flats of the octagon internally at ground level, tapering to 16ft. at the top of the walls, which are 2ft. thick and contained two floors. It was the last of the Sampford mills to work, passing from Charles Hall (1890, 94) to George Day (1898) and John Day (1906), who in 1912 was stated by *Kelly* to be using wind power. Dr Turner noted in 1921 that the mill had been taken down more than seven years previously[18], and other informants state that this was done by Scott of Radwinter, millwright. The mill was in fact recorded on the third O.S. 6in. map (1919) as 'Corn Mill', but evidently in reference to the use of power-driven stones in the base.

The Sampfords are probably the most barren of all Essex villages in respect of a pictorial record of windmills which could still be seen in the mind's eye of the aged in 1975. Until 1985, and therefore after 16 years of systematic research for these volumes, the four Sampford mills were unrepresented pictorially except for the base. Then a curious chain of circumstances led to the discovery[19] of an old photograph of the village smock mill of particular interest in that it bore features elsewhere unremarked in Essex, most likely the product of a Cambridgeshire millwright.

The smock body appears white-painted and smooth, best explained as the result of laying sheets of canvas over vertical boarding, the latter being nailed over a skin of horizontal boards. Graham (Chris.) Wilson, an authority on the mills of Cambridgeshire, and a practising miller at Over tower mill in that county, supports the presumption that the builder of Sampford mill came from his side of the Essex border. He cites the positioning of the window frames in relation to the framing of the smock, and the style of the braces connecting the top of the flyposts to the top of the cap. He also finds the cap shape — allowing for the fact that it has been retouched in the photo somewhat inaccurately, along with the fantail — similar to that in some former Cambridgeshire mills, for example Downham Road Mill, Ely, now gone. Mr Wilson comments: 'Vertical weatherboarding was often fixed over old horizontal boards in Cambridgeshire; first each side of the smock was measured so the vertical boards could be cut in the workshop, the boards often being grooved down each edge and provided with a false tongue. The assembly on site was reduced to a minimum; often the original horizontal boarding was left in place, but this was not such a good idea because there was very little sound wood left at the corners to nail into later, and the vertical boards came off as a result. A good example of this was to be seen at Shade Mill, Soham. Usually narrow laths were nailed over the joints to protect the false tongues . . . at Sampford there may not have been any laths covering the butt joints and tongues: this would account for the mainly smooth look. Canvas was sometimes saturated in lead paint and fixed to vertical weatherboarding on smocks, as often on caps. This system of weatherproofing is very good only if the painting is to be repeated every few years at a very great expense in paint, time and labour. Today such a system would be ridiculous.'

Mr Wilson cites Histon Mill as an example once canvas-covered.

Vincent Pargeter (Essex County Millwright) hazards an explanation for the presence of the heavy timber slabs applied externally to the upper few feet of the cant posts. They may have been used in conjunction with a system of tie rods to bring a distorted curb into the round.

The mill sails appear to be tapered towards the tips, not a feature normally seen in eastern England, and certainly not in Essex. Curiously, the taper seems to derive partly, if not wholly, from the width of the leading board allowed, the indistinctness of the photograph leaving uncertain the extent of variation in shutter width. Why this eccentricity? Once again our attention is riveted by the capacity of the windmill builders and repairers to surprise and entertain us by quirks of design. No striking tackle is visible at the rear of the cap, and the two pairs of single-shuttered sails may, therefore, have been spring-operated, or have been of patent type with internal striking gear, as at Great Bardfield and Southminster, Cripplegate, Mills. The smock frame evidently contained three floors above the two in the brick base.

223b Great Sampford smock base, 1985

NOTES

1 E.R.O. D/A CR 14 p. 458. Jas. Coe miller in 1757 (E.R.O. Q/SBb 212/16)

2 C.C. 18.12.1801

3 E.S. 3 & 10.11.1843

4 E.W.N. 1.10.1886

5 R.E. Pol. No. 151356 10.6.1796 per H.E.S. Simmons

6 Ibid. No. 202881 24.9.1803 per H.E.S. Simmons

7 C.C. 28.8.1801

8 C.C. 11.12.1807; E.R.O. D/CT 310A; E.S. 10.12.1841

9 E.W.N. 24.9.1880. Last directory entry; Starling in 1882

10 Recorded as 'Old Windmill (Corn)' on O.S. 1:2500 (surv. 1896)

11 *Essex Poll Book* per G. W. Martin. Given as Wm. Harrard in 1826 land tax (E.R.O.)

12 E.R.O. D/A BR 35 p. 295

13 I.J. 9.5.1817

14 Information supplied by Ann Furlong of Waterford, Herts., 18.10.1972

15 E.R.O. D/A CR 20 p. 241

16 E.R.O. D/CT 309 A

17 E.W.N. 25.10.1878

18 Probably in 1914, for the windmill is marked as such on the O.S. 1 in. Popular edition (surv. 1914-15)

19 By E. F. Goatcher of Sawbridgeworth, Herts.

Shalford

Post mill. Stood on the north side of the Wethersfield road 175 yards south west of the turning to Jaspers Green. A bungalow stands in the mill enclosure (1974). TL 710270

THE windmill shown by Warburton, Bland and Smyth (*c*1724) at approximately 706264 was probably intended for Shalford mill, which is on a plan of 1730[1] and on county maps from 1777 to 1896. It had comparatively few changes of ownership after 1800, appears seldom in sale notices, and then receives scant description. It is the subject of insurance registrations with the Royal Exchange in 1779, 1783 and 1797, when the policy holders were Thomas Darby of Shalford, miller, in the case of the first two, and Thomas Lee jun., in the last, the sum insured on the timber-built mill decreasing from £250 to £200 to £150. A roundhouse was not mentioned[2]. Probably the mill was replaced in the early 19th century. In November, 1791, the freehold of the premises, then occupied by Jacob Medcalf, was for auction, enquiries to be addressed to Abraham Barnard of White Notley[3].

On miller John Webb's death in 1795, his wife, Martha, put to auction the freehold of the mill and the copyhold associated buildings and land[4]; the property was later in the hands of the Butcher family (1815, 1830)[5], and in the late 1840s was owned by Thomas Legerton and occupied by his kinsman John[6]. The last were succeeded by first Thomas, then Daniel West, who held the mill from *c*1850 until its demolition *c*1896.

In the late 1870s at least one pair of patent sails was acquired as well as new stones preparatory to attracting a lessee[7], but the Wests nevertheless continued to be returned as millers at Shalford Green, in 1890 and 1894 using wind and steam. There were two pairs of stones in the mill head. The claim in a sale notice of 1880 that the mill was 'wonderfully well and strongly built' and 'in splendid condition' received later support from the fact that, on demolition *c*1896, component parts were put to use elsewhere[8]. David Young, carpenter, of Bannister Green, Felsted, who took down the mill, commandeered the body for himself, and delivered the fan gear to Cock Green nearby. The roundhouse was for a while used to house pigeons.

NOTES

1 E.R.O. T/M 472

2 R.E. Pol. Nos. 76716 10.11.1799, 88075 24.11.1783, 155830 25.3.1797 per H.E.S. Simmons

3 C.C. 18.11.1791 per R. Hawksley

4 E.R.O. D/A BR 28 p. 547; C.C. 20.3. & 5.6.1795

5 E.R.O. D/A BR 32 p. 472; *Essex Poll Book*, 1830 per G.W. Martin; Thos. Letch, miller (*Pigot*, 1839). Land tax (E.R.O.) 1826: George Butcher owner-occupier; 1832: owned Robt. Andrews, occupied Letch

6 E.R.O. D/CT 312A; P.O. directory 1850

7 *The Miller*. Vol. IV. 1.7.1878, p. 332; E.W.N. 11.6.1880

8 Per D. W. Muggeridge as related by Mr Crow of Felsted, April, 1942, who put the date of demolition as *c*1896 (corroborated by land tax records). See also C.C. 5.6.1896. p. 4. col. 6 for auction notice of mill and premises.

Shenfield

(1) Two mills. One was a post mill, whose site is in the grounds of High House, about 300 yards west south west of the pond on Shenfield Common, and 70 yards from the north side of the existing mill chase. The other, probably of post type, stood close to Mill House nearer the common, also north of the chase. TQ 597934 and 598935

(2) Smock mill. Site lies at or close to Mill Hill House, part of Brentwood School, on the west side of Middleton Hall Lane (formerly Tasker's Lane), 150 yards north of Priest's Lane. TQ 601937

(1) THE PAIR OF MILLS, SHENFIELD COMMON

The maps of Ogilby and Morgan (1678) and Warburton, Bland and Smyth (c1724) mark one windmill on Shenfield Common. It must have been the easterly of the pair shown by Chapman and André (1777), as indicated by the abutments of the property cited in a mortgage in 1712 effected by Anne and James Barnes, when Edward Lee was in occupation[1]. Barnes had entered in 1695, purchasing from John Ward[2]. The miller in 1755 was Thomas Osborn[3], who was also mentioned as having one windmill in Shenfield in a conveyance of 1782[4], so that it would appear that the two mills mapped in 1777 were more in series than in parallel in the temporal sense, and their co-existence is not otherwise recorded. The later, westerly, of the two, appears on the drawings (1799) for the first O.S. 1in. map, and is precisely indicated on the tithe map (1837)[5]. This — Alexander's mill in 1816 — was described in 1829 as a 'capital post windmill', when Alexander's retirement heralded the arrival apparently of James Woodfine from Kelvedon Hatch mill[6], who appears in directories of 1832 and 1838. In 1839 Woodfine was tenant to Edward Kemp[7], and in 1848 Kemp himself was named in a directory as miller, and William Roper was operating the smock mill at site (2).

The post mill was sold in 1849 as part of a freehold estate to John and Nehemiah Taylor, who paid £2,000 for the mill property, including 10 acres, let at £100 per annum[8]. These owners advertised the mill for letting in 1854, declaring it to be in good working condition and near the railway station[9]. There was a rapid succession of millers at both Shenfield windmills as times grew harder, and the directories give no help in coupling them with their mills. Dr Turner, writing c1920, quotes a correspondent as stating that the westerly mill was a small wooden post mill, last worked by an old man named Hawkins, and was blown or pulled down about 1860[10], but it is present in *Kelly* and on the first O.S. 6in. map in 1866. Furthermore, John Hawkins was given in the electoral register of 1869-70 as holding the mill, though he does not appear in *Kelly's* 1870. Both this mill and that off Tasker's Lane were retained, probably in error, in the 1893 revision of the O.S. 1in. map, but

were absent from the 1895 6in. survey. At about the time of the doctor's enquiries, the west mill was still remembered. Mill House stands today (1975) at the entrance to the chase, and was formerly a bakery.

(2) THE SMOCK MILL: TASKER'S LANE MILL

According to a sale notice of 1828, this mill was built in 1810, being a 'nearly new and substantially built freehold smock windmill'. It drove two pairs of stones and claimed a weekly potential output of six loads. There was a brick-fronted dwelling house and an acre of pasturage. J. Eckworth, deceased, was the late proprietor[11]. It may have been at this mill that labour relations took an unhappy turn in 1816[12]:

> Left his Master, on the 27th December last, A Young Man, 19 years of age, five feet six or seven inches high, thin face, dark eyes, with a downward look, stoutly made, hair cut remarkably close, supposed to be in his working dress. If any Miller or other person who may have set him to work, will address a line to Mr Edward Clay, Shenfield Hall, near Brentwood, he will relieve the distresses of an afflicted family.

Pigot (1832) gives Wm. Roper as miller and baker. In 1839, Joseph Tasker and William Roper were respectively landlord and tenant, and from the 1851 census we learn that this, Roper's mill, was run by George Slater, a journeyman miller from Suffolk[13]. Two millers were entered by directories as at Shenfield Common in 1863: Richard Giblin, stated by Dr Turner to have been the last to operate at Tasker's Lane, and Charles Welham. Welham was therefore presumably at the post mill. In 1870 and 74 there was one miller only: Charles Roffey, and in 1878 Mrs L. Roffey. According to Dr Turner's information the east mill was taken down in about 1880. As stated above, it is shown on the revised O.S. 1in. map (1893), which is highly suspect as regards undeleted mill symbols in this part of Essex.

Addendum

Mill Hill is a residential cul-de-sac leading south from the A12 at 604947. Reason for naming obscure.

NOTES

1 E.R.O. D/DSx 266
2 E.R.O. D/DC 23/604
3 E.R.O. Q/SBb 204/3
4 E.R.O. D/DSx 267
5 E.R.O. D/CT 316
6 C.C. 1.3.1816; 15.5.1829; 26.3.1830
7 E.R.O. D/CT 316A
8 E.S. 19.10. & 16.11.1849. The P.O. directory for 1850 gives Richard Woodfine at the Steam Mills, High Str., Brentwood
9 *Stamford Mercury* 15.9.1854 per H.E.S. Simmons
10 Dr Turner: Notes on Essex windmills. Southend R.L., but *Kelly* (1866) gives: Jn. Hawkins, Common, Joseph Chas. Simpson, Shenfield Mill, Shenfield Common; 1870: only Chas. Roffey at the eastern mill

11 C.C. 19.9.1828
12 C.C. 12.1.1816
13 P.R.O. HO 107 1774. See also C.C. 3.1.1851, p. 1, col. 5: 'large and capital windmill', etc., to be let

Southminster

(1) Post Mill. Stood just west of Ratsborough farm buildings. TQ 953985

(2) Smock mill. Known as West Windmill. Stood south of the junction of Kings Road with Burnham road, and a few yards south of the existing Mill House. The mill approach still survives. TQ 955993 (□ I 51)

(3) Smock mill. Known as East Windmill, alias Cripplegate Mill, alias North End Mill. Site approximately by 'Oude Molen', a modern bungalow. TM 962001 (□ 224)

(4) Mill drawn in some detail as a post mill on an estate map of 1610 (E.R.O. T/M 165). Known as Moor Mill. Stood south of the approach to 'Old-moor' east of the Asheldham road. Shown by Ogilby and Morgan (1678) and Warburton, Bland and Smyth (c1724). See under Asheldham (Vol. I, Appendix A) for a likely allusion (1662). TM 968005

(1) RATSBOROUGH MILL

Ratsborough mill is marked on the maps of Ogilby and Morgan (1678), Warburton, Bland and Smyth (c1724) and Chapman and André (1777). It was the subject of a conveyance in 1705 by James Quilter to John Danby, when occupied by John Chalk, formerly by William Starling[1]. The 200-acre farm, of which the mill was part, was offered for sale in 1778 by private contract and in 1780 by auction; the 1780 notice mentions a post mill with a bricked roundhouse, and a horse bolting mill[2]. The occupier, paying a rent of £40 per annum, was Thomas Lewin, who raised his insurance from the 1776 figure of £50 each on stock and utensils in the windmill and in the 'flour house and stable under one roof, timber and tiled' to £150 and £200, respectively, in 1779[3]. The 1778 notice of sale mentioned extensive repairs and improvements to farm buildings, and the windmill was possibly then provided with a second pair of stones.

In November, 1781, appeared the brief notice in the *Chelmsford Chronicle*:[4]

> On Saturday morning last, about one o'clock, a fire broke out in a wind-mill, at Southminster, in this county, which entirely consumed the same, with corn, meal and every thing therein. The stock, &c. was insured in the Sun Fire Office.

No other Southminster windmill is known to have been standing at that date, and no more is known of a Ratsborough mill.

(2) WEST MILL, BURNHAM ROAD

By October, 1783, Southminster was served by another windmill standing in the parish. It was in the possession of Thomas Lewin and was marked by an octagon in the parish plan of 1790[5]. That this smock mill was built to no great height, at least at that time, is suggested by the following news item, if accurately reported, in the *Chelmsford Chronicle* for 14th August, 1789: 'Last Tuesday the son of Mr Laver, of Southminster, about 8 years of age, happening to go too near the windmill, near his father's house, the sails struck him so violent a blow, that he died soon after.'

Two windmill symbols are present in the parish area on the drawings (1799) for the first O.S. 1in. map, and both windmills were insured by the Essex and Suffolk in 1817[6]: in the case of the mill on the Burnham road by Thomas Lewin, for a total of £1300, £500 of which was to cover the contents. Such a large sum indicates a mill of generous capacity; the fabric itself, insured for £800, was rated 'double hazardous' at 5s. premium per £100. Lewin was a man of substance, employing several hands and holding properties in Burnham and Earls Colne, besides a number in Southminster, his total cover being £3000. From this empire he engaged Matson, a farmer who accused him of supplying short measure, in a series of defamatory exchanges which, by the agency of the *Chelmsford Chronicle*, were assured a wide publicity. This episode took place in the spring of 1813 (see Vol. I, *Dust and Vitriol*).

By Lewin's will, proved in 1818[7], his mill passed to his son Thomas, who died intestate in 1827, and so to the widow of Thomas[8]. The tithe apportionment (1843) records Thomas Lewin as owner and occupier at this, the west site, and 'Smith and others' at the east site as tenants under John Crick[9], but for Smith should be read Alexander Allen Smyth. The west mill c 1844 came into the occupation and probably the ownership of Jonathan Stacey Summers, who was certainly the proprietor in 1868, and who was reputed to have been the first in the district to make and distribute 'charity bread' for the poor[10]. In 1872 the 'tower' mill, having two pairs of stones, using patent sails and an iron windshaft, was offered for sale, and in a further sale notice of May, 1886, it was stated to have four floors[11]. Dr Turner gave G. and C. Reeve as millers at this site in 1878, which assertion is supported by the land tax records for 1875 (Summers and Reeve owner and occupier), and the electoral registers suggest that milling ceased in 1879-80[12]. Efforts to sell the mill in 1886 must have been unfruitful.

The mill was burnt down in about 1895 after being struck by lightning according to several informants, but another gives 1889 as the date of disappearance. The mill is not shown on the revised second O.S. 1in. map (surv.\1893), giving support to the second assertion. A surviving photograph, taken from Kings Road, shows the sails in damaged condition; they appear to have been single-shuttered, but trees intervene and little detail emerges. No fantail is visible.

(3) EAST OR CRIPPLEGATE MILL

This smock mill was built in 1790 by William Stebbing, miller and mealman[13]. It was insured by him in 1802 with the Royal Exchange for £500, the cover for the contents being £100. In 1817 he switched to the Essex and Suffolk, maintaining the sum insured at £500[14]. In 1830, when Stebbing died, the mill was working three pairs of French stones under the direction of John Hammond, foreman. It supplied a bakery opposite the church[15]. John Crick assumed ownership, insuring the mill in January, 1832, for £350, and the machinery for £100[16]. When in 1859 John Crick, described as of Maldon, solicitor, insured the mill for £500, steam power had not by then been introduced.[17]

224 *Southminster: East or Cripplegate Mill. Believed demolished in 1929*

The miller for many years was Alexander Allen Smyth, who in 1837 insured his stock and utensils in the windmill for £200, and to whom reference was made in 1859[18]. He was succeeded by William Smyth (1862, 3), but for the ensuing two decades the succession of millers at both parish mills is difficult to unravel, and it is possible that the owner of the West Mill, Jonathan Stacey Summers, ran East Mill for part of that time[19]. In 1865 or before the owner of the freehold of East Mill was Thomas Clarke, whose executors sold the mill to one Fisk in 1884 for £510[20], succeeded as owner by Mrs S. G. Fisk (1886) and James William Fisk (1890, 1912)[21]. In 1895, when the running of the business was in the hands of Messrs Payne and Murton, the notes made by the Essex and Suffolk agent in his policy register give us the insurer's-eye-view of such premises[22]:

> The mill is 5 floors in height; it is lighted by candles and night work is done therein. It is worked by wind power and occasionally by steam by a portable engine standing in the open yard. There are four pairs of stones therein, 3 worked by wind and 1 by steam. The bridge trees or spindle beams ... (are) of wood. No kiln therein or in communication therewith, and no oats, paddy or rice ground or shelled therein, but oats are allowed to be crushed; one screen, but no rollers, discs, exhaust disintegrator, middlings purifier, dismembered smutter or exhaust machine allowed therein.

In 1886, Baker of Danbury did some work on the sails. A new middling 42ft. long, sawn to size, cost £5 4s. 6d. and two new whips and sail bars cost £3 5s. 6d. For these and other materials and labour, mainly on the sails, £46 6s. 8d. was expended by Fisk. In 1889 he had a new hurst and stones 'with crane and all complete' installed for £87 6s. 0d., probably coinciding with the introduction of a steam engine. Baker's expenses included journeys to Ipswich and Maldon.

In 1890 the same millwright painted the wooden frame of the mill white and apprently tarred the brick base; a breakdown of the charges gives the following:

1890 Mr. Fisk Southminster

July 22				
Son & 3 men painting mill & repairing same 354 hours		8	17	3
6lb putty			1	9
12 gallons linseed oil		2	2	0
2 gallons tar & 2lb nails			2	0
2½ cwt white lead		4	15	0
5lb lead & black paint			5	6
Other colours for mill			7	6
Lodging & rail fare			9	0

The labour charge proves to have been 6d. per hour. However, Baker charged 1s hourly for his own labour; in 1890 he fitted a new iron gudgeon and iron bands to the wooden upright shaft, he and his son being engaged 15 hours for the sum of £1 10s. 0d, the materials costing £2 12s. 0d.[23]

With the above references to the Fisk family as owners we come within reach of living memory. E. G. Brand recalled in 1963 his days at the mill in 1912, when, aged 14, he helped in the work using wind and steam power[24]. 'The sail shutters were opened and shut from inside the mill by ropes operated from the top storey, and the driving wheel with cogs on the sail shaft had a large brake which when a strong wind occurred used to be hung with ½ cwt. weights to hold the sails. Owing to the failure to replace some cogs made of apple wood underneath the cap, the fan that used to turn the cap to keep the sails head to the wind failed to work and the sails had the wind behind them. During a high wind one half of a sail came down across a stable, wrecking it and just missing a horse. That was the end of the sails.'

The mill was visited by Dr Turner in 1921. It stood bereft of sails, but was producing grist by steam power. The photographic record shows the mill both with and without sails, the last working set being a pair each of single and double-shuttered patents. The six-bladed fantail sat incongruously over the rear of the cap, with the least of visible supports, clearly not part and parcel of the original structure. The cap was built to protect the former hand-winding gear at the rear in a practical but far from comely fashion, unrelieved by petticoat or gallery. The brick base was stepped on the exterior in a manner reminiscent of the larger example at Bulmer. The mill is said locally to have been demolished in 1929.

Addendum

Will of Bartholomew Averal of Southminster, 1562: 'My wife shall have the profits of the manor of Southminster called the Moor with the windmill.' (*Elizabethan Life: Essex Gentry's Wills*, Emmison, p. 151). Relates to site at 968005.

NOTES

1 E.R.O. D/DGn 76.
2 C.C. 16.10.1778, 7.1.1780; I.J. 8.1.1780
3 Sun Pol. Nos. 363664 9.1.1776 & 408644 20.1.1779 per H.E.S. Simmons
4 C.C. 23.11.1781
5 E.R.O. D/P 259/11/1 & 259/28/1
6 E.R.O. D/F 21/1, pp. 102, 107
7 E.R.O. D/A BR 31, p. 435
8 C.C. 25.1.1828
9 E.R.O. D/CT 321A
10 *Kelly* (1845); land tax, E.R.O. (1868); E.C. No. 78, p. 397
11 E.W.N. 28.6.1872, 21.5.1886
12 Dr Turner: notes on Essex windmills, Southend R.L.; land tax and electoral registers, E.R.O.
13 E.R.O. D/P 259/11/1 & 259/28/1; see also C.C. 21 & 28.5.1830
14 R.E. Pol. No. 190610 9.4.1802; E.R.O. D/F 21/1, p. 107
15 C.C. 1.1.1830, 21 & 28.5.1830
16 E.R.O. D/F 21/6, p. 57
17 E.R.O. D/F 21/16, p. 19; see also 21/12, p. 174 (March, 1857)
18 E.R.O. D/F 21/8, p. 54 (1837); D/F 21/16, p. 19 (1859)
19 Suggested by R. Hawksley from sources studied
20 1865: land tax, E.R.O.; E.W.N. 2.1.1874, p. 8, col. 1; 14 & 21.11. & 12.12.1884
21 Per *Kelly's* directories, etc.
22 E.R.O. D/F 21/25, p. 115
23 Ledgers in possession of Baker & Sons (Danbury) Ltd
24 E.C. No. 78, p. 397. Note, however, C.C. 7.11.1873, p. 5, col. 7, which reports the fall of a sail on a stable and the miraculous escape of a horse! Furthermore, this occurred at the mill of G. and C. Reeve, which — Dr Turner was informed locally in 1921 — was the West Mill!

Springfield

(1) Post mill. Stood 80 yards west of Arbour Lane behind the site of the later-built Alma public house. TL 716074

(2) Post mill. Stood immediately west of the residence 'Windmill Pastures' and 300 yards east south east of the site of the former Broomfield watermill. TL 717102 (□ 225)

(3) Smock mill, known as Pease Hall Mill. Stood 150 yards south of Sandford Mill Road, Brook End, at a point 80 yards east of the surviving Windmill Cottage. TL 733066 (□ 226)

(4) Mill of unknown character at Springfield Gaol, 1874. TL 717072

(1) ARBOUR LANE MILL

A deed of 1655 refers to a windmill on land known as Knott's Croft abutting to the east on the highway leading from Springfield church toward Faircross[1]. A mill traceable to this site is listed in a rate book for 1765[2], and other references occur up to the 1790s. No mill is indicated, however, on the maps of Ogilby and Morgan (1678) and Warburton, Bland and Smyth (c 1724), but a symbol is given by Chapman and André (1777). The will of Edward Bilding the elder, of Moulsham, miller, dated 1767, makes mention of a newly erected windmill in Springfield[3] — demonstrably at site (1), which, taken in conjunction with map evidence, suggests, but does not prove, that there was a lengthy gap in the milling occupation at this site. The first windmill was apparently not associated with a watermill in 1655, but the second was throughout its known existence. Examples of discontinuous occupation of an identical or proximate site did occur in Essex, as at Radwinter, Walton-on-the-Naze, and probably Mountnessing.

The Arbour Lane mill further appears on a map of the proposed Chelmer and Blackwater Navigation (1792-4)[4], but is not seen on the drawings (1799) for the first O.S. 1 in. map, by which time it probably no longer existed. On the canal map the mill is clearly drawn as an open trestle post mill, as are Moulsham, Barnes and Little Totham mills, known to have been of post type at that time. A plan of the plot on which the mill stood contains the mill similarly drawn. This accompanies an abstract of title recording the sale for £232 by Edward Bilding of Moulsham, miller, to Shadrach Bullen, in 1767, of 'all that windmill . . . situated upon the freehold close . . . called Knotts Croft otherwise Gravel Pit Field . . . in Springfield'. The property was in 1785 left by will to Abraham Bullen in tail, and then worked in conjunction with the watermill nearby. The watermill alone receives mention in 1802. Indentures of November, 1816, show that by then the mill had certainly gone[5].

(2) 'BROOMFIELD' WINDMILL, SPRINGFIELD

In July, 1782, Robert Dixon of Broomfield, miller, insured for £400 his 'Wind Mill and Round House adjoining, Timber built and covered with Boards, situate at Springfield'; the 'utensils and (stock in) trade therein' were insured for £200[6]. In 1787 Richard and Robert Dixon, described as of Felsted, insured the Felsted, Hartford End and Broomfield watermills and their contents for a total of nearly £5000, and the Springfield windmill just beyond the Broomfield boundary for £400[7]. Thomas Digby of Springfield, miller and mealman, insured his windmill in the same parish in July, 1799, and again in August, 1803; this was the mill under discussion[8]. The Marriage family were established in Broomfield by 1800, and probably held the nearby Springfield windmill soon after. In 1842 Henry and William Marriage were in possession,[9] and indeed their descendants still occupy the site.

225 *Springfield: mill near Broomfield. Stated to have been standing until 1918*

The mill is recorded on the second O.S. 6 in. map (1895) as 'Old Windmill', and on the third O.S. 1 in. map (surv. 1904). A photograph exists showing the then remaining two common sails, which turned anti-clockwise, and a plain weatherboarded body over a single-storied brick roundhouse. Winding was by tail pole. Instead of windows the body had ports. The sails descended very low, and perhaps this was the 'Broom-field Mill' whose sails struck a child of about 10 years in 1787, brought to recovery by a trepanning of the skull[10].

A legal document, mentioned in *150 Years of Milling and Farming 1824-1974* by Stan Jarvis (relating to W. & H. Marriage & Sons Ltd.), describes the mill as dilapidated in 1918. R. Hawksley questioned an old resident (1977) who confirmed that it was then standing. The mill was, however, not marked on the Popular edition of the O.S. 1 in. (surv. 1914-19).

(3) PEASE HALL MILL

Greenwood's map (1825) is the first to show this mill, which appears to have been the 'capital tower windmill' to be sold or let in November, 1816, enquiries to be addressed to John Baker of Great Baddow.[11] The mill was stated to be situated within a short distance of water carriage to London, and capable of grinding 10-12 loads per week. The 10 acres of land included correspond with Thomas Marriage's holding at the time of the tithe apportionment (1842); the mill was evidently not sold in 1816, for Marriage held the land in 1815 and for many years after, and land tax records suggest that Pease Hall mill may have been built as early as 1804. Joseph Marriage at about that time became occupier in addition to owner of the estate, to be succeeded in due course by Thomas, who in 1828 was owner of farm and mill and joint occupier with Abraham Wallis[12]. Wallis continued as miller until *c* 1839. The tithe apportionment records Thomas Marriage as owner-occupier of windmill and yard comprising 26 perches; a Thomas Marriage also ran Barnes watermill, then owned by Lady Mildmay. Thomas Marriage senior, on his death in 1840, left to his son Thomas the 'tower mill at Springfield ... with the mill yard and road of fifteen feet wide from the hedge stake leading from such mill to the public road', and also the cottage nearby and the post mill standing near Barnes watermill in Great Baddow parish[13].

In the early 1860s Henry Cottee was at Pease Mill, with cottage and garden, the freehold of which was purchased in June, 1860, for £500 by William Bott junior, who also bought the Pease Hall estate, then of 42 acres, with premises, for £3000[14]. The last miller was Tom Peatfield, who is stated to have worked the mill from the early 1870s until 1894 or later. The windmill appears to have stood in idleness for over 30 years, and its use as an observation post during the first world war did nothing to improve the fabric[15]. It is included in Donald Smith's survey[16], and is thought locally to have been pulled down *c*1932.

A number of photographs show features broadly comparable with those of other smock mills in south and central Essex, and we may presume that we are viewing the work of one of the Moulsham-based millwrights. There was a boat-shaped cap with deep petticoat and four boarded floors over a single-storied brick base, and also a distinctive 7-bladed fantail as at Hatfield Peverel. The full complement of sails does not appear in known views; the pair which remained in the derelict period were single-shuttered turning anti-clockwise. There was a mill stage, but apparently no gallery around the cap. Several interior views and external shots through gaping weatherboarding reveal a wooden clasp-arm brake wheel on an iron windshaft, a wooden upright shaft and a wooden great spur gear, also of clasp-arm construction. The stones were arranged underdrift on the second floor, and their weight

226 Springfield: Pease Hall Mill. Stood unused approximately 1896-1932, then demolished

and that of the driving machinery was transferred down to ground level by four vertical posts of stout section supporting the main stone-floor beams. There were probably three pairs of stones.

The mill site was still traceable in 1971 by the differing texture of the grasses; the base measured approximately 24 ft. across the flats internally.

(4) WINDMILL AT SPRINGFIELD GAOL

This is known only from the first printing of the O.S. 10 ft. to 1 mile map (1874), on which it appears as a rectangle described as 'Windmill'. It represented an area of about 21 × 18 ft. A treadmill was inside the inner wall with a corn mill at the end, and the windmill was outside the inner wall, but within the wings of the prison, so that it must have been very tall. Essex Record Office have many competing plans for enlarging the prison in the 1840s, but none shows the windmill. The specification for the pump (1848) stated that it was to be worked by treadmill.[17]

NOTES

1 E.R.O. D/DU 567/17

2 E.R.O. D/P 211/11/1 per R. Hawksley
3 E.R.O. D/A BR 25 p.576 per R.W. Smith
4 E.R.O. Q/RUm 1/1, 1/2
5 E.R.O. D/DCh T16
6 R.E. Pol. No. 84033 16.7.1782 per H.E.S. Simmons
7 Ibid. No. 104272 23.11.1787 per H.E.S. Simmons
8 Ibid. Nos. 168405 10.7.1799 & 202213 22.8.1803 per H.E.S. Simmons. See also E.R.O. D/A BR 29 p.42: Richard Dixon's will, proved 1797
9 E.R.O. D/CT 322A
10 C.C. 8.6.1787
11 C.C. 15.11.1816
12 Researches by R. Hawksley
13 E.R.O. D/A BR 35 p.2
14 E.S. 6.7.1860
15 E.C. No. 98, March, 1965, p.308: letter from Leonard Gregory; see also trade directories.
16 *English Windmills*, Vol. 2, 1932, pp.65-6.
17 Notes by R. Hawksley

Stambourne

(1) Mill of unknown type. Stood away from roads in the east of the parish beyond Dyers End and south of the Yeldham road, probably at about 250 yards north north east of Elms Farm (727381) and ½ mile south east of Stambourne church. Approx. TL 727383

(2) Mill of unknown type. Stood a little west of Hill Farm at the junction of the Ridgewell road. TL 716393

(3) Mill of unknown type. On the north side of the Yeldham road 450 yards east of the Finchingfield road. TL 727388

(4) Post mill. Stood at Chestnut Horse Farm on the south side of the Bumpstead road, here named Mill Road, 350 yards west of Wesley End Road, the turning to Ridgewell (as site (2) above). TL 714391 (□ 227)

IN REFERENCE to the first three sites there is little apart from map symbols to put on record. At (1) a mill is placed by Warburton, Bland and Smyth (c1724). An abstract of title deeds relating to Greenfields or Greenvills Farm (726387) cites for 1729 the farm and the 'Mill House ... with the Mill and Hill it stood on as it was then inclosed with a Mote', Robert Chote (sic) being in occupation.[1] A deed of 1771 gave Edward Choate (sic) in occupation but without reference to a mill. The tithe map (1837-8)[2] names Little Mill Croft and Mill Field at site (1), corresponding with fields named in the above-mentioned abstract in a conveyance of 1821.

Chapman and André (1777) record a windmill symbol only at site (2), and the drawings (1799-1800) for the first O.S. 1 in. map place a symbol only at (3), which is not noted on other maps examined. A dwelling west of Stump's Cross at 731387 was named Mill Farm on the first and second O.S. 6 in. maps, and was presumably connected with mill (3). The Jarvis family were evidently here: Edward in 1804, advertising for a pair of mill-stones of large diameter, and Robert, listed as potential juror in 1815[3]. Greenwood (1825) has no mills in Stambourne. Mill (4) is seen on the revised first O.S. 1 in. (rev'd 1836-7). The Hill Farm mill (2) may have been included in the former area of Ridgewell parish.[4]

The last mill (4) is seen in two post-1900 photographs as devoid of roundhouse and standing on tall brick piers. It is of note that the mill was held with Hill Farm in 1834 when in the occupation of Messrs Unwin, and was then for sale by auction[5]. It had two pairs of French stones, which a note recorded in 1936 described as in the breast[6]. Daniel Unwin held the mill in 1834 and also in 1866. There followed George Unwin (1870, 74) and Daniel Unwin junior (1878, 82), and so to Mrs E. Unwin (1906) and Daniel Herbert Unwin (1908). The last were prepared to lavish money on repairs at this comparatively late date, but the mill was dislocated beyond redemption on Friday, 3rd December, 1909. A press report stated[7]:

Stambourne. Mill Wrecked. During the storm which raged at the end of last week, the Stambourne windmill, one of the few that still exist in motion, which is in the occupation of Mrs Unwin, was practically wrecked. The

227 Stambourne, Mill Road. Stated to have been blown down c 1909. Note the roving stage for access to the sails

mill, which stands on an eminence, had been in constant work. It was just undergoing repair, and the ladders and scaffolding were in position. The terrific force of the wind early on Friday morning caused the mill to be wrenched over on to one side, and rendered useless for further business operations. Nobody appears to have heard the crash. The machinery was put out of gear, the driving wheel being irreparably damaged. We understand that the amount of damage done was considerable.

About a month later, the same paper announced the demolition of the mill 'injured during the recent gale', and in May, 1910, a sale by auction on the premises of mill parts was advertised. These included two pairs of stones, sails, gear wheels, plummer blocks and so forth[8].

As revealed by photographs, the white-painted mill body was plainly built, without porch or projections at the rear, and was winded by tail pole with a simple yoke attached. A sack slide descended the rear ladder. There were four spring sails, single-shuttered and turning anti-clockwise, and a wheeled staging was pushed round the mill for shutter adjustment. The brick piers rose to above head height and the base timbers bore evidence of the depredations of the weather, having reinforcement at the lower joints.

Addendum

Windmill, etc., 1540, in Ridgewell and Stambourne. (*Feet of Fines, Essex*, Vol. IV, p. 235).

NOTES
1 E.R.O. D/DU 751/165
2 E.R.O. D/CT 323A. Note also (per R. Hawksley): Will of Jn. Claye of Stambourne (7.8.1613) includes windmill. Will in form for realty (E.R.O. D/A BW 11 p.58)
3 C.C. 10.8.1804; E.R.O. Q/RJ 12
4 Per R. Hawksley
5 E. & H.M. 22.7. & 5.8.1834
6 Per D. W. Muggeridge
7 *Halstead Gazette* 9.12.1909 per A. Corder-Birch of Little Yeldham. *Kelly* (1910) gives Unwin as farmer
8 Ibid. 6.1. & 26.8.1910

Stanford Rivers

(1) Post mill. Stood 20 yards from the south side of the lane to Littlebury watermill and 80 yards from the Ongar road: hence nearly opposite Great Colemans. TL 547014

(2) Post mill. Stood on a bluff overlooking the westward meander of the Roding 100 yards north of the lane to the Shonks watermill site from the Ongar road, and 500 yards from the nearest point on the main road. TQ 527984

(3) Post mill. Stood on the site now occupied by 'Trethvas', a bungalow on the south side of Mill

Lane, and about 40 yards from the T-junction to the east. Known as Toothill Mill. TL 515026 (□ 228, I 10)

WHEN conditions were propitious, the Roding, pursuing a leisurely, meandering course on the southern flank of Stanford Rivers parish, spawned watermills at broadly equal intervals, themselves the forebears of windmills which never attained to a truly independent existence. Thus arose the pairs at Littlebury and Shonks, and another at Passingford Mill in the next parish downstream. Shonks windmill is shown on Warburton, Bland and Smyth (c1724), and all three windmills along this stretch of the Roding are seen on Chapman and André (1777).

(1) LITTLEBURY WINDMILL

The tithe map for Stanford Rivers (1839), beautifully executed in colour, records windmills close to Littlebury and Shonks (Navestock) watermills, and at Toothill[1]. The last two mentioned are indicated by small circles, suggesting a roundhouse in plan, but the mill opposite Great Colemans by the lane to Littlebury has a small blocked-in circle with four dots spaced evenly outside it, intended, doubtless, to represent an open substructure. This presumption finds support in the fact that insurance records and sale notices for this mill fail to mention a roundhouse. Daniel Corney in January, 1781, insured his 'timber and tiled water corn mill' at Littlebury for £400 and the contents for £300, while the figures for the windmill were £200 and £100 respectively[2]. Two years later Corney was bankrupt[3]. In 1802 this property belonged to Joseph Waight of Andover, gent, and was occupied by Timothy and William Phillips, farmers[4]. The discrepancy in the overall insurance cover on building, machinery, stock and utensils between the water and wind mills was now greater: £900 as opposed to £350; the windmill was described as boarded. In August, 1832, trustees under the will of Timothy Phillips, deceased, offered the freehold for sale[5]. The watermill drove two pairs of French stones and the post mill two further pairs of 4ft. 10in. diameter, probably placed head and tail in conformity with the normal 18th-century construction in Essex. The lease of the whole, including 15 acres, was held by John Smitheman at £160 rent per annum. At the sale the freehold was knocked down at £3020[6]. The tithe apportionment (1842) records Smitheman as tenant to John Kynaston, and the mill is included on the revised O.S. 1in. map (1844). William Kynaston was rated for Littlebury mills in 1854, but for one mill only in the following year[7], that being the watermill. Steam and electricity, superseding wind and water power, carried the business forward a further century.

(2) SHONKS WINDMILL

The Shonks windmill, successor to an earlier mill, stood about 100 yards distant from the lane leading to the watermill, apparently in isolation, and the two mills lay 350 yards apart. James Grove of Navestock, miller, leased in June, 1703, from the Hon. George Petre of Bell House, Stanford Rivers, a piece of land called Old Bury, doubtless corresponding to the site under consideration, which the map by Warburton, Bland and Smyth (c1724) shows as possessing a windmill. John Grove, of Shonks Mill, Navestock, miller, renewed this lease in 1796, reserving the right to 'carry away the windmill' and convert the materials to his own use. He demolished the 'old' mill, erected a new one, and in 1797 sold the leasehold mill and land to John Chaplin for £2100[8]. The old mill appears on the maps of Kitchin (c1761)[9] and Chapman and André (1777). In February, 1835, Chaplin sold the land and windmill to his nephew John Abraham Chaplin of Navestock, miller, for an annuity of £150. The Chaplin family, who included maltsters and brewers at Harlow, retained an interest in the windmill until 1860. In 1842 Thomas Sadler was in actual occupation[10]; he is described as of Shonks, Navestock, in White's directory for 1848. Cruchley's map of 1856 shows the windmill. In June, 1860, the lease of mill and land was surrendered by the head lessee to the landowner, Sir Chas. Cunliffe Smith[11]. The windmill probably fell into disuse at this time, and it ceases to figure in the church rate lists after 1862[12].

(3) TOOTHILL MILL

The post mill at Toothill was described as newly-erected in a sale notice[13] of September, 1828, but Greenwood (1825) and a sale of the lease[14] under a deed of assignment for the benefit of the creditors of Charles Shuttleworth in 1826 show that it had already seen some years of active service. In 1829 the builder of the mill was described as the late Mr Corder. Corder entered the land tax records in 1814, and Rayner, the eventual owner, as occupier under Corder in 1816. The mill was therefore probably erected c1815[15]. The 1828 auction notice mentions two pairs of stones, a bricked roundhouse, a detached brewhouse and one acre of land. Robinson the miller could hardly have timed his departure more opportunely. He was succeeded by the luckless Joseph Knight, hitherto an obscure and honest miller with a large family, whose multiple injuries, acquired in the mill under spectacular circumstances in June 1829, attracted the interest, morbid, compassionate, or other, of a public far beyond the bounds of Essex. The Chelmsford Chronicle of 26th June, 1829, devoted the larger part of a column to the disaster. By this publicity and their helpful initiatives the editors sought to alleviate the plight of the stricken miller.

The main substance of the account reads as follows:[16]

Awful effects of a thunderstorm

About half-past five o'clock in the afternoon of Thursday the 18th., Ongar and its vicinity was visited by a dreadful storm of thunder, accompanied by lightning, from the effects of which a windmill, the property of Mr

Rayner, situated at Toothill, in the parish of Stanford Rivers, was nearly destroyed, and the miller so shockingly mutilated that his recovery is considered doubtful.

A very heavy cloud was observed to descend over the mill, which stands upon an eminence, and at the same instant a hissing noise was succeeded by an explosion resembling the discharge of artillery. The wife of the unfortunate miller, hearing the report, opened the door of her cottage, and was the first to observe the unthought-of calamity: she was nearly suffocated by the sulphureous vapour which impregnated the air, and quickly filled the house. She had scarcely viewed the appalling demolition of the mill, when the heartrending shrieks of her husband, calling for her assistance, met her ear. In a state of distraction she alarmed Mr Randal, a neighbour, who, with several others, soon assembled; but the awful spectacle so riveted them to the spot, that some time elapsed before sufficient courage enabled them to ascend the stairs. A young man, (nephew to Mr Rayner), as soon as he was aware of the circumstance, without hesitation, led the way, and, followed by others, immediately went to the assistance of the unfortunate sufferer. The scene which presented itself on reaching the second floor baffles all description. The poor man was discovered lying on a sack, his head most shockingly and indescribably lacerated — his right leg hung over the ladder communicating with the first floor, and connected with his body by a small portion of flesh only — the bone protruding through the stocking. His right eye was so injured, that its powers of vision are, it is supposed, for ever destroyed, and his right hand mangled in a frightful manner. Apparently insensible of pain, and regardless of the injuries he had sustained, his first enquiry was as to the state of the mill and the corn. When the spectators had recovered from the alarm excited by the mutilated appearance of the sufferer, they conveyed him to a house and the assistance of a surgeon was speedily obtained. Upon further examinations, large splinters of wood, and even grains of wheat from the hopper were found driven into various parts of his body. The hair of his head was much singed. In short, the unfortunate man presents a horrible spectacle of mangled flesh. The most singular penetration of the fluid was observable in the partial destruction of a pad in the neckcloth he wore at the time. His hairy cap was found lying by his side, torn into innumerable pieces, and the floor was covered with blood. Mr. Potter, surgeon, of Ongar, assisted by several other professional gentlemen, removed the leg. Owing to the splintered state of the bone, the use of the saw became necessary, but from the skilful manner in which this operation was performed, the poor man suffered comparatively but little.

To describe the state of the mill is a task more difficult but less painful. The lightning, it would appear, first struck the middlings end, a term given to some iron braces which afford support to the sails, and proceeded in the track of a number of bolts, removing some and slightly damaging others, until it reached the neck, when it took the parcels, and then commenced its work in the interior of the mill by shivering a great part of the nearly new oaken shaft. The fluid continued its course in nearly the centre of the sack chain, and on reaching the second floor, came in contact with the beam and scales, forcing two half-hundredweights through the side of the mill. In its progress so far, it completely cut off two of the sails, which it split into innumerable pieces, and hurled to a great distance. Some of these fragments were found sticking in the earth as to require great strength to effect their removal. The roof of the mill was struck off in a similar manner, and the sides were nearly stripped of their boarding. The ceiling of the mill was divided and thrown on either side upon the grass. The machinery was thus completely exposed to the view, enclosed in the skeleton building. The two other sails remain in their places, but will need much repair to make them again fit for use. The whole of the machinery was deranged, and the cloths, where nailed, were much burnt. The electric fluid, having affected nearly all the iron in the mill, forced its way out by tearing up part of the flooring, and cutting a piece of sheer-tree away, thus escaping to the iron sheeting which covered the roundhouse. Part of this it raised, and concluded its destructive course by passing down the back of the stairs, which were iron braced; and, forcing out a number of very strong-nutted screws, it finally disappeared in the earth, making a cavity to a considerable extent. Even a pen in the inkstand did not escape, being singed, as were also the brooms and brushes.

The situation of the sufferer appears to be accurately portrayed by the poet:

> Swiftly like sudden death it came;
> Like travellers by lightning killed,
> I burnt the moment I beheld.

228 *Stanford Rivers: Toothill Mill. Demolished 1935*

The poor man states that shortly before the accident occurred, he closed the loop-hole in order to keep out the rain, and having done so, sat himself down upon some sacks by the wheat hopper. Whilst in the act of looking up in order to see whether the rain came in, he received the shock, but remembers nothing more until the persons came to his assistance. His injuries appear to be confined, in a great measure, to his exterior, although at times he is delirious; but the extraordinary patience which he displays astonishes those who visit him.

The name of the poor man thus injured is Joseph Knight — he is about fifty years of age — has a wife and seven children, one of them is deaf and dumb. He is said to have been an industrious and honest character. Under these circumstances his situation will, we have no doubt, open the charitable hearts of those around him, as well as those who through curiosity view the shattered fabric and the afflicted state of the suffering individual.

Mr Rayner, the proprietor of the mill, had but a short time previous to the calamity, in company with his nephew, left the building. He will be the loser of between £300 and £400, the mill being uninsured. It was built by the late Mr. Corder. A great many persons have visited the spot, all of whom were struck by the destructive powers of the fluid. Several gentlemen took sketches of the scene [see □ I 10] which we understand were drawn with the laudable intention of publishing engravings, to be sold for the poor man and his family, who, if he survives, will be a cripple for the remainder of his days. Upwards of 1,000 persons are said to have viewed the scene of destruction on Sunday last. A petition has been drawn up on behalf of the sufferer, and lies at the Green Man, Toothill.

A fortnight after the publication of this account, the *Chelmsford Chronicle* was able to report:

> Joseph Knight, the sufferer by lightning at Toothill, is living, and favourable symptoms are apparent as to his ultimate recovery. The hint of our correspondent H.C. will no doubt be attended to; an election of 25 children to the Asylum takes place, we understand, in a few days, and we hope that Knight's deaf and dumb child will be thought a fit object for charity; in the mean time, we shall be happy to convey any sum which the charitable may be disposed to contribute, to soften the afflictions of this distressed man and his family.

After the further lapse of a fortnight came a contribution to the *Mechanics' Magazine* by one Thomas Squire of Epping, who had zealously traced the course of the lightning through the mill and recorded its effects in minute detail. According to his findings, the 'whizzing noise' of the lightning was succeeded by a crash of thunder consisting of three distinct and rapid consecutive reports, attributable to the imperfect nature of the conductors in the mill, down which the lightning was channelled. With impressive perspicuity Squire continues his chronicle:

> At the time of this accident the head of the mill was to the north, so that the windshaft lay nearly in the plane of the meridian, and the sails were standing at an angle of 45 degrees to the horizon, or what the millers term "cross sail". The right hand or eastern upper sail was first struck by the electric fluid not at the extremity or highest point, but near the middle, where there was an iron band and bolt which fastened the sail to the arm; here it drove out the latter and separated the former, snapped in two the timbers, then descended to the axis, and struck off the opposite sail. It then entered the upper part of the mill by the head of the shaft, and as it here came in contact with very imperfect conductors, its powerful effects were most visible; for it not only rived, but drove off a large portion of the shaft on the western side, destroyed the framework of the crown or cog-wheel, and in other respects damaged or displaced every part of the machinery; the roof it completely drove off, and nearly all the boards round the mill as far as the floor. The electric fluid now became concentrated in the chain which was used for drawing up the sacks; this was in part fused, as the links were welded together in one solid mass. The good effect of the conducting power of the chain was very perceptible, as little or no damage was done in that section of the mill through which that part of the chain passed. By this chain the ethereal fire entered the lower compartment, and was diverted from its downward course by some half-hundred and other weights standing on the floor near the western side of the mill; here it tore up a large space of the floor, the weights were ejected into the yard to a considerable distance, and the boards were forced off as before with great violence, and thrown in every direction. From this part the lightning passed to the roof of the round house, which rises nearly to the lower floor; and as this was covered with plates of iron, it here met with a ready passage, and, darting a short distance through the air to the iron braces under the stairs, it was thence conducted to the earth without doing any further damage. As the braces did not quite reach the ground, its course by that means was again a little interrupted; and in its last effort to overcome every effort *(sic)* opposed to its furious velocity, it tore up the stones and gravel, and finally made its exit by forming a large hole near the western side of the steps, in an oblique direction, and in size and appearance somewhat like a rabbit's burrow. Such was the violence of the explosion, that a great many pieces of the boards and large fragments of the mill were thrown into adjoining fields to an amazing distance, and some of them must have ascended to a great height in the air, as they were observed sticking upright in the hard ground, as if driven there by a pile driver.

Squire put Knight's survival down to the fact that he was out of the direct line of the 'fluid' and partly sheltered by sections of the machinery. A further report in the *Mechanics' Magazine* of August 1st stated that the miller was likely to recover. Splinters of wood and grains of wheat were still being taken out of his body, more than a cupful having been extracted to date. His complexion, as black as a tinker's after the catastrophe, was now changing to normal. Several sketches of the ruined mill had been engraved and were on sale to the public in aid of the victim. We are told also that millwrights were busy repairing the damage, and that

Rayner, the owner, proposed to erect a conductor at a short distance from the mill.

Almost a century later, in its latter days of dereliction, the mill was again struck by lightning on 10th February, 1928. Paul Baker quotes reports that three engines of the Epping Brigade within two hours extinguished the flames in the mill roof, but this was merely a reprieve for the structure, already described as ruinous by Dr Turner (c 1920). The mill shed a stone during its prolonged decline and was finally condemned to demolition in 1935. As a last gesture it carried the flag on high on the occasion of the Silver Jubilee of George V; the unfortunate who hoisted it is said to have fallen through one of the floors[17]. The end came when the roundhouse was taken down and the body pulled over by rope. The larger timbers were sent to a sawmill and the smaller found their way to local hearths. The brick piers lingered on for some time[18].

Apart from its rare eruptions into the headlines, the mill worked in comparative obscurity. Edward Rayner was owner-occupier in 1832 and 1842; later millers were John Crisford Rippington (1851), and, in rapid succession, as recorded in the rate books: George Lambert (1853), Henry Moor (1858), J.S.A. Willis (1860) and Daniel Surridge (1865). The last-named appears in Kelly's 1894, to be followed by Comyns Owers in 1898. The mill is said to have ceased work in 1904[19].

The derelict was much photographed. The mill body, with oval ports, stood over a large roundhouse having two floors, and winding was by tail pole. There were four single-shuttered, anti-clockwise sails, which from photographic views appear to have been spring-patents with laminated springs to form the cross. The striking gear was inside the mill, and the weatherboarded body showed no external feature worthy of comment.

Addendum

Tithe, 1840. Plot 66: Mill Grove (522038), and plot 307: Mill Mead (533016) may have been windmill sites.

NOTES

1 E.R.O. D/CT 327.
2 Sun Pol. No. 437416 2.1.1781 per H.E.S. Simmons
3 *Lond. Gaz.* Oct. 21-25, 1783
4 Sun Pol. No. 728287 22.1.1802
5 C.C. 17.8.1832
6 C.C. 31.8.1832
7 E.R.O. D/P 40/4/1
8 E.R.O. D/DSd T31: bundle of deeds covers mill's history.
9 In the Passmore Edwards Museum, Newham: *The Environs or Counties Twenty Miles Round London Drawn from Accurate Surveys by Thomas Kitchin, Geographer,* 1755-1765. (Shonks windmill probably taken from W.B. & S. c1724).
10 See note 1
11 See note 8
12 E.R.O. D/P 40/4/1, 2
13 C.C. 26.9.1828
14 C.C. 10.3.1826. See also E.R.O. D/DSd T21
15 C.C. 26.6.1829: land tax in E.R.O.

16 The Passmore Edwards Museum has an account by Paul Baker: *Toothill. The Story of an Essex Windmill.* See also *The Essex Naturalist.* Vol. 28, pt.2, pp. 51-4. Some post-1928 and other references extracted.
17 E.C. No. 98, March, 1965, p. 308. Letter from A. J. Young.
18 V.C.H. *Essex*, Vol. IV, 1956, p. 210
19 *Trans. Newcomen Soc.*, Vol. XXXI, 1958, p. 155. *Kelly's* directory, 1898: Comyns Owers — baker and miller; 1902 — baker only.

Stansted Mountfitchet

(1) Post mill, joined by a second post mill, evidently to the south, at a distance of some 300 yards, but whose site is unknown. The first mill stood near Walpole House, a modern conversion from cottages and a bakery on the west side of the Quendon road (B 1383) three-quarters of a mile north of Standsted crossroads. TL 513260 (□ 229)

(2) Tower mill. Preserved. Stands about 70 yards east of the main road (B 1383) on the north side of the narrow turning, Mill Lane, 350 yards south of Stansted crossroads. TL 510248 (□ 230a, b; I 49; II 98,99)

(3) Smock mill. Wisbey's Mill, sometimes referred to as Elsenham Windmill. Stood by the track 60 yards south east of the existing Mill Cottages on the south side of the Stansted road 530 yards south west of Elsenham crossroads. TL 531259

(1) THE QUENDON ROAD MILLS

The north Stansted site bears a mill on maps from Warburton, Bland and Smyth (c1724) onwards until the mid-19th century. The will of Robert Camp, miller, of Stansted Mountfitchet, proved in 1732, makes reference to the parcel commonly known as Windmill Hill, together with a piece of ground late of Read's Hill 'containing twelve feet in breadth and one hundred and thirteen and a half in length ... used for a way ... from the King's Highway ... to the said Mill'[1]. A windmill was insured for £220 in June, 1779, by Lawrence Webb, miller of Stansted[2], whose name is later linked with Thaxted tower mill. During Webb's occupation a second mill was built. A sale notice in 1788 advertised to be let or sold 'two Substantial Post Wind Mills, with a Pair of French Stones and Flour Mills and a very good Horse Mill for the convenience of dressing flour'. These were situated by the turnpike road and were stated to be 'within threescore rods' (330 yards) of each other. The proprietor was going into 'another way of business'[3]. No subsequent reference to two co-existing mills in this location has been traced. In 1794 Laurence *(sic)* Webb, this time disclosing his name, and inviting enquiries at Thaxted, announced the sale of one post mill with one pair of French stones, and a horse bolting mill.[4]

Thomas Girtin painted a water-colour in 1798

229 'The Old Mill, Stansted, Essex' by Thomas Girtin. Water-colour, 1798, evidently featuring the north-west mill off the Quendon road

formerly entitled 'The Old Mill in Stansted, Essex', but since renamed 'A Mill in Essex',[5] and probably featuring the long established mill at site (1). The painting has been much exhibited this century and was to be seen at the Victoria and Albert Museum in April, 1975. The windmill is depicted with four anti-clockwise cloth-spread sails and an open substructure, the crosstrees being slightly over ground level and set on a low mound. Three thatched buildings and a pond complete a most attractive grouping. In 1795 Webb as proprietor and William Whitehead of Stebbing, baker, as mortgagee, insured a windmill, timber-built, for £100, and the gears &c. for £40, William May being occupier, and in this and a later insurance policy secured by May himself, the property is described as near or in The Chapel[6], which is so named on Chapman and André's map (1777), and relates to the north-west quadrant of the village.

Greenwood's map, surveyed in 1824, omits the post mill, which certainly continued to exist until as late as 1866[7]. In the early 19th century, the millers of Stansted were prone to bankruptcy. In 1808 the freehold premises under discussion were for auction for the benefit of the creditors of Charles Littlechild[8]. There was one post mill with a pair of French stones, but a horse mill was not mentioned. William Haiden insured mill and contents for £150 each in 1809[9], and in 1814 the land tax returns give William Clark as owner of the property, late Haiden's. In c1815 George Nottage was bankrupt while in occupation of one of the parish mills[10]. At Stansted north in 1830 Simon Horsnell was owner and James Sharp occupier[11]; on the death of the former, the mill was for auction in 1833, then run by Abraham Speller using two pairs of stones[12]. It was bought by Charles Porter[13], whose tenant was soon to be Joseph Felsted. The tithe apportionment (1844) returns John Porter and John Felsted as owner and occupier[14]. Mill Field lay north west of the mill premises. A map dated

1847 is perhaps the last to offer a windmill symbol for this mill[15], which does not appear on the first O.S. 6 in. map (surv. 1875). However, a sale notice dated 1866 showed the mill as still active, then with patent spring sails and a brick and slated roundhouse[16]. There was a bakery, and the reference to 'a well of good water' repeats the phrase of sale notices 70 years earlier. Joseph Chopping was yearly tenant, and with his eventual departure the mill probably ceased to work.

(2) STANSTED TOWER MILL

Historical and technical information on the existing Stansted mill, and an outline of the late efforts towards preservation have been separately treated in these volumes. The reader who requires a 'straight run-through' is referred to the Pictorial Guide issued by the Stansted Mountfitchet Windmill Committee. Here, a brief note must suffice.

The mill was built in 1787 for Joseph Lindsell, and was worked until 1910, for much of the period after 1850 by the Hicks family as tenants, who also operated the malting. Charles Smith was miller in the 1830s. There were a few changes in ownership following upon illuminating sale notices, and the mill proved very demanding both on those who bought it as an investment, and those who tried to eke out a livelihood by running it. Although enjoying a head start over most of its Essex contemporaries in terms of initial outlay and capacity, the mill had to wait many decades for serious efforts at modernisation, and the chance preservation of the correspondence bearing on this and on the running costs for the period 1845-65 offers a most rewarding bonanza. That 1910 was the last year of work, according to Donald Smith, is supported by local enquiry, though the last directory reference is in 1894. Possibly the business was ultimately run by a master miller operating in Bishops Stortford.

The mill today, by the robust nature of its construction and by its advantageous situation amid an appreciative community, has found willing contributors towards its upkeep and the practical demands of its exhibition to the public. The 'Stansted Millers' have grown out of the initiatives of the second Lord Blyth, who in 1934 had the mill put in good repair, and presented it to the parish.

As an example of the vigilance and financial backing needed to keep a preserved windmill in being and of the care which must be exercised if the option of future restoration to working order is not to be lost, we may note the work done at Stansted mill in 1984-5 following the launching of a £14,000 project by the parish council as trustees of the windmill to enable both the cap and the sails to turn. The work was entrusted to Millwrights International Ltd., a comparatively new enterprise based at Mapledurham near Reading, with Christopher Wallis, M.I.C.E., as a leading consultant. The firm, active over a wide area, had already exercised its skills in Essex at Bocking windmill. As son of Barnes Wallis, who designed the bouncing bombs for the 'dam-busters' of World War Two, Chris. Wallis can clearly lay claim to that inborn ingenuity for which the old and successful master millwrights were much commended, and from an early age it was impressed upon him that 'the greatest

230a *Stansted tower mill, August, 1940*

creativity comes from a combination of brain work with the use of hand tools'.

Apart from the question of replacing the sails at Stansted, damaged by a storm and weakened by hidden decay, other matters awaited resolution. School parties on mill visits can bring their own hazards such as weight concentration where undesirable; core samples of the Stansted stone-floor beams showed them to be no more than adequate for their normal function of stone support. They were therefore propped in the traditional manner from the ground-floor ceiling beams (the latter having central cast-iron columns beneath), using three of the sail whips lately removed.

A new set of sails cannot be safely fitted to a windmill without regard to the strength of the mill structure. In Volume II, p. 78, reference is made to the weatherbeam bowed outwards to follow the curb and to the makeshift manner of its support following earlier repairs. This

inadequacy was overcome by Mr Wallis as described in a letter to the writer dated January, 1985:

While sitting in the cap deliberating, I noticed the heavy torsional distortion of the weather beam under the main bearing; this had been "held" by removing the cap circle wheels and blocking the cap circle off the curb with folding wedges. The whole assembly of the cap circle, weather beam and bearing blocks was structurally unsound, and I felt very unhappy about adding $4\frac{1}{2}$ tons of stocks and new sweeps to the existing $2\frac{1}{2}$ tons of windshaft and brake wheel, which would push it downwards and outwards via the main bearing. Worst of all, those who follow would have no choice of making the cap turn again. The curved weather beam arrangement was copied in many mills, but the end joints between the weather beam and the sheers having no torsion resistance, the resulting twist always transferred the bearing load on to the two wheels directly below. How could I cure this without heavy and expensive alterations? The answer was a light steel "A" frame of 2 in. square rolled hollow steel, prefabricated, with the three members bolted together in situ, free-standing except for locating coach screws into the sheers at each end. This is placed astride the sheers with its apex over, and leaning slightly back from, the main bearing. High tensile steel cables are anchored to each of the two main bearing fixing bolts, pass over the "A" frame and the top of the brake wheel and are anchored to eyebolts through the cap circle at the rear of the mill. The main bearing fixing bolts are elongated to reach down below a large annular ring washer under the cap circle, i.e. 6 ft. long by 1 ft. wide, to grasp all the bits and pieces of timber in the cap circle under the weather beam. Bottle screws in each of the cables ensure that they can be tensioned to share the load between the four new cap circle wheels and the cables. At present all is in place and the weather beam is back in line, with the cap circle wheels just *not* carrying load i.e. can be rotated by hand.

230b *Stansted. Tail of two-part windshaft, with tail bearing. 1972*

Mr Wallis further remarked that the new sails were being designed at the request of the parish council as patents to take the piles of 4 ft. × 9 in. shutters stored in the mill on the trailing side only; there would be an 11 in. wide plywood windboard on the driving side. With new sails in position and the mill having retrieved its popular image, an increased flow of casual visitors and of organised groups can be expected; funds trickle in, and — like the grain of yesteryear — help to preserve in being a cherished local landmark.

(3) WISBEY'S MILL

This mill appears in the land tax records for 1820, when it was owned by Michael Phillips. It is not on Greenwood's map (1825), but is shown on the London to Cambridge railway plan of 1835, still in the ownership and occupation of Phillips[17]. It is also on the railway revision of the first O.S. 1 in. map (post-1840), and in the tithe records (1844), which give Michael Phillips also at the watermill close by in Elsenham (1841 for that parish)[18].

Edward Wisbey, mentioned in directories of 1878 and 1886, is recorded by Donald Muggeridge as in possession of this mill when a storm arose which blew off the cap, brake wheel, sails and fantail. This was the storm reported in the *Herts. and Essex Observer* dated 5th November, 1887, which caused damage to several other local mills. The late Rev. Clarke was told that the sprag normally fitted when the mill stopped work was not put in position on this occasion. Wisbey was laid up for some time after, and it is probable that the mill was left in disrepair and sooner or later was demolished. *Kelly* (1890) records steam in use. The windmill carried four double-shuttered patent sails. No illustration is known.[19]

NOTES

1 E.R.O. D/A BR 21, p.99
2 Sun Pol. No. 415536 26.6.1779 per H.E.S. Simmons
3 C.C. 11.4.1788
4 C.C. 16.5.1794
5 See: *The Art of Thomas Girtin,* Thomas Girtin and David Loshak, Adam & Charles Black, 1954, pp.171, 272
6 R.E. Pol. Nos. 146622 26.11.1795 & 187127 3.11.1801 per H.E.S. Simmons
7 E.R.O. B2173. Sale on 23.10.1866
8 C.C. 27.5.1808
9 R.E. Pol. No. 245597 25.3.1809
10 *Lond. Gaz.* 16.5. & 29.7.1815 & 13.7.1816. E.R.O. T/M 457/8: Chas. Hicks occupier
11 *Essex Poll Book,* per G.W. Martin
12 E. & H.M. 19.11.1833
13 As note 7
14 E.R.O. D/CT 328A
15 E.R.O. Q/RDc 36
16 As note 7   17 E.R.O. Q/RUm 1/53   18 E.R.O. D/CT 130A
19 R. Hawksley reports that the second 6in. map suggests that the steam mill was away from the windmill, so the latter was probably pulled down when the cap blew off.

Stapleford Abbots and Stapleford Tawney

(1) Mill of unknown type. Stood in the parish of Stapleford Abbots evidently over the watermill which up to *c*1775 lay possibly as much as 220 yards west of the surviving mill building and therefore 440 yards west of Passingford Bridge. TQ 500976.

(2) Mill of unknown type. Stood on the south side of the T-junction about ¾ mile south of Stapleford Tawney church, and within that parish. TQ 502978.

(3) Post mill known as Boyland's Oak Mill, Stapleford Abbots. Stood 100 yards to the south west of the Havering road from a point opposite the Royal Oak public house. TQ 512944 (□231)

(1) & (2) PASSINGFORD MILLS

In 1740 John Clarke was admitted to land previously part of the waste of the manor of Stapleford Abbots 'between the old river (Roding) and the cut in the new river'; by 1743 he had erected 'two watermills and one windmill' at the position shown by Chapman and André (1777)[1]. We may interpret the 'two watermills' as two pairs of millstones driven by one water-wheel and we must note that Chapman and André place their windmill symbol directly over the watermill. This indication that the watermill structure supported the windmill is reinforced by the fact that court book entries from 1779 refer to the rebuilt watermill as having replaced the windmill and two watermills 'decayed and pulled down'. Had the wind and watermills stood apart it is unlikely that they would separately have decayed and needed replacement after the remarkably short time of 30 years. Indeed, the 'decay' may have been brought on by a disaster of more immediate impact, granted the vulnerability of windmills, resulting in damage beyond economic repair.

John Clarke, the initiator of the milling at this site, sold the property in 1744 for £350 to Robert Goodwin, all the mill fixtures to be surrendered except the 'Skreens, Sieves, Boulting Cloths, Sacks, Weights, Beam & Scales, Shovells, Bushells'. Goodwin, when insuring in 1757 his wind and water mills in Fyfield, was described as of Passingford Bridge, miller[2]. In 1779 Mary Goodwin, widow of Robert, was admitted to the by then rebuilt copyhold watermill in pursuance of her late husband's will, by which the property was eventually to pass to William Taylor, son-in-law. William Taylor, Fellow of Magdalene College, Cambridge, had a freehold windmill erected 500 yards to the north of the watermill (at site (2)) in Stapleford Tawney. Both the earlier water and windmills were therefore replaced, the windmill being sited in a more favourable position for wind. Later maps suggest a change of site for the watermill also, and in this are supported by documentary references.

In 1784 Taylor sold both mills to Joseph Browne, and in 1792 they were offered for sale by auction[3] at Garraway's Coffee House, Change Alley, Cornhill, London, the freehold and copyhold estate being grouped in one lot under the title 'Stapleford Corn Mills'. It comprised the watermill with a 17 ft. wheel working two pairs of stones, a dwelling, 14 acres of meadow, and a 'very substantial' windmill. The lessee was James Browne, paying a rent of £90 per annum. The purchaser — in 1793 — was Charles Smith, who left the mills to his son John Charles Joshua Smith, admitted to the copyhold in 1821. He was followed by Sir Charles Cunliffe Smith in 1832. From the date of appearance of the 'second generation' mills there had been a succession of operating millers, including Richard Moss (1779), Lancelot Tuck (1784), John Cooper (1795), Fincham and Evans (1798), the dates given being years of their known occupation. The last-named insured in 1798 various items in the watermill for £1000, and in the windmill (including sail cloths) for £200[4].

The Stapleford Tawney windmill is indicated on the revised first O.S. 1in. map (1844) but not on the first 6in., here surveyed c1865. The tithe apportionment (1838) records two Windmill Fields adjacent to the south west and north east, but does not mention a windmill[5]. However, the field containing the mill site was occupied by Charles Stevens, who ran the watermill at this time, and the plan and reference book for the London and Bury St Edmunds Railway[6] (deposited Nov. 1845) place an open rectangle at the site, suggesting a post mill with open trestle, and describe the pasture field and windmill as occupied by Stevens under the ownership of Spencer Smith (trustee under Chas. Smith's will). The church rates[7] show a considerable reduction in Stevens' rental in 1858, possibly stemming from the disappearance of the windmill.

The mill is included on two maps published in the 1850s: Cruchley's 'Survey of the Country Thirty Miles round London' (with additions to 1856), and Davies' 'Environs of London' (1859), but these are derivative.

(3) BOYLAND'S OAK MILL

This is not shown by Greenwood (1825) or by earlier cartographers. It appears to have been a comparative latecomer, and occupied a small plot on the property of Richard Palmer Roupell in 1846 when in the occupation of Jonas Crouchman, miller, a man of 47 years in 1851, employing an 11-year-old apprentice[8]. Later millers, using wind only, were William Dewing (1866, 1878) and Herbert Balls (1882). Balls presumably responded to notices in 1880 regarding the letting of Boyland's Oak Farm, of 108 acres, together with the post windmill containing three pairs of stones, a bolter and jumper,

occupying 'a high and healthy' position[9]. There were spring sails on an iron shaft. The mill has not been noted on later directory lists, though Balls can be traced to 1884 in electoral registers[10].

There was evidently some reluctance to clear the remains of this mill from the landscape, in which Dr Turner viewed it as 'a conspicuous object with its gaunt sails seen on all sides for a considerable distance'. He mentions the owner's — Lord O'Hagan's — intention to have it repaired, but the outbreak of war scotched the idea. According to George Tasker, writing in the *Essex Review,* the remains of the sails were blown off on Sunday, 21st October, 1923. The mill was demolished shortly after, in December[11]. Photographs of its ruinous condition show four single-shuttered anti-clockwise sails, and the absence of weatherboarding exposes a side framing very much akin to that at Mill Green, Ingatestone. Possibly it was an old mill brought from elsewhere. The side girts ran to the main rear corner posts, behind which lay an 'extended' section housing the dresser. The body was tarred, winded by tail pole, and stood over a single-storied roundhouse.

231 *Stapleford Abbots: Boyland's Oak Mill. Demolished 1923 after many years of dereliction*

NOTES

1 E.R.O. D/DSd T9; documents relating to the period 1740-1832
2 R.E. Pol. No. 33676 5.12.1757 per H. E. S. Simmons
3 C.C. 13.4.1792

4 R.E. Pol. No. 164670 12.11.1798 per H.E.S. Simmons

5 E.R.O. D/CT 331A

6 E.R.O. Q/RUm 2/34 per R. Hawksley

7 E.R.O. D/P 144/4/1 per R. Hawksley

8 E.R.O. D/CT 330A and P.R.O. HO 107 1771

9 E.W.N. 13.2. & 25.6.1880. Also E.R.O. Sage Coll., Vol. 9, 22.7.1880

10 E.R.O. per R. Hawksley

11 E.R. Vol. XXXIII, p. 94 et seq.; p. 148: footnote by Harold Smith

Stebbing

(1) Mill of unknown type. Playle's Mill. Stood prior to 1770 on a site thought to have been in the eastern angle of the main T-junction at Bran End (TL 654253).

(2) Post mill at Bran End. Stood 50 yards beyond the end of Barrack Lane, a cul-de-sac. TL 658258

(3) Mill at Bran End. Stood behind 'Firs', a house on the west side of the Great Bardfield road, 900 yards north of the watermill and 90 yards south of Barrack Lane. The house is now named 'Malt House'. TL 655257

(4) Smock mill at Bran End. Stood in the corner of a field 300 yards south west of the watermill and nearly 100 yards west of the Dunmow road. TL 649251

(5) Post mill. Stood a few yards north of 'Windmill Orchard', and 180 yards south of the turning westwards to the parish church. TL 669241

MILLING was a leading industry in Stebbing, where in mid-19th century stood contemporarily two water-mills and three windmills, for the most part driving two pairs of stones. Some operated in conjunction, and thereby become harder to differentiate in the records, and the loose description 'Bran End' as a site location, though adequate at the time, lacks the precision now needed for certain identification. The first O.S. 1 in. map (1805) failed to record the one windmill then standing in the parish.

(1) PLAYLE'S MILL

In 1756, Samuel Playle of Stebbing, miller, devised to his eldest son John, his 'parcel of copyhold ground with the windmill erected on part thereof'[1]. John's entry in 1757 was recorded at a court of the manor of Stebbing Hall in 1770, the reference being to a close called Stones 'whereon stood a windmill which is since pulled down'[2]. A further reference to the mill plot occurs in 1790, but not allowing its identification[3]. The Playle family were at Bran End watermill, employing two pairs of French

stones, which property they were offering to let in 1816[4]; it is likely, therefore, that their former windmill stood in the vicinity. A local researcher, K.J. Ellis, stated in 1979 that he had identified 'Stone's Garden' of earlier days at the position given in (1) of the mill list above. This was probably the mill site.

(2) BARRACK LANE MILL

In 1752 William Tunbridge, of Stebbing, miller, bought a copyhold plot of land without mention of a windmill, but by 1754 was in possession of one situated as described above, and mortgaged for £76 7s. 6d[5]. By his will in 1774, William left his daughter 'one shilling only', but lavished on his son James the windmill and appurtenances to which the latter was admitted in 1778. The mill appears on the map by Chapman and André (1777).

In March, 1786, the 'substantial copyhold post wind mill' called Brand (sic) End Mill was auctioned, having one pair of French stones and a bolting mill, with half an acre of ground, late in the occupation of William Barker. Thomas Butcher, miller, of Finchingfield, made a successful bid of £70, and sealed it with a deposit of 10s. 6d[6]. In 1805, Butcher sold the mill to John Bambridge, already in occupation, from whom it passed in 1811 to John Cornell jun., of Lindsell, miller, and in 1820 for £475 to John Green. To Samuel Chopping jun., of Stebbing, Green sold in 1821 for £120 the cottage and land 'upon the site whereof a windmill once stood which has been lately blown down'[7]. One of the milling Choppings was sent in 1818 to the House of Correction at Newport for a term as a 'rogue and vagabond', having used 'subtle craft' to impute a theft to an innocent person with intent to deceive another[8].

The parts of the grounded windmill were offered for auction in April, 1820. It had 4 ft. 7 in. and 3 ft. 6 in. French stones, head and tail wheels of 7 ft. 8 in. and 5 ft. 10 in. diameter respectively, a nearly new wooden windshaft 15 ft. 6 in. long, 21 in. sq. at the poll, and a complete set of ground timbers[9].

A replacement post mill appeared by the date of Greenwood's survey (1824), and was sketched as a post mill without roundhouse on the tithe map (1840); the apportionment returned Samuel Chopping as owner and occupier of both Barrack Lane mill and that at the Firs[10]. In the land tax records[11] of the same year (1840) Chopping's premises were entered as cottages, mills, lands and a malting. In 1841 'mills' had become 'mill', presumably indicating that the one in Barrack Lane had gone out of use, and prematurely, in fact, if it was new-built in 1820, and not an importation.

(3) THE 'FIRS' SITE: CHOPPING'S MILL

Samuel Chopping junior, miller, was given as holding mills and land in Stebbing in the Essex Poll Book

(1830), and in 1832 held freehold his 'New Mill' near Bran End. There is no evidence of its existence before 1830, and one must note that Chopping's other mill at site (2) was copyhold. The name 'New Mill' persisted to the 1890s, though the mill was older than the two other surviving parish windmills[12]. The suggestion made in Volume I (p. 72) that the Black Notley mill might have been moved to sites (3) or (5) in Stebbing c 1839 must be withdrawn in the light of additional information.

In 1850 Chopping combined the trades of baker, miller, maltster and brickmaker. The Choppings are said at one time to have owned also the south-east mill near the Watch House[13]. After Samuel (1863), the last miller at the Firs site, the main windmilling base of the family, was William, returned by *Kelly's* directory in 1894 as using steam and wind, and last given in the electoral register for 1895-6.

A local inhabitant aged 76 in 1971 could just recall the demolition of the mill c 1900, achieved by the substitution of timber props for supporting brickwork, the timbers being burnt away.[14]

(4) BRAN END SMOCK MILL: WHITEHEAD'S

This mill started life as Herbert's mill in Maldon, whence it was removed to Stebbing in 1842. The frame was broken during the initial loading and was therefore transported in dismembered form[15]. It was worked in conjunction with the watermill, from which it lay distant 300 yards by road and 90 yards up a field track to the hilltop site bought by Joseph Whitehead in October, 1842, from Samuel Chopping. In 1844 it was working on cloth sails, the canvas being completely torn off in a whirlwind in October of that year[16]. Joseph Whitehead was recorded as miller in 1863; in 1874 and '78 Joseph Barrett was at Bran End Mills, presumably employing the windmill.

Whitehead's trustees under his will put the water and wind mills to auction in September, 1886[17]. The combined water and steam mills were by then amply housed in a 4-floored brick building, and drove four pairs of 4ft. millstones; the windmill, described as small at the time of the move, drove only two. The water and steam mills were withdrawn at £390, and the windmill was also withdrawn[18]. In March, 1895, the windmill was blown down in a 'great hurricane'; it was stated not to have been worked for some years, and to have had its sails 'blown out' c 1873[19]. The first O.S. 6in. map (surv. 1875) records the mill as working.

(5) POST MILL NEAR THE WATCH HOUSE: LATTERLY CUSTANCE'S MILL

This mill receives its first mention in 1833, when owned by Robert Dixon (of Felsted Mills) and others, and occupied by Joseph Dixon. It was then described as near Warehouse Farm, which lay to the south. In 1840 it was in the hands of the executors of Robert Dixon and

still occupied by Joseph Dixon, who in c 1845 insured the mill for £300 and the machinery and contents for £170[20]. After Joseph's decease c 1848[21], the miller was Zachariah Nicholls (1850, 66). The freehold post mill, with brick roundhouse, known as 'Watch-House Windmill', and having patent sails driving two pairs of stones, was so described when offered for sale in January 1884. It was then occupied by Edward Hynds at a rent of £30 p.a.[22] A further sale notice, apparently relating to this mill (since steam is not mentioned, but was in use at site (3)) was published in October 1888, application to be made to Charles Crusha, at Great Leighs[23]. The last miller was Albert Ernest Custance of Mill House, using wind power solely from 1890 or earlier until 1895, after which the mill is no longer given in the land tax returns. It is described as 'Old Windmill' on the second O.S. 6in. map (1896), but is not shown on the third O.S. 1in. map (surv. 1902). Francis, miller at Little Saling, is recorded as stating (1948) that this, the last Stebbing windmill, had two pairs of stones and four spring sails, and that it was pulled down by Custance[24].

Included in the recollections in 1971 of Frank Howland, a Stebbing villager, were the roundhouse of this mill, and also a notable character, Davy Chopping, who was struck by a sail at this site in about 1840 when a mere boy of 12 years[25]. Chopping's skull was fractured, and a silver plate let into it; he was also paralysed down the right side and able only to hobble about with the aid of a stick. For close on 80 years his laboured perambulations arounds the village would have been worth a score of warning signs to the inhabitants in preventing further mishaps of like nature, and, indeed, none such is on record. He died at the advanced age of 91, in 1919.

NOTES

1 E.R.O. D/A BR p. 323

2 E.R.O. D/DU 222/1 pp. 87-8

3 Ibid. 222/2 (1790)

4 C.C. 8.3.1816.

5 E.R.O. D/DO T616, which also gives the 1778 ref.

6 E.R.O. D/DU 192/10; C.C. 3.3.1786

7 E.R.O. D/DU 222/2, 3, 4

8 C.C. 16.10.1818   9 C.C. 7.4.1820   10 E.R.O. D/CT 332

11 At E.R.O., examined by R. Hawksley

12 Per R. Hawksley

13 & 14 Recollections of Frank Howland, 1971, recorded by R. W. Smith. See also E.S. 13.3.1840: Samuel Chopping robbed on the highway. R. Hawksley states that this must have been a smock or tower mill, as the base had a long extension on the first 1/2,500 map (1876) and the second of 1896.

15 See under Maldon

16 E.S. 18.10.1844

17 E.R.O. B2587

18 E.W.N. 24.9.1886

19 *Essex County Chronicle*, 29.3.1895, per H. E. S. Simmons

20 1833: E.R.O. Q/RPl 328 per R. Hawksley; 1840: D/CT 332A; c 1845: D/F 21/10 p. 15

21 E.R.O. D/A BR 36 p. 83

22 E.W.N. 4 & 18.1.1884. Hynds' death: E.W.N. 13.3.1891, p. 5, col. 2, but an Edward Hynds succeeded (at watermill)

23 *The Miller*, 1.10.1888, per H.E.S. Simmons

24 Per H.E.S. Simmons

25 As reported to R.W. Smith (see notes 13, 14 above)

Stock

(1) Post mill. Threadgold's Mill. Stood literally on the boundary of Stock and the former Buttsbury parishes, which bisected the roundhouse. The site is on the south side of Common Road, at or close to the British Legion Hall standing east of the Baker's Arms (formerly the Jolly Miller). TQ 693991

(2) Post and tower mills, the latter north of the former, subsequently joined by (1) above. The tower mill is preserved by Essex County Council and stands on the east side of Mill Lane 130 yards north of its junction with Mill Road leading east towards Wickford. TQ 698987 (□ 232a,b; I 7; II 92-4)

(1) THREADGOLD'S MILL AND THE ORIGINS OF THE THREE MILLS ON STOCK COMMON

The earliest reference discovered to the western site is in 1779, when William Threadgold, of Stock, was miller[1]. In October, 1780, he insured his windmill and going gears for £400, a sum suggesting a new mill[2]. The Threadgolds were described in the early 19th century as of Buttsbury. In April, 1784, were for sale 'two capital freehold Wind Corn Mills, with Store-houses under the same' together with a dwelling house and two acres on Stock Common, and in July of that year a repeat notice refers to the 'new' mill[3]. The description suggests post mills with roundhouses, presumably one at each of the sites (1) and (2). Chapman and André (1777) record on their map a mill at the east site, shown also by Warburton, Bland and Smyth (c1724), and by estate maps of dates c1685 and 1733[4]. None of these maps indicates a mill mound, but a plan of Lord Petre's estates in Stock (1779), besides showing a windmill where expected at the east site, places 'Windmill Hill', a small circle of hachures, 375 yards to the south east in a corner of the common, clearly the position of an earlier windmill[5]. The map of 1733 records a Mill Hill Field at approximately 691969 in the demesne of Blunts manor in the extreme south of the parish[6]. References to 16th-century millers in Stock will be found under *The First Five Hundred Years* (Vol. I, pp. 98-100).

On the preliminary survey for the O.S. 1in. map (1799), two mills appear, one to the west and one to the east. According to family tradition, the tower mill was built c1800[7], and it may be noted that John Madle of Stock, miller and mealman, insured in 1796 the contents of one mill only in the parish, described as timber-built[8]. Access to additional material since the publication of the second volume of the present work suggests that the tower mill was erected c1816. William Moss, who appears first in local records in 1802,[9] insured his milling property in 1806 for £1400, including the post mill and roundhouse, perhaps newly built, for £500, the machinery for £100 and the stock and utensils for £370.[10] In 1815 a private enclosure map shows the post, but not the tower, mill; however, the schedule indicates the late acquisition by Moss of the tower site[11]. In 1818 there was a press reference to Stock Mills, and in the following year a parish survey included the tower mill[12]; these records place the mill's origin to within a year or two of 1816.

In 1802, William Threadgold, miller and farmer, insured his post mill with roundhouse for £300 and contents for £110[13], and his name was coupled until his death at the age of 80 in 1826 with the sale of mill parts, which, in 1827, at the time of the disposal of his stock, included a pair of new 5ft. French stones, a mill shaft 21ft. long, a crowntree and two crosstrees, and 200 French burrs[14]. George Threadgold, also of Buttsbury Mill, took as wife in 1818 the eldest daughter of William Moss, of Stock Mills. Threadgold's mill was destined to make that short journey also, on a carriage, being erected in 1845 between the tower and post mills[15]. It was held freehold by George Threadgold in 1832, and by William Threadgold as owner-occupier in 1843, when in the tithe apportionment for Stock he was recorded at 'Mill (part of)'[16]. A perambulation of the bounds of Stock in 1817 proceeded to a mark on the roundhouse of Threadgold's mill[17].

(2) THE TWO, AND LATER THREE, MILLS ON STOCK COMMON

The post mill here, at the east site, was held in 1795 by Robert Woodgate[18], who received letters in 1798 threatening to burn it down; the offenders were easily traced as debtors to Woodgate, and were arrested and brought before the assizes[19]. William Moss, born in 1774, came from Thaxted to take over the post mill, probably in or shortly before 1802[20]. He was active in helping to found the local Congregational Church in 1813, prior to which the mill house was specially licensed for use as a place of worship[21]. As William Moss the elder, he died in 1859[22]. He made his mark locally for his strong support of the temperance movement, and the Stock historian, L. Donald Jarvis, rescued from oblivion one of a number of verses extolling the miller's virtues, as recollected by an elderly resident. It is insubstantial but authentic Victoriana:

> Oh, have you heard the miller-saint? —
> With heart so stout, though voice so faint,
> Who says the poisons beer and gin
> Make earth to weep and hell to grin —
> The champion of teetotallers!

232a *Stock Mills, a painting dated c 1834, showing the two mills then standing. The tower mill, now preserved, then had hand winding and a stage*

William Moss junior, of Stock, miller, dissolved partnership with John Moss in 1838, and eventually became insolvent in 1852[23]. This William Moss was less hardy than his founding-father, and had the special misfortune (for a miller) to be asthmatic. It is said that on leaving Stock mills, probably following the sale of 1853, Moss took on some 13 milling situations in 12 years, including the business at Windmill Hill, Gravesend, Kent, and that at Wimbledon Common, Surrey[24]. The milling at Stock was still nominally run by William Moss junior according to *Kelly's* 1855 and 1859. Moss died in 1865, aged 63. Later known millers were John Pertwee (1863, 66), Joseph Clover (1870, 90), Mrs Mary Clover (1894, 98), William Mayes (1902, 17) and Frank Semmens (1926, 29). The tower mill stopped work c1930; the two post mills are said to have been demolished c1890. All three mills were stated to be driving two pairs of stones in 1853, when they were offered for sale following Moss' insolvency[25].

Two paintings of dates c1834 and c1862 have survived, and a comparison of them is of interest, since they pre- and post-date the arrival of the third mill. The earlier painting shows the tower mill with hand winding from a stage at first-floor level from which the four anti-clockwise common sails were reefed. The white post mill was similarly equipped with respect to sails, and was winded by tail pole. There was a projection at the lower rear of the body, perhaps to accommodate a small office, as at Moreton, and this is seen in the later painting, in which Threadgold's mill appears placed about midway between its predecessors, which were 90 yards apart, the tower being the more northerly. All sails turned in the same sense. The newcomer was drawn smaller than the other post mill, and a notable feature of both was a mobile staging mounted on four wheels, not unlike a costermonger's barrow in appearance, which was braced up by angled timbers to the

forward corner posts and perhaps to the side girts also. This turned with the mill, gave protection from the moving sails, and also access to them when needed, an arrangement not noted on other Essex mills.

The author regrets that the sequence of the mode of drive to the stones in the tower mill is incorrectly stated in two earlier volumes (I 36, II 71, 80). There was in fact one change only — from overdrive on the present bin floor to underdrive to the stones on their transfer to the floor below. Vincent Pargeter points out that two of the 14 ft. 8 in. long posts supporting the bridgetrees and the upright shaft (see the technical description in Vol. II) have been cut from the main post of a post mill. Their identity is revealed by quarterbar mortises and by traces of score marks left by former sheers. It is possible that the modifications to the machinery took place at the time of the demolition of the adjacent post mills, allegedly c1890, when Joseph Clover was miller. The tower mill had still only two pairs of stones in 1853, and Christy, who put in the iron machinery, operated from 1869. If Clover had visions c1890 of applying steam power to the great spur gear, they were evidently dissipated by his death, for Mrs Mary Clover succeeded him as miller for much of the 1890s, and it is not until 1902 that *Kelly* records the use of wind and steam against the name of William Mays *(sic)*.

Several late sale notices relating to the tower mill are preserved; that dated 1906 refers to the iron windshaft and engine shed, and gives Mayes' rent as £50 for the mill, dwelling house, &c. and 4 acres[26]. A detailed

232b *Stock tower mill. The great spur wheel, a stone nut (disengaged), and the bevel gear for engine drive*

description is offered in 1920[27], in which year the property was bought by R. Spurling for £1040, and, Mayes having died, the mill was wind and steam driven by Frank Semmens, one of his employees, until about 1930, after which an engine continued in use. In 1936 the windmill was scheduled as a building of historic interest, and in 1943 was offered for sale by the executors of the late Spurling[28]. It has been taken over by the county council, who preserve it as a landmark and permit viewing by appointment. The mill still sports its handsome boat-shaped cap, but with the added fantail removed, so that a side view approximates to the original, showing a large rear overhang. It is the sole survivor of a complex of mills and outbuildings; the mill house itself, which so often is the last survivor, is said to have been the only building in Stock to have been destroyed by bombing in the second world war. The tower mill, apart from losing its entourage, has been further diminished by the Lilliputian freeholders who have settled within an arm's length of the potential swing of the sails.

Addendum

Further to the references to the Whiskerds, millers at Stock in the 16th century (see I, 98), Dr F. G. Emmison contributes from his *Wills at Chelmsford*, Vol. 5, 1584-91:

'Will No. 249: of Charles Whiskerd of Stock, dated 20 Aug. 1587, proved 23 Jan. 1587/8. To Henry Motte my mill with the mill house in Stock until John son of John Whiskerd late of Southminster deceased is 21, on condition that Henry enter into bond to my overseers to maintain the mill with all implements belonging, as stones, brass and all iron and timber work with sufficient reparation (and by other of the same occupation of millers if occasion shall so serve); if he refuse, my gift to be void. I will that Henry shall pay to his mother for 3 years and she being unmarried (i.e. not re-married) such a yearly rent out of my mill as they shall agree upon, and after the 3 years £5 to my executrix, and she shall occupy the mill house until John son of John Whiskerd is 21. To George Whiskerd my mill called London Mill in St Martin's-in-the-Fields (co. Middx.) in the tenure of Henry Hatton. To John son of John Whiskered of Southminster deceased and his heirs male my said mill called Stock Mill with the mill house and outhouses at 21; if he die without such issue, the mill and land to George Whiskerd and his heirs male; for default of issue, to Robert Whiskerd minister [*sic*: not identified as a cleric] and his heirs male.'

NOTES

1 E.R.O. Q/SBb 296/9
2 Sun Pol. No. 433634 4.10.1780 H.E.S. Simmons
3 C.C. 23.4. & 16.7.1784. Also C.C. 30.4. & 11.7.1788 refer to the new-built post mill with 2 pr. stones, late the property of Stephen Saxbe, deceased. Edward Lee was miller at Stock in 1758 (E.R.O. Q/SBb 215/19)
4 E.R.O. D/DP P14/2 (*c* 1685); D/DU 431 (1733)
5 E.R.O. D/DP P34 (1779). For pre-1700 references see *Rectors of Two Parishes and Their Times*, Rev. F. W. Austen, 1943, pp. 35, 57, 80-1, 87 &c.
6 Per R. Hawksley. See also E.R.O. D/DU 266/18, 20 (1638, 1663)
7 *Stock, Essex*, L. Donald Jarvis, 1934, p. 37
8 R.E. Pol. No. 154004 25.11.1796 per H.E.S. Simmons
9 E.R.O. land tax, per R. Hawksley
10 Sun Pol. No. 786476 31.1.1806
11 E.R.O. D/DP P52 per R. Hawksley
12 C.C. 14.8.1818; E.R.O. 54/28/2 (1819)
13 Sun Pol. No. 736858 *c* Oct. 1802
14 C.C. 8.9.1826, 25.5.1827
15 See Vol. I, 'Windmills in Transit,' p. 64
16 K. & E.M. 24.4.1832; E.R.O. D/CT 336A
17 Per Dr Turner. Notes on Essex windmills, Southend R.L.
18 C.C. 17.4.1795
19 C.C. 27.7. & 3.8.1798
20 See Note 9
21 See Note 7
22 Per L. D. Jarvis, interviewed by R. W. Smith (1972)
23 *Lond. Gaz.* 24.7.1838 & 13.1.1852 per H.E.S. Simmons
24 See Note 22
25 E.S. 25.2.1853
26 E.R.O. B4194
27 E.R.O. B3678
28 See Note 22

Takeley

(1) Mill of unknown type. Stood on the north side of Stane Street (A120) approximately 250 yards west of the church approach. TL 552213

(2) Post mill: Piper's Mill. Stood in the north-east corner of a field behind the existing 'The Old Mill' inn, and 110 yards from it on the north side of Takeley Street. TL 540213

(3) Post mill, known as Takeley Old Mill or Clarke's Mill. Stood a few yards east of the mill house south of the road to Molehill Green, and 220 yards east of the T-junction. TL 557233 (□233)

(1) SITE WEST OF 'MILLERS' NEAR THE CHURCH

A mill is placed at the top of the rise from the west by Chapman and André (1777), the first O.S. 1in. map (surv. 1799) and Greenwood (1825), none of which shows a mill site (2) at Takeley Street further west. The only press reference to this earlier mill discovered is in the *Chelmsford Chronicle* dated 2nd October, 1791, which reads: 'The lease of a good-accustomed windmill to be disposed of, with French stones, and flour mill, and all necessities complete, standing by the roadside in the parish of Takeley, near the street. Inquire at the mill of John Trott'. Probably Edward Mumford then entered; he left to mill at Quendon in 1793[1]. It is possible that this mill was eventually moved to the position behind the inn, as Piper's mill was by all accounts of a primitive nature.

(2) PIPER'S MILL

Takeley Street mill was described as 'Old Windmill' on the O.S. 1 in. map surveyed in 1902. Like the Clarkes at the other end of the parish, the Pipers resolutely held their mill prow to wind over many decades. The land tax records give Isaac Piper in 1820 in succession to Samuel Clarke junior in 1819, and list him in 1826 as miller and farmer under Nicholas Patmore as owner[2], presumably at site (1). Later Pipers were John (1832), Isaac (1839, 63), Henry (1870, 94). Again like the Clarkes, they combined flour with beer retailing. The mill property was let at an annual rent of £30 to Henry Piper in 1884 when it was sold to J. Flinn for £500, comprising a post windmill, indoor brewhouse and 4 acres of land[3]. Local descendants of the Pipers state that the mill stopped work in 1896-7 and was pulled down 1904-5.

On the tithe map (1838) the mill is indicated by four brick piers in plan[4], and it was remembered by the Clarke family as devoid of roundhouse. The sails were two spring and two cloth, the middlings being mortised through a wooden windshaft. They drove one pair of stones[5].

(3) TAKELEY OLD MILL or CLARKE'S MILL

This post mill was said to have been in the occupation of the Clarke family for some 200 years. It was part of the Clulow and later Mumford property of Waltham Hall Farm, and is mentioned in those connections in documents covering 1796-1854[6]. It was insured in 1776 by Henry Clarke of Hallingbury, miller and farmer, for £80, and by James Stanes of Ashdon in 1780 for £150, then in the occupation of Samuel Clarke[7]. In the millers' invasion returns of 1798, two millers, Peter Harris and Samuel Clarke, each describing himself as at Takeley Mill, promised six 280lb. sacks of flour daily 'if wind permits'.[8] So Clarke succeeded Clarke, always Samuel in the directories from 1832 until 1890, when Mrs. Elizabeth Clarke is given at Mill End, to be followed by Samuel again. The traditional occupation was continued by another Samuel, one of some ten children of the last to mill by wind, who was employed at Hasler's, Dunmow.

Details of the 'Old Mill' — so called by the family — were recorded in 1936 by Donald W. Muggeridge from that source. Latterly it had four single-shuttered spring sails, one pair with wooden and one with canvas shutters, but had formerly worked on four cloth sails, then two cloth and two spring, and, from c1886, on four spring. In the middle 1880s some capital expenditure was made for 'modernisation'. Fred Chopping,

233 *Takeley Old Mill, Molehill Green. Pulled down just before 1900*

employed by Gentry of Braintree, millwright, fitted a cast-iron windshaft to replace the old wooden one, and the substructure, hitherto open, was enclosed in a 16-sided weatherboarded roundhouse. The tail pole, which had a yoke for turning, was sawn off at the rear steps and a six-bladed fantail provided for winding.

The internal arrangements were unusual. The brake wheel, of wood, with applewood cogs, drove two pairs of stones: one very large pair of French burrs, of 5ft. diameter, direct through an ordinary gear, and a small pair, of 3ft. diameter, consisting of a peak bedstone and a burr runner, by a belt drive. The late Rev. F. G. Clarke recorded that the small pair of stones was on the top floor, an arrangement otherwise unknown to him. Presumably there was a short vertical shaft above the windshaft with a gear to receive the drive from the top of the brake wheel, and also a pulley to transmit the belt drive horizontally to the rear to turn the stones. It would represent a relatively inexpensive device to increase a primitive mill's output. One may note that St Leonard's Mill, Winchelsea, Sussex, had a pair of 3ft. stones in the top floor, but driven from the tail wheel.[9] Takeley mill also had a flour dresser and an oat crusher.

The mill body was supported by an oak post and substructure and an elm crowntree, substantial parts of which were eventually incorporated in the building of an 'old' house in Cambridge. The single known photograph shows the mill with later additions, and Sam Clarke, the miller, standing by the roundhouse door. It was clearly a mill with small capacity, probably built originally to take only one pair of stones. The sails turned anti-clockwise. The forward corner posts were apparently of the 'gunstock-head' variety, thickened out forwards from the waist upwards, in a manner more pronounced than at Mill Green, Ingatestone, and pointing, perhaps, to the use of inverted tree trunks, cut and trimmed to suit their function in the mill.

In c1897 the mill was falling into disrepair and Clarke asked Gentry for an estimate for work needed; as this amounted to some £400 instead of the £100-£150 expected, the mill was pulled down. The last miller said that it was once possible to count seven windmills from his tail steps: Takeley (Piper's) mill; Little Canfield, Hatfield Broad Oak, Elsenham (sic), Broxted, Great Easton and Henham. Not one of these remains.

Addendum

Windmill, 1550. (*Feet of Fines, Essex*, Vol. V, p. 33).

NOTES

1 E.R.O. D/DYv 217-18.
2 In E.R.O.
3 E.W.N. 18.7. & 15.8.1884.
4 E.R.O. D/CT 342.
5 Per D. W. Muggeridge as informed by Samuel Clarke senior.
6 E.R.O. D/DHp T1.
7 Sun Pol. No. 363210 1.1.1776 & R.E.Pol. No. 79059 9.10.1780 per H. E. S. Simmons.
8 E.R.O. L/R 1/1.
9 *The Windmills of Sussex*, Brunnarius, 1979, p. 108. R. Hawksley states that the drive was by belt.

Tendring

(1) Mill of unknown type, but probably a smock mill c1840. Site occupied by an octagonal cottage on the west side of Crow Lane opposite the narrow turning to Far Thorpe Green. TM 152235

(2) Tower mill. Stood integrally with the now converted granary immediately north of Mill House, which lies 200 yards west of the Weeley road from a point 100 yards from its north end. TM 150239 (□ 234)

(1) THE SOUTH MILL

Chapman and André (1777) and Greenwood (1825) place a windmill at this point, and the tithe map (1842) and apportionment (1843) have 'Old Mill and Yard' in the ownership of John Cardinall and occupation of John Bones, who held also the tower windmill to the north.[1] The mill was doubtless worked in conjunction with a water corn mill which lay on the Holland Brook below, at Crow Bridge, and which was described as 'lately disannulled' in a notice relating to the sale of machinery in 1786.[2]

In July, 1843, and April, 1844, two 'very substantial tower windmills' at an unspecified location were to be let according to press notices emanating from Thorpe and Mistley.[3] Six pairs of stones, patent sails and self-winding tackle were to be had, together with 22 acres of farmland, 'centrically situated in a capital corn district' and 2½ miles from a wharf. These details leave little room for doubt that the Tendring mills were for disposal; the wharf would have been at Beaumont Quay, and Cardinall's mill property at the time of the tithe apportionment comprised close on 22 acres. The 'Old Mill', which may have been so called merely to distinguish it from the new brick tower mill, has not been traced further, but one questions whether it may not have become the Bradfield windmill apparently set up by 1846, but burnt down in 1857.

The present octagonal cottage at the south Tendring site does not appear to be a converted mill base.

(2) THE TOWER MILL

The precise date of erection of the tower mill is uncertain, but Greenwood (surv. 1824) records a symbol at the site. In 1827 Charles Bones, miller, when under financial duress, surrendered the copyhold premises to the lord of the manor of New Hall in Tendring, John Cardinall Esq., including 'the entirety of the windmill lately erected on the copyhold hereditaments . . . and also the round house thereof'.[4] The mill was in the tenure of John Bones, son of Charles, who was miller and farmer in 1841 on the lord's land, and in 1848 was held by Jonathan Bones. Subsequently it was run by William Balls (1863, 1874, with steam also in 1882), by Mrs Margaret Balls (1890), and then by A. Goddard using both wind and steam (1894, 1910). The Cardinall estate was sold in 1910, when Goddard was leasing the mill at £48 per annum.[5] The massive brick-built windmill worked three pairs of stones, each of 52in. diameter, and had very extensive storage space, having on two flanks a two-storey granary built on, over which turned four double-shuttered anti-clockwise patent sails winded by a six-bladed fantail. The mill was later taken over by A. E. Borneman, who ran the business by oil engine, the mill sails having been removed at about the time of his arrival c1910 according to one local informant, and some two years later according to others. The mill was described as disused on the third O.S. 6in. map (1921).

Harry Gooch, born in 1894, recorded in 1970 his memories of the mill, to which he took his gleanings as a boy.[6] He believed that Goddard entered c1894 and bought the mill in 1910, and thought that the sails had by then already been removed following the cracking of a middling in the poll end. He stated that the mill had six floors. During hostilities the buildings became quarters for prisoners of war, who were taken under escort into

234 *Tendring tower mill. Demolished c 1921*

the fields to work. The windmill tower was finally demolished in 1921-2.

NOTES
1 E.R.O. D/CT 343
2 I.J. 15.4.1786.
3 E.S. 28.7.1843 & 19.4.1844.
4 E.R.O. D/DSz T7. The mill is not mentioned in a mortgage of the land in 1817 (D/DBm M270).
5 Sale notice in private possession.
6 Notes from Roland W. Smith.

Terling

Smock mill. Stands today, preserved as a landmark and private residence, half a mile west of the village centre. TL 764150 (□ 221a; I 34; II 89, 90)

TERLING mill harbours a number of secrets in its loose-knit frame which have not been wrested from it despite diligent enquiry. There is the persistent tradition that it was erected in Cressing in about 1770 and removed to Terling some 60 years later. Neither date has been substantiated or disproved and both appear to stem from the writings — part conjecture — of Alfred Hills in 1930.[1] He spoke with Bonner, the last miller, and presumably recorded bona fide such shreds of truth as a hundred years of village tattle had left intact. In submitting to the *Essex Review* a fervent apologia for the windmill as a feature of the cultural landscape and for Bonner's mill in particular, Hills refrained from pushing his luck as far as the press reporter of later years, according to whom 'the great sails first began to turn a year or two after the winds of Heaven had scattered the Spanish Armada'.[2] What seems probable is that the mill was built or re-erected c1818, and was initially designed for grinding bark. In 1818, one Wood, for whom a mill

in Terling was erected, announced that he was removing to Witham, and that his new windmill, now for sale, could be converted to corn grinding at 'an inconsiderable expense'.[3] Chappell, of Witham, millwright, may have had a hand in the building. He was available for consultation to any prospective purchaser, and was doubtless a descendant of the Thomas Chappell, Terling millwright, of 1733.[4] The question of removal and the form of construction of this windmill are separately treated in Volumes I and II. The tithe apportionment of 1844 records field names indicating a plurality of windmill sites in the parish, one of which may have carried a windmill for a short period after 1700.[5]

Formerly part of a large estate, the 19th-century windmill at Terling was seldom paraded before the public eye in sale particulars. It was held in 1844 by Arthur Robert Goodday, whose family name was coupled with the mill until 1883. Among tenant-millers were Frederick Rust (1859), who dissolved partnership with Goodday in 1850,[6] and Charles Joseph Doe (1882, 1902). Rust was summoned in 1859 for using light weights amounting to a loss of about 10oz. per 56 lb.; in adjudging that 12 months' wear could so reduce a weight, the court fined him 2s. with 3s. costs and he was obliged to forfeit the weights; he escaped lightly, there being found no intention to defraud.[7]

Martin Bonner was miller after Doe (1902, 12), followed by Herbert Bonner (1914-1950), who worked at the mill for almost 50 years, retaining an active interest during the short time when Leslie, his son, carried the main burden of the business.[8] At the age of 78, still 'running about the top of the mill like a cat', and reportedly within two days of completing his half century at the mill, it fell to him to bring the whole of the county's 750 years of windmill history to a truly tragic close.[9] Alone in the mill on the morning of 30th March, 1950, when the tractor in a shed nearby was driving the machinery by belt, he climbed up in the region of the great spur wheel for some purpose unknown. Here, in a position not normally accessible, the Factories Act required no guard. As had befallen so many of his trade, in a second's disregard he was seized by the turning cogs. His cries for help were heard outside and his son and others rushed in to see what was amiss. The victim gave directions for his release and the frantic rescuers strove to reverse the direction of the cogs, but each time a gain was made the weight of the machinery edged them back. The services were summoned and the weight of the trapped miller's body was supported on a board. When finally freed by firemen, Herbert Bonner was dead, without having been able to gasp an explanation for his plight.

At the inquest, death was held due to multiple injuries and a verdict of accidental death given. Bonner had served on the parish council for 40 years and had acted as churchwarden for most of that time. His passing was deeply regretted by a wide circle of friends and by those who had espoused the cause of windmill preservation.

One working mill is worth a dozen derelicts in the opinion of many. In July, 1921, Bonner had bought the mill and cottage for £550 from Praed Wood, of Sparrows, Terling, farmer; his daughter-in-law eventually sold in 1968 to Lord Rayleigh's Farms Incorporated for £3,500. The windmill and cottage stood untenanted for a spell while planning permission for conversion of the mill into a residence was sought. This was granted in 1970 to Mr A. Cater, a building expert, and the cottage was hived off as a separate entity. Both properties are now well cared for and retain much of their external charm. The mill had developed an ominous lean towards the head, as one may now rightly say, the sails and cap having been immobile for some years and locked facing west. The cost of repairs and modifications to the mill, and of the erection of a built-on two-storied house, were initially estimated at £6,000 each, and indeed, in 1950 the mill was in no condition to work indefinitely by wind without a radical overhaul. Alone to make good the weatherboarding in 1970, the cost was estimated at approximately Bonner's purchase price for the whole property in 1921. By mid-1974 the conversion to a residence was completed, only the largest items of machinery being retained.

In 1935 the mill was struck by a violent gale which carried parts of the fan assembly to a distance of several hundred yards, and the main sails were held with difficulty. The mill was nevertheless put into repair, and worked until 1949 on four double-shuttered anti-clock-wise patents, which, with a white domed cap over the latterly tarred body, were highly photogenic. This attribute drew in 1937 the director of the comedy film 'Oh, Mr Porter!' featuring Will Hay, who chose this mill for the hilarious sequence when a round trip on the sails gave the hunted a respite from the pursuit of the hunters. As the mill was temporarily inactive, the sails were turned by hand. It is said that first dummies, then professional acrobats, were employed, and that the miller climbed on to a sail and freed one of the latter when his rope became entangled.[10] These sails turned three pairs of millstones and an oat crusher at the same time, the stones being underdriven, though in later days Bonner was by no means satisfied with such air currents as came his way; he felt aggrieved at the many trees which had been left to spring up around, and it is said that he sought legal protection against the spread of housing towards his beloved mill.

Addendum

Harry Apling in *Norfolk Corn Windmills*, Vol. I, p. 92 (1984) states in his account of Diss tower mill: 'The last pair of sails, which had come from Framlingham post mill when that was pulled down in August 1921, were later taken to Terling, Essex, and put on the smock mill there.'

NOTES

1 E.R. Vol. XXXIX, 1930, p.84. Article: *Four Essex Windmills*.

2 E.C. 7.4.1950.

3 C.C. 17.4.1818. For full details see Vol. I, *Windmills in Transit*.

4 E.R.O. D/A CR 13, p. 392.

5 E.R.O. D/CT 344A. See Vol. I, Appendix A.

6 *Lond. Gaz.*, 2.7.1850, per H. E. S. Simmons.

7 E.S. 17.6.1859.

8 Deeds relating to mill property in private possession, 1883-1968, summarised by Roland W. Smith.

9 See note 2.

10 E.C. No. 102, July 1965. Article by Jean Gumbrell.

Great Tey

(1) Mill of unknown type. Stood in the angle between Top Road and New Barn Road a little north of New Barn Farm at Tey Hall Green (late 18th century). TL 887264

(2) Post mill. Sparkes' Mill *c*1845-55. Stood 330 yards north west of the church and in the north-west corner of a field in the neighbourhood of the modern Greenfield Drive. TL 890259

(1) TEY HALL GREEN MILL

This mill is marked by Chapman and André (1777). On 2nd June, 1740, a licence was granted to James Pain to build a windmill on waste land belonging to the manor of Great Tey, of which the copyhold was later confirmed. James Deadman entered in 1754, James Walsh, miller, of Great Tey, in 1757, and Benjamin Digby in 1760, whose brother and heir James sold in 1763 to William Barrett, already installed as miller. From Barrett the mill passed to his wife and then grand-daughter, who, immediately on entering, in 1782, sold to Richard Rand.[1] Rand secured a mortgage loan of £200 from John Deeks senior in December, 1782, conveying conditionally 'all that windmill for the grinding of corn . . . upon Tey Hall Green'.[2] The mill was gone by 1795 or before, as noted below, and the site today is flat and under cultivation.

(2) SPARKES', LATER SACH'S MILL

Rand demolished the old mill and erected a new one on the later site while in possession of the land at both points before and after the discontinuity of operation, and there is no evidence of the two mills' co-existence.

The switch in milling site may have taken place in late 1791, for in January, 1792, Rand, described as miller and shopkeeper, then insured his tenements and shop in Great Tey for £80, and his windmill 'near' with contents and a brick roundhouse for £300.[3] The mill house stood on the north side of the village street opposite Warrens Farm, and Rand would obviously have benefited by operating his mill 500 yards nearer; nevertheless he was bankrupt in 1795. In a statement of property mortgaged was included 1½ acres . . . 'with a windmill thereon erected . . . by Richard Rand . . . and also all that parcel

. . . whereon a windmill . . . lately stood upon Tey Hall Green'. A sale notice of 28th July, 1795, referred to the latter as the old windmill, while describing its successor as lately built and having a roundhouse 'in which may be pitched 20 score or upwards of sacks'.[4] Thus there was no mill transfer involved. In response to the forced sale of Rand's estates, John Green of Fordham, farmer, bought the mill at an auction for £493 9s. Green sold for £430 in September, 1802, to Zachariah Lewsey, who later moved to Ardleigh, selling the windmill and lands to John Collis in April, 1810, for £500.

The mill, with bricked roundhouse, was before the sale advertised as having a good pair of French stones and was part of a compact estate.[5] For nearly 30 years after c1820, the Willsher family, farmers in Great Tey, owned the property, leasing it to Samuel Ely of Copford, miller, in 1825 for six years at a rent of £36, and subsequently to the Sparkes.[6] In 1840 Ephraim Willsher had as tenant Susan Sparkes, but George Sparkes carried on the milling until a little before his death in 1859.[7] In 1857 the executors of the will of Jane Willsher sold the windmill to Josiah Nice for £400 and the fixtures for £108. Nice took a loan of £250 and let the mill to Thomas Winson for £50 annual rent, but sold to John and Frederick Sach in 1859 for £659 14s. 6d, £550 being paid for the mill alone. In 1857 it had two pairs of stones at the head, while still occupied by G. Sparkes[8], but in 1859 a sale notice mentioned three pairs of 4ft. 2in. French burrs, two driven by wind and one by portable steam power.[9] The mill had evidently been radically altered since 1810, and the body contained three floors in the manner of Bocking and Mill Green mills.

The Sachs' use of the windmill ended in January, 1865:[10]

'On Friday night a post windmill at Great Tey, belonging to Mr Sach, of Coggeshall, and in the occupation of a person named Sexton, was totally destroyed by fire. It appears that the weather on the night in question was very stormy, and the sails of the mill were blown round with such forcible rapidity that the men were unable to stop them; the continued friction caused the timber-work to ignite, and the mill was burnt to the ground. The property is insured in the Essex and Suffolk Fire Office.'

The first and second O.S. 6in. maps, surveyed in 1875 and 1896, both show an open circle with the words 'Old Windmill', indicating some remains, presumably including part of the mill body.

NOTES

1 E.R.O. D/DU 304/28-31 per R. Hawksley.
2 Deeds in private possession (1782-1859) include windmill.
3 Sun Pol. No. 594988 18.1.1792 per H. E. S. Simmons.
4 *County Chronicle* 28.7.1795.
5 C.C. 24.11.1809.
6 E.R.O. D/DE1 T142.

7 E.R.O. D/CT 345A & E.S. 12.8.1859.
8 E.S. 17.7.1857.
9 See note 2.
10 E.S. 13.1.1865.

Little Tey

Mill of unknown type. Stood near the parish church; exact site unknown. TL 892237

LITTLE TEY mill is known only from a sale notice in the *Essex Standard* of 8th November, 1861, announcing the auction, under a distress for rent, of: 'The Small Windmill, with going gears, pair of 3ft. French stones and iron shaft, driving and spur wheel, sails &c., situate near the Church . . . (and other items) of Mr Samuel Evans'.

Today, near the church, is Church Farm, and one quarter of a mile distant lies Knave Farm. A Mill Lane appears on the first O.S. 6in. map (1875) half a mile south west of the church.

Marks Tey

Windmill Fields, 1624. (E.R.O. D/DC 5/87).

Thaxted

(1) Post mill. Stood on the east side of the Dunmow road about 100 yards south of the Bardfield road and roughly opposite Totman's Farm. TL 615306

(2) Post mill. Stood at Mill End to the south of the town centre in the area behind the Rose and Crown public house. TL 613309

(3) Post mill. Known as Newbiggin or Boyton End Mill. Stood immediately north east of the Fox and Hounds public house (now hotel) and south of the Sampford road. TL 611317 (□ 235)

(4) Post mill. Stood immediately south of 'The Mill House' at Cutlers Green, on the west side of the Debden road approximately opposite the track to Millhill Farm. TL 592311

(5) Post mill. Stood near Sibley's Green, 500 yards east of the Dunmow road and 120 yards south of 'Grace's Farm House', which stands at the exit of the former mill approach. The mill stood against the east side of the track. TL 617283

(6) Tower mill. Lowe's Mill. Stands in restored condition 200 yards south west of the church. TL 609308 (□ 236; II 95-7)

WITH its majestic church, set in a bedrock of exquisite period architecture, Thaxted is an exciting discovery for those who, with the perception of a Wordsworth, are disposed to roam his 'mighty world of eye and ear'. All is intact and authentic, it would appear, even to the sturdy brick windmill, which — odd omission! — was brought as an afterthought under the blanket preservation order over the ancient nucleus, following pressure from the Thaxted Society. And yet, one vitalising element of centuries' standing no longer obtains: the play of wind-mill sails. Greenwood, or his surveyors, in the years around 1820, could count four sets from south to north above the roof tops, and two more within the parish boundary, the highest number attained. Two or more windmills were in work here from the early days of their inception, cocking a snook at the infant Chelmer below. If the tower mill's sails are made to turn again, it will be no more than Thaxted's due.

(1) & (2) The Mill End post mills

A number of sale notices and other records relating to these mills occur in the period 1790-1830, which make it possible to trace broadly the sequence of owners and occupiers in each case, but the allocation of the two groupings to their rightful sites remains tentative.

The windmill described as near the Saracen's Head in 1790 and near the King's Arms in 1808, was probably that whose site lies close to the Rose and Crown of today (site (2)). Joseph Butcher insured in 1790 for £150 a windmill, timber built, 'with roundhouse under', near the first-mentioned inn, and in 1805 John Abbott entered as tenant on a lease expiring in 1811.[1] The free-hold was to be put to auction by Thomas Butcher of Shalford, miller, in 1808, the post mill then being stated to contain one pair of stones, but was again offered by Butcher in 1814 and 1815.[2] Abraham Barnard suc-ceeded, remaining until 1823, after which further changes occurred,[3] and there is no record to suggest that this mill survived after 1824. Like its close neighbour, it appeared both on Chapman and André (1777) and on Greenwood's map (surv. 1824). Both mills were described as post mills in the church rates.[4]

A mill at site (1), south of the Bardfield road, was evidently that mentioned in 1584 in the Quarter Sessions rolls, when it was recorded that Christopher Kents of Thaxted 'for lack of a bridge laying over a brook near Ryc(h)monds Grene, doth annoy the footway to church, market and mill'.[5] Continued occupation is indicated by Ogilby's *Britannia* (1675) and by Warburton, Bland and Smyth (c1724). The windmill is likely to have been that 'known as Old Mill' insured by Samuel Clift in 1778, and stated to have a roundhouse. The cover was doubled to £100 three years later.[6] Samuel Root insured what may further be presumed to have been the south mill in 1795; the figure of £200 on the timber structure and round-house points to substantial repairs or a total replace-ment.[7] From Root's widow in 1802, the tenancy at least of the mill was conveyed to James Camp, who, on his death in 1821, passed the freehold to Kezia, his wife.[8] In May, 1829, was offered at the Rose and Crown by Franklin and Glascock, auctioneers, a capital post windmill with two pairs of stones, 'standing in a superior

position for wind and trade near Mill End in the town of Thaxted'.[9] This must have been the mill held by Kezia Kempton in 1830, who was given under Town Street in the land tax returns. George Cowell was recorded as in occupation 1826-30, but in 1831 we have 'land, late Camp's mill' in the church rate lists.

The tithe apportionment (1844) lists Mill Pasture and Mill Field opposite Totman's Farm, whence the ground slopes away to north, south, and west. There is no hint of the former position of the north mill.

(3) Newbiggin or Boyton End Mill, by the Fox and Hounds

This does not appear to have been the site of the north mill or the church mill of the 14th century,[10] though it is still plainly marked by the substantial remains of a mound 10-12ft. high, with a ditch on the northern side. In 1623 the abutments of a pasture in Thaxted make reference to 'Reades Lane near the new mill' and to 'Dameries Mead'.[11] Damary's Mead on the first O.S. 6in. map shows the 'new mill' to have been at site (3), but it is unwise to assume unreservedly that we have come across the initiation of a milling operation. A mill replacement is possible, and 'new' as a name element can live to a ripe old age: the mill at site (3) under Stebbing serves as an illustration. Ogilby's *Britannia* (1675) and Warburton, Bland and Smyth (c1724) record the

235 *Thaxted: Fox and Hounds Mill. Probably gone by 1893*

Boyton End mill, which is not shown on the revised second O.S. 1in. (1893) or on the second 6in. (1896), though said to have been demolished in 1897.[12] Two surviving photographs give the impression of a long enduring mill which retained primitive features to the end.

In 1796 the mill, with contents, was insured for £200.[13] It was bequeathed in 1817 by James Guyver, previously in his own occupation, to his son James, who was returned as miller at Boyton End in 1830.[14] There was then no mention of the inn adjacent, but on the death of the second James in 1835 was offered the lease of the free public house called the Fox and Hounds, with brew-house and premises, in addition to the windmill driving one pair of French stones.[15] In 1844, Daniel Britton was tenant under Richard and William Randall, brewers, of Dunmow.[16] Further millers and also victuallers were John Belsham (1848) and Thomas Belsham (1878); in 1880 the brewers Randall advertised the tenancy with pinch-penny economy:[17]

> Fox and Hounds Public-House and Flour-Mill, Thaxted. This well-known property to be let; it has been in the same family for upwards of 50 years. — Apply personally to R. and W. Randall, Brewery, Great Dunmow.

Kelly's directory of 1882 gives Frederick Charles Heath at the Fox and Hounds, but makes no mention of milling.

No details of the mill's interior are to hand, but its salient external features are enough to show that it would have made a fascinating contrast to its sophisticated counterpart by the church, had it been spared another century. The substructure stood exposed, with the down-curved crosstrees supported just over ground level, providing a convenient seat and a platform for sacks. Winding was by tail pole. The body was clearly of small capacity, and must have worked a single pair of stones to the last. There were small elliptical portholes in the centre sides of stone and spout floors. The weather beam was carried forward of the front corner posts with externally provided diagonals to support its ends, and the roof boards ran forward above to give cover. The windshaft was of wood, and was mortised for four common sails turning clockwise, all spread with canvas in the photograph, the motley and threadbare patch-work in one sail advertising the dire poverty, extreme thrift, or disillusionment of the licensee. The weather-boarding on the prow progressed downwards through horizontal lines to a pronounced herringbone pattern, with moulded pendants to discharge the drips.

(4) CUTLERS GREEN MILL

Barely more than sixty years were granted to this post mill. It was to be auctioned at the Sun Inn, Thaxted, in November, 1815, when described as follows[18]:

> A substantial and eminently situated post windmill, built within seven years, with one pair of good French stones and going gears, also 16 rods of leasehold ground, 92 years of which are unexpired; together with a freehold messuage ... and half an acre of garden ground ... situated at Cutler's Green.

Less than two years later it was for sale by private contract as a 'four-post windmill' in the occupation of John Harvey,[19] who was returned by Pigot's directory as miller in 1823, but replaced by John Brown in 1826. In 1830 it was held by the executors of Thomas Woodham Francis,[20] and in 1844 by Thomas Francis junior, under Robert Sackville. Later, it was in the hands of the Giblin family: William (1859) and Elizabeth (1863), and was still in their possession when its career ended violently:

> Essex Weekly News, 14th January, 1870. 'Thaxted. The Late Gale. About twelve (noon on the previous Saturday) a post windmill was blown down on Cutlers Green, belonging to Mr E. Gibling, whose brother-in-law had left the mill only about ten minutes. The body of the mill was broken, but only one sail was injured.'

Today, the mill plot, adjoining the mill house, still preserves the outline as drawn on the tithe map of 1844.

(5) SIBLEYS GREEN MILL

Here was the case of a mill taken to the corn when confidence in the future of wind was running at a high level. The site is flat and featureless, though open enough to take all winds sent, but its comparative remoteness must have proved a factor in the windmill's premature demise. The mill is said to have come into the hands of the Barnard family, farmers, from the Watkinsons by marriage; first Robert, then his son Abraham ran the business.[21] The windmill was insured by Abraham Barnard in September, 1806, for £300, and the stock in trade for a further £100[22]. This is the first known reference.

Abraham was listed as miller by Pigot in 1823, and by his will, proved in 1841, empowered trustees to auction the freehold post mill, farmstead, and 33 acres of land.[23] The mill had one pair of patent sails and two pairs of French stones, undertaking a fair proportion of grist work. A miller's cottage was provided. The whole was bought by William Barnard junior of Stebbing for £1,350.[24] There were Barnards, also, at Folly Mill Farm in Thaxted, and a Samuel Barnard, son of the late Abraham Barnard, in possession of a mill at Finching-field.

Directories enter James Pettit as miller in 1845 and Samuel Pettit in 1848 and in 1859; Charles Ketley was miller and farmer, partnered by Brock, in 1866, 74. In 1862, 63, Charles Wicks was given in Kelly's and White's, probably as the working miller under Ketley.

In April, 1877, Franklin & Son, auctioneers, announced the sale of the entire structure, including two pairs of French stones, stating that the mill had been taken down and that excellent pieces of oak fit for church repairs were to be had.[25] The first O.S. 1:2,500 (1876) indicates that there was no roundhouse.

236 *Thaxted Mill in working order, probably in the early 1900s*

(6) THE TOWER MILL

The ace of Thaxted's windmills is said to have been composed of locally won or fabricated materials: timber from the Park and Borough farms and bricks prepared close by.[26] It was commissioned by John Webb in 1804, as an inscription on the mill exterior testifies, and the stones ran dry at the last around 1910. The rock-like stability of the tower, four feet thick at the base, was paralleled by the constancy of the millers: one Lowe was milling for Webb in 1837 and Harry Lowe ground doggedly on until the last turn of the sails.

The 1837 reference was to an assault and robbery, in which Lowe, on leaving the mill premises in the darkness of a winter's evening, was waylaid by three men and relieved of two to three pounds of silver belonging to his master.[27] A Webb, always John, is recorded as miller in earlier directories, as in *Pigot's* (1823), *White's* (1848), *Post Office* (1850). The Webb of 1853 was an extensive property owner in the town.[28] There was a reference to Laurence Webb, miller, of Thaxted, in 1794.[29]

In 1907 a forlorn attempt was made to sell the freehold of the mill, when Harry Lowe, the then yearly tenant, was paying an annual rent of £35. The notice outlined the salient features: four floors, two double and two single patent sails and three pairs of French stones of 4ft. 3in., 4ft. 6in. and 5ft. diameter. Space adjoining was hopefully offered for the erection of a steam mill, but a buyer did not come forward.[30] The mill stood unattended for more than twenty years until the Thaxted Civic Trust did essential repairs, making the lower floors available to scouts and youth groups, and waterproofing the cap. From the Trust the mill passed to the parish council in the mid-1950s, since when the Thaxted Society, formed in 1964, have taken strenuous action to restore the structure.[31]

A full technical account of this mill will be found in Volume II; a brief outline is here added.

The mill stands 54ft. to the top of the cap internally, and the inside dimensions of the tower are 24ft. at the base and about 15ft. at the curb. The floors in order of descent were dust, bin, stone, spout and ground, but the dust-floor level has been altered. Of the three pairs of overdrift stones, two occupied the original positions, the third was added. Both the windshaft and the upright shaft were of iron and in two parts coupled together. All the main, heavy, components down to the stones have been preserved, partly, no doubt, because there were two capacious floors below, adequate for later, non-milling, uses. Exterior photographs of the mill in working order show sails corresponding to the 1907 sale notice; also visible is a stage at first-floor level and a gallery around the domed cap, behind which was a fantail with eight blades. The windmill and the church seen from afar make an arresting composition.

Addenda

1595: John Tytterell versus Richard Cofylde and wife Joan. One windmill & ½ acre of land in Thaxted. (Per Dr F. G. Emmison, extracted from *Feet of Fines*). The first party in a Fine is normally the purchaser, the second party the vendor.

Lawrence Webb of Thaxted, miller, in 1798 charged with stealing flour worth 4d from the mill of Samuel Choppin. Webb claimed it was taken only as a sample. (E.R.O. Q/SBb 371).

NOTES

1 R.E. Pol. No. 116681 30.6.1790; E.R.O. D/P 16/11/1-3.
2 C.C. 18.11.1808, 15.7.1814, 6.1.1815.
3 E.R.O. D/P 16/11/1-3 (poor rate); land tax and church rate.
4 E.R.O. D/P 16/5/14 per R. Hawksley.
5 *Essex Journal*, Vol. 8, p. 121.
6 R.E. Pol. Nos. 73665 27.8.1778 & 81531 27.8.1781.
7 R.E. Pol. No. 145752 24.6.1795.
8 Root's (or Roote's) will, proved 1798: E.R.O. D/A BR 29, p. 163; Camp's will: E.R.O. D/A BR 32, p. 109, which, with *Pigot's* directory (1826), points to Thos. Everitt (Town Street) as then practising miller
9 C.C. 8.5.1829.
10 *Thaxted in the Fourteenth Century*, K. C. Newton, E.R.O. Publications No. 33, 1960.
11 E.R.O. D/DYq 5 per R. Hawksley.
12 *The Thaxted Bulletin*, No. 4, Autumn, 1969, p. 17.
13 R.E. Pol. No. 151352 10.6.1796.
14 E.R.O. D/A BR 31, p. 327 & land tax returns.
15 C.C. 10.4.1835 per H. E. S. Simmons.
16 E.R.O. D/CT 348A.
17 E.W.N. 20.8.1880.
18 C.C. 20.10.1815.
19 C.C. 13.6.1817.
20 E.R.O.: land tax returns.
21 Per G. W. Martin from private correspondence.
22 R.E. Pol. No. 225371 29.9.1806.
23 E.R.O. D/A BR 35, p. 35.
24 E.S. 10 & 24.6.1842.
25 E.W.N. 13.4.1877.
26 *English Windmills*, Vol. 2, Donald Smith, 1932, p. 81.
27 E.S. 10.2.1837.
28 *The Thaxted Bulletin*, No. 6, Autumn, 1970, pp. 8, 9.
29 C.C. 16.5.1794.
30 E.R.O. B1051.
31 As note 12 above, pp. 5, 6.

Thorpe-le-Soken

(1) Post mill. At Far Thorpe Green near 'Old Mill Cottage', part of which stood derelict in 1971 in the acute angle between the Weeley road and the lane to Barnard's Farm. Approximately TM 164226

(2) A pair of post mills. The surviving base of the westerly mill stands 280 yards south of the village centre off Mill Lane. The other mill stood 120 yards to the south east, in a field. TM 178223 and 179223 (□ 237a, b; I 20)

(3) Mill of unknown type. Marked on the map by Warburton, Bland and Smyth (*c*1724) in the area between Whitehall and Bradley Hall on Whitehall Lane leading north from Thorpe Green, where was also Mill Hill Field on the tithe map east of T-junction. Probably the 'Thorpe Great Mill' mentioned in manor court records, 1752, 58 (ERO D/DBm M220). No further information. Approximately TM 162232

(1) FAR THORPE GREEN MILL

The mills at Thorpe Green and at Thorpe Street or village were held copyhold of the manor of Thorpe, and the surviving court rolls therefore throw some light on their 18th-century history.[1] Robert Stone was admitted in 1700 on the death of Richard Stone to the windmill and land known as Heath, Richard having been admitted the previous year. Other field or place names associated with the site: Moses, Eight Acres, Taylors and Rush Green, enable it to be traced through to the 19th century.

The mill was mortgaged by Richard Barnard in 1723, shortly after which it failed to appear on the map by Warburton, Bland and Smyth (*c*1724). In 1759 one John Barnard was replaced by another, and on 26th July, 1794, William Barnard surrendered his copyhold messuage and windmill then in the occupation of Ann Drake, widow, to Thomas Annis of Kelvedon, miller. The windmill, which appears on Chapman and André (1777), stood on a small parcel of waste, part of Rush Green, belonging to the manor, and contiguous with Barnard's holding by the name of Taylor's, but the precise site and the dates of building of successive mills are unknown. Annis, on entry, mortgaged to William Barnard for £250 at 5% interest, and insured the mill, 'brick and timber built', near his dwelling house, for £290.[2] In default of payment by Annis, Barnard was re-admitted in July, 1799, conveying in 1801 to Porter Everitt, the occupier then being William Goodrich.

237a *Thorpe-le-Soken. Drawing sketched c 1900 from an old photo*

In September, 1805, the post mill, with two pairs of 4ft. 10in. French stones, roundhouse, dwelling house, and appurtenances was for sale, complete with flour mill, jumper and going gears 'on the most improved principles'. The mill could grind 15 loads weekly and lay one mile from Weeley barracks.[3] Matthew Howland Pattrick bought the property for £605, and in all probability transferred the windmill to Thorpe village, as local tradition suggests, to enlarge the family business.

(2) THORPE VILLAGE MILLS

Milling by wind at this site dates from before 1700. Ogilby and Morgan (1678) indicate a windmill south of the village, and Warburton, Bland and Smyth (c1724) and Chapman and André (1777) mark one mill; Greenwood (1825) and the tithe map (1842) show two. Francis Hodge occupied the windmill known as Thorpe Little Mill in 1739, when he mortgaged the property for £157 10s., but surrendered to Thomas Rolfe of Thorpe, baker, in 1742. Bradbrook and Wm. Swift had been previous occupiers.

The Pattricks were bakers in Thorpe in 1791, and in 1810 held Thorpe mills.[4] The original mill was referred to as old and well-accustomed in February, 1786, and in excellent repair, having been 'lately rebuilt near the street'.[5] It was sold in that year to John Pattrick, of Marks Tey, by William Rose. The mill did not figure on the first O.S. 1 in. map (surv. c1799), though the other Thorpe mill then still at Far Green was shown. The village mill was worked by George Pattrick, miller and baker, in the 1840s, in conjunction with the second post mill on 'Further Mill Pightle' to the east.[6] In October, 1847, the unnamed owner offered the extensive property for auction at the Bell Inn, Thorpe.[7] The two post mills, with brick-built roundhouse, driving four pairs of stones, the mill house containing 'six lofty bed-rooms', and the large bake-office, were then laid before the public in rhapsodic terms:

Taking it as a whole, whether you look at the suitable description of the very capital family residence, which is most agreeably and (for business) most advantageously situate directly in the centre of Thorpe Street; at the old-established and lucrative trade connected with the bake-office; at the convenient situation of the mills, whether as regards their elevation, or the population around them; to the convenient sized enclosure close by; to the state of repair of the buildings; the trifling amount of yearly outgoing; to the general compactness of the entire property; or to the important and extensive business which has for one hundred years been conducted thereupon; it would be difficult to find a property, which, to the man of business, presents such a field for enterprise, and the profitable employment of capital (by the extension of the present trade and the annexation of the malting, coal and other mercantile occupations, which its proximity to Thorpe, and several thickly populated villages, fully justifies the idea of establishing), as that above described.

From 1855 to 1878 Robert Beckwith operated Thorpe Mills, but only one is subsequently mentioned, worked by R. Gilders from 1882-9; however, the first O.S. 6 in. map (surv. 1874) does not include the east mill. Philip Bendall Harris took over in 1889. By that time a third pair of burr stones had been set up for wind drive and a fourth pair and an oat crusher were worked

237b *James Salmon (photo 1936), the last miller at Thorpe. In 1882 he climbed the topmost sail to see the first train to Clacton on the newly opened railway*

by steam in the roundhouse.[8] James Salmon related in 1936 how he started milling in 1881 at Thorpe for Robert Gilders, and how he, Salmon, had climbed the topmost sail of the mill in the summer of 1882 to see the first train pass along the newly opened Clacton line. Salmon remembered having ground as many as 50 sacks in a week from the two pairs of stones in the mill breast.[9]

In 1900 the unacceptable state of the centre post and difficulty of replacement brought to an end milling by wind, and the body was taken down in 1906.

Mr Harris, aged 84 in 1972, son of the last windmiller, remembered winding the mill by hand crank when a boy.[10] Photographs show two pairs of double-shuttered patents turning anti-clockwise and struck from the rear exterior, where a Y-wheel was mounted above the tail platform. The mill was automatically winded by a 6-bladed fantail over the rear steps. The body was evidently raised in height during the century or more of its existence, and the roundhouse contained two floors with large bins and a storage room, doubtless a vermin-proof 'pastry'.

Mrs Emily J. Harris, using steam power, is returned by directories as miller for most of the inter-war years. In 1945 the mill roundhouse was sold to Mr Hudgell, still in residence in his converted dwelling in 1973.

NOTES

1 History of Far Thorpe Green mill from deeds in private possession and from manor court proceedings (E.R.O. D/DBm M204, 206, 220, 223).
2 R.E. Pol. No. 140801 9.8.1794 per H. E. S. Simmons.
3 I.J. 21.9.1805.
4 Per G. W. Martin. Owner-occupier: 1826 M. H. Pattrick, 1831 George Pattrick (E.R.O. land tax records).
5 I.J. 11.2.1786.
6 E.R.O. D/CT 352A (1842).
7 E.S. 15.10.1847.
8 The Miller, Vol. XV, 1889, p. 282.
9 Notes by D. W. Muggeridge.
10 Personally interviewed 21.10.1972.

Thorrington

Post mill. Stood on the levelled corner of the field behind the lodge on the south side of the drive to the tide mill and Mill Farm. The site lies immediately off the Brightlingsea road. TM 083193 (□ I 53)

THORRINGTON windmill was erected for William Walker, of Butt Mill, Colchester, possibly as early as 1740, when he entered the property; on the marriage of his daughter Mary to Daniel Clapton in 1757, the windmill and tide mill passed to them, and subsequently to their children, who in the 1790s conveyed to Daniel Poole, nephew of John Clapton[1]. Poole was in occupation with oppressive mortgage commitments until the entry of William Eve, senior, in 1814, and of his son, of

like name, in 1816. Thereafter, the title to the estate becomes very involved; for instance, with eight-part indentures of lease and release in April, 1832.

In October, 1810, Poole arranged the sale of the freehold tide mill and windmill, probably under pressure from the mortgagee, but the sale was cancelled and the mortgage transferred elsewhere.[2] Both mills were then driving two pairs of French stones. The capacious tide mill had four flour dressers and the windmill one; together, it was stated, the mills could produce 100 quarters of flour weekly, which could be despatched to London, 58 miles away, from the mooring for 70-ton vessels on the estate. The ample buildings included a millwright's workshop, and were attractively set in 16 acres of arable, marsh and woodland. A baker's shop with a 'perpetual' oven formed a second lot in Brightlingsea.

In the 1820s a lime kiln and 'Roman cement manufactory' had been added, making a diversity of product not confined to millstones; Charles Bones' — the ex-miller's — stock, for sale in 1827, included 1000 new hoops and 470 very dry beech mill cogs.[3] In 1832 John Pyman, miller, mortgaged the premises for a loan of £1300 at 4½% and sold to George Cooper of Aldham, Suffolk, miller, in 1841 for £2430. It is possible that Cooper constructed a post mill on the premises for carriage away, for in the Essex Standard of 2.1.1846, the following interesting announcement appeared, but with the builder's name withheld:

A Windmill for Sale, at Thorrington (To be removed, for which a reasonable time will be allowed).
By auction by W. F. Dawson, At the Red Lion Inn, on Thursday the 15th of January, 1846, at Five o'clock in the Afternoon, Comprising a small new-built Post-Windmill, very completely fitted with two pair of French Stones, flour mill, corn bins, and the usual gear complete.
The property is most conveniently situated for removal, and it is presumed would be an acquisition to an extensive agricultural occupation.

Cooper, like a number of master millers, intolerant of the patter of little feet, advertised in 1856 for a strong active married man, without a family, and of good character, able to drive a miller's wain and make himself generally useful.[4] In January, 1857, a violent gale blew three sails off the mill and dashed them to pieces, breaking also the windshaft, probably of wood, causing damage estimated at £120.[5] The opportunity was seized to fit an iron windshaft and patent sails, mentioned in extravagant terms below. In 1859 Cooper was 'declining business', and took steps to sell the tide mill, now with three pairs of stones, and the windmill, still with two, by private contract, but apparently without success, and when he died, in 1862, his wife Harriett came into possession.[6] Harriett took the fateful step of selling for £1500 to Henry Chopping of Roxwell, miller, in 1866, including a land holding of 19 acres, allowing Chopping the very high mortgage of £1300 at 5%. The ensuing litigation is described elsewhere.[7]

Chopping moved on in 1870 shortly after the windmill had met its end in circumstances which drew forth an arresting press account, owing not a little of its dramatic and authentic ring to the ebullient personality of the miller:[8]

Thorrington. The Late Gale — Destruction of a Mill. The gale of the 16th Dec. 1869 caused great havoc in this neighbourhood, many sheds being blown down and stacks unroofed. Much to the regret of his neighbours and friends, Mr Chopping's windmill was much injured — in fact, wrecked. The evening, it will be remembered, was wet and windy, but towards midnight the rain partially cleared off, the wind increasing to a perfect hurricane, and about twelve o'clock so sudden was the shift from South to Westward, that it carried away the nearly new and capital wind tackle, with the mill stairs and everything connected with them. The latter snapped off close to the mill, and falling down, enabled the mill to work itself still more out of wind. Efforts, attended with great danger, were made to prevent the disaster by roping back the mill sails and shutters, to prevent their closing. This was without effect. So violent was the storm that Mr Chopping and his son and two men ran great risk of their lives by holding on to the last, when the windshaft snapped below the neck, carrying with it four of the finest and most complete double-patents in Essex. The yard was strewn with huge timbers, the shutters flying in the air. It is wonderful, says Mr Chopping, that not one of the four received any injury, as three minutes before they were holding a rope on the very spot where this great mass of shivered timbers and iron work fell, of several tons weight, shaking the foundations. Mr Chopping, who is a practical man, had recently put the mill into thorough repair, at considerable cost. The same gentleman met with a similar accident at his mill at Roxwell, during the heavy gale of October 31st, when damage was done to about £150. The present damage is estimated at £200.

A water-colour, dated 1868, of the windmill and its late-added fantail, has been preserved, and, allowing for some artistic inaccuracies, gives a fair impression of the mill, and also, as a check, of the surviving mill house.[9] The mill is standing on the part-mound overlooking the sunken drive entrance leading down to the tide mill. Four double-shuttered patents, a single-storied roundhouse, and a six-bladed fantail over the steps are seen, and there is a built-out extension over the rear door, probably for the flour dresser. Whether it is to be taken as Walker's original mill is an open question, but the small depth of the body as portrayed by the artist suggests the affirmative. This pictorial record proved to be a timely one.

NOTES

1 Devolution of the mills from deeds in private possession. Mills insured for £250 each in 1787: Sun Pol. No. 529251 4.4.1787 per H. E. S. Simmons.

2 I.J. 6 & 20.10.1810 per G. W. Martin.

3 C.C. 17.3. & 28.4.1826, 15.6.1827, 18.7.1828.

4 E.S. 18.1.1856.

5 E.S. 9.1.1857.

6 E.S. 12.8.1859.

7 See *Three Jolly Millers*, Vol. I.

8 E.W.N. 24.12.1869.

9 In possession of Mr Aldridge, Thorrington, 1973.

Grays Thurrock

Presumed post mill, unconfirmed. Stood a few yards east of Grays Wharf overlooking the Thames. TQ 615774

A POST-1700 mill stood on this site according to two maps: that of Warburton, Bland and Smyth (c1724), and that resulting from the survey made by the trustees of Pinnock's Charity in 1739[1]. On the Pinnock map it is drawn as a post mill with an open substructure, as no doubt it was. Nothing more is known of it. It is very probable that a windmill, apparently bought for removal in 1624, stood at or close to this site, for it was stated to be on the west side of the salt marsh and sometimes let with the ferry.[2] Edward Kighley Esq., of Grays Thurrock, sold for £60 to Sir Edward Barrett, Kt., of Bellhowse (sic) in Aveley, the windmill, gears and utensils, and guaranteed the right of 'ingress and egress . . . to enable men to take down and carry away the said windmill before the 25 July, 1624'. It may conceivably have become one of the sequence of Aveley mills which stood near the Barrett mansion.

For a note on a presumed pumping mill in the parish see under East Tilbury.

NOTES

1 Details supplied by Randal Bingley, Curator, Thurrock Museum, Grays.

2 E.R.O. D/DL T1/739.

West Thurrock

Smock mill. Stood a few yards from the head of the small tidal inlet on the premises of Wouldham Cement Works, about 120 yards back from the Thames bank. TQ 598775 (□ 238)

THE WINDMILL erected at the close of the 18th century in West Thurrock was evidently built with the high profitability of the London flour trade in view; it was accessible to river vessels, and doubtless benefited from the dearth of watermills and the low density of windmills in the hinterland. The site as shown on the first O.S. 6 in. map (surv. c1864) was approached by Mill Lane southwards from its junction with the Purfleet-Grays road opposite Millwood Lane. On that map the

238 *West Thurrock. Chalk drawing, 27 Sept. 1846, showing wind and steam mills.*
Windmill evidently discontinued in use or demolished c 1861

mill buildings are described as Steam Mill (Corn), with no reference to the use of wind power, which may have been discontinued shortly before.

The only known illustration of the mill is a chalk drawing dated 27th September 1846, and timed precisely at 2 pm![1] Here we see a sturdily built smock mill of five floors, two in the brick base and three above, in a strongly battered, octagonal wooden body. There were both road and water approaches with corresponding loading facilities at two levels. The fantail for self-winding, the artist's representation of double-shuttered anti-clockwise sails and the view of the chimney close by convey the impression of a dynamically pursued business, as emerges from documentary evidence.

The first reference to the mill noted concerns James Gillbee, of West Thurrock, miller, who in 1799 insured the contents of the wind corn mill with the Sun Office for £999, a high figure for this category, which excluded the fixed machinery and the main structure.[2] In 1815 the mill was advertised to be let on lease in the following terms:[3]

A capital windmill in the county of Essex, situated in West Thurrock, on the banks of the Thames, within three miles of Grays, twelve of Romford and twenty from London, surrounded by the finest wheat land, in perfect repair, and capable of doing as much business as any windmill in the kingdom — having four pair of French stones. Two workmen's cottages, a kiln (built about two years since), stabling, pig and poultry houses, and about two acres of land adjoining. The roads are excellent. A good opportunity offers to unite the coal and timber trade with the mealing concern, as a creek runs up to the foot of the mill, where vessels and barges can load and discharge.

For over fifty years the Nokes family, farmers and millers, were lessees of Thurrock mill, and they ran a parallel concern at Upminster. In 1817, William Nokes junior, of Upminster, insured the windmill at Thurrock, together with the gears and utensils, for £1500. The stock-in-trade was insured for £1800 and a timber and tiled cottage nearby for £100, making a grand total of £3400. Within the year Nokes further insured a steam engine and a brick and slated engine house for £500; in this provision of auxiliary power in an Essex windmill situated well outside the sprawl of the metropolis, he may be regarded as a pioneer. In the next year or two Nokes continued to extend the premises, until by November, 1819, the insurance cover totalled £4,400, and there was a reference to an oil mill.[4]

That Nokes' suppliers were not purely local was shown by a successful court action fought in 1822 against a hoyman by a farmer at Steeple, who entrusted to him a cargo of fifty quarters of wheat at 80s. a quarter for delivery to West Thurrock mill by Monday, 17th September, Nokes agreeing to purchase this lot if punctually received. As the consignment arrived late, Nokes would not accept it. It was therefore sent on to London, but it deteriorated and was adversely affected by a change in market prices. The farmer-plaintiff was awarded damages and costs.[5]

In 1839, Thomas Nokes held of Lady Wilder 12 acres of land, including a salting and the mill property of one acre; five years later the steam mill working four pairs of French stones and the windmill three pairs were to be let, Thomas Nokes having announced his intention to quit.[6] He was followed as miller by Thomas Nokes jun., who towards the end of the 1850s was facing bankruptcy. In June, 1856, the freehold of the property was for auction, the sale notice making only the briefest of references to the use of wind power:[7] 'The West Thurrock Flour Mills, in the occupation of Mr Nokes, subject to two years' notice, at a low rent. They comprise, exclusive of the Windmill, a spacious 3-floor Mill, worked by a powerful steam-engine, and altogether 7 pair of stones; . . . and private approach from the Turnpike Road, within 3 miles of Grays Railway Station'. In October, 1860, came the public announcement of 'The Failure of Mr Nokes'.[8] His creditors met at West Thurrock, and, finding liabilities of £18,051 and assets of £5,090, agreed to accept 6s. in the £, calculating that if the estate were placed to bankruptcy, not more than 2/6d in the £ would be salvaged. Thanks to the fecundity of the Nokes family, this breach in the milling business was made good by Charles in 1863 and T. Nokes in 1866 operating the steam mill, but if wind was still in favour, its use was not acknowledged. The first O.S. 1:2500 map (surv. 1864) gives an octagonal plan for the base, but omits the description 'Windmill'.

Addenda

A windmill in Torrells Hall manor was mentioned in 1267, and later up to 1595. (V.C.H. *Essex*, Vol. VIII, p. 65). This stood in the east of the parish and is evidently the mill included in a conveyance of 1581. (P.R.O. CP25(2)/131/1681, No. 23 per F. G. Emmison)

Feet of Fines, Essex, Vol. V, p. 3 records a windmill in 1547, which (pp. 149-50) was at West Thurrock, evidently at Purfleet. V.C.H. *Essex*, Vol. VIII, p. 66, states Purfleet windmill was last recorded 1653.

NOTES

1 Southend R.L. Ref. No. W.12.1. '68. Accession No. 470 P.
2 Sun Pol. No. 686931 2.3.1799.
3 *Suffolk Chronicle*, 4.11.1815, per G. W. Martin.
4 E.R.O. D/F 21/2, pp. 124, 158, 165; 21/3, pp. 12, 35, 72.
5 C.C. 15.3.1822.
6 E.R.O. D/CT 357A; E.S. 9.8.1844.
7 E.S. 16.5.1856.
8 E.S. 12.10.1860. See also E.W.N. 13.8.1869, p. 2, col. 6.

East Tilbury

with a note on Thurrock windpumps

(1) Smock-framed drainage mill. Stood 820 yards east of the road leading from Muckingford southwards to East Tilbury measured from a point 560 yards south of the railway crossing. The site lies 510 yards south east of Gobions Farm. TQ 686789 (□ 239)

(2) Mill of unknown type. Stood at Muckingford in the neighbourhood of Halt Road, north of East Tilbury station and south of Muckingford Road. Approximately TQ 676790

(3) Windpumps of the Thurrock area.

(1) EAST TILBURY DRAINAGE PUMP NEAR GOBIONS

This 'wind engine', as these devices were sometimes named — and rightly so — had appeared by the date of the survey of this area (1862-5) for the first O.S. 6in. map Judging by its condition in 1926, when photographed by L. S. Harley, it probably continued in use until the first world war; it was pulled down *c*1939-40, but its inoffensive remains were suffered to linger on until well after December, 1956, when Denis Sanders was able belatedly to record a few details.[1] R. Hawksley found scattered vestiges in 1976.

As Donald Smith stated in 1932,[2] the mill was built over a ditch and supported on a hollow square of concrete of side 8ft. resting on angle iron laid across brick piers. The wooden framework above was seen by R. Hawksley to be octagonal and not hexagonal, as recorded by Smith. It was covered by a metal-sheeted domed cap with a neat ogee finish. A fantail at the rear turned four single-shuttered anti-clockwise patent sails into the wind. The sails had 8 bays of 2 shutters in each, and were held at centre by an iron cross, though the precise nature of the fixing is not clear. All the gearing and the brake were of iron. The brake wheel drove an upright shaft, which, through a pair of bevel gears, turned an iron-cased archimedean screw with its long axis in line with the ditch. The action was to lift the water from a lower to a higher level. Denis Sanders found in 1956 the remains of the iron cylinder, of about 16in. diameter, but was evidently not able to record the length. The driven bevel on the shaft of the screw was 32in. in diameter and had about 72 teeth. At each cant post position on the concrete base, a pair of irons had been cast in, projecting up 15in., and having a turned lip at top to notch into the cant post for greater locking power. The posts, probably about 7in. square, were held by two sets of three bolts, one set to each of the irons, the bolts being suitably staggered at right angles. Such was the robust construction which had doubtless endured since before c1864. The boss of the fantail was also found in 1956, showing provision for six blades; the casting included forked outer ends to carry the blades, giving an overall diameter for the ironwork of 4ft. 4in.

The first O.S. 6in. map indicates the smock pump with the words 'Windmill (Pumping)'. Nearly 600 yards in a south-easterly direction a pond was marked where a windpump symbol appeared on later maps.

(2) WINDMILL AT MUCKINGFORD

The nature of this mill, occupying a dead flat site, remains unknown. It appears on the revised first O.S. 1 in. map (1843), but is not shown on the 6in. survey made in 1863-5. The tithe apportionment (1839) records Mill Pightle as a field of close on 2 acres at the site in the possession of Mary Driver and occupation of James Lockwood, and three other fields adjoining have names containing 'Mill', but no mill is indicated on the map

239 *East Tilbury drainage mill with archimedean screw. Pulled down c 1939*

(1836). Neither is a reference to a mill to be found in the land tax returns for 1832. *Pigot's* directory for 1839 returns John Harris as miller in East Tilbury.

(3) WINDPUMPS IN THE THURROCK AREA

The windpump near Gobions Farm with the archimedean screw is shown in the O.S. 1in. map, revised in 1931 and published in 1940, by the windpump symbol, as are several other water-pumping wind machines in the Grays-Chadwell-Tilbury area, which merit brief comments.[3]

East Tilbury (683785): not on first O.S. 6in.; shown on third 1:2500 map (1915) and later maps. Iron wind-pump, probably for cattle.

East Tilbury: Low Street (671778): O.S. 1in. 1940. Remembered as an iron windpump, used for cattle.

Little Thurrock (638781): second O.S. 6in. (surv. 1895). Remembered as an iron windpump for cattle.

Chadwell St. Mary (637767): second O.S. 6in.; also on third 6in. Iron windpump.

Grays Thurrock (624783): first O.S. 6in. Shown north of quarry which later extended north beyond the site. To north of mill lay 'Wash Mills'. Evidently a pumping mill. Marked as an open square on first O.S. 1:2500 (surv. c1864).

NOTES

1 Notes supplied to the author.
2 *English Windmills*, Vol. 2, Donald Smith, 1932, p. 58.
3 Incorporating notes on maps and sites by R. Hawksley.

West Tilbury

One or more post mills, followed by a smock mill, of which the base remains in the north-west angle of the crossroads 1000 yards north of West Tilbury church. TQ 659787 (□ 240)

THE ABOVE SITE was occupied by a post mill in 1584 according to a map by John Walker[1], and no doubt was in continuous occupation for centuries. Morant referred in 1768 to a windmill then standing at the point where the military camp had been set up at the time of the Spanish Armada[2] — a reference to the West Tilbury windmill — and reputable county cartographers unfailingly record this milling site.

In 1767 a windmill of undefined type, built of timber, was insured for £150 by Edward Leader, and Chapman and André (1777) represent it on their map by a smock symbol. The drawing gains credibility from the fact that Barling mill, in this part of the county, was truly depicted as of smock type. The first positive mention of a smock mill at West Tilbury comes with a notice of 1784, in which the mill, so described, was to be let, having a pair each of French and peak stones and also a bolting mill.[3] The rate books first recorded Edward Leader, miller, in 1766. He succeeded William Sweeting (1761-5) and one Spray (1765). An Edward Leader was buried at West Tilbury in 1770, and another, 'Farmer and Miller', in 1782. The latter's will, dated 1781 and proved 1784, shows that he leased High House Farm together with the adjoining windmill; by it he appointed trustees either to carry on or dispose of the business, the income to be devoted to the 'Maintenance, Education and bringing up of my . . . Son James Leader'. The succeeding miller has not been identified, but John Burles was operating the mill from 1803 or before to 1809, when Thomas James took over.[4]

The freehold wind and steam mills, property of the late Thomas James, were to be auctioned in May, 1834, at Jack's Coffee House in Mark Lane, London, comprising the smock windmill with three pairs of stones and a brick-built steam mill with two pairs driven by an 8 h.p. low pressure engine.[5] There were five acres of land, and milling was still combined with farming. Particulars of the sale were distributed to inns on both sides of the river from Chatham and Gravesend to Chelmsford, and in solicitors' offices in the City. With reference to the early use of steam power, the Curator[6] of the Thurrock Local History Museum, in a letter to the author, wrote: 'One of the attractions of going into steam-business, must, I imagine, have been its position, because a coal-carrying business (from the collier dump at Coalhouse Point) had been in operation since at least the 1780s under John Button of Becksland, and by the 1830s under the Asplin family of East Tilbury Place. The "road" — a waggon track running directly across the common field from East Tilbury — passed the Mill frontage on its course onward to (we believe) Warley barracks'.

The mill property remained with the James family, Joseph and Richard being owner-occupiers in 1840; the partnership was dissolved in 1843, leaving Joseph in sole charge.[7] In 1851, Joseph, then aged 38, was described as master miller employing three men, two of whom were journeymen aged 21 years, unattached, and living in Mill House.[8] For looking after the windmill in 1865, a journeyman could expect board, lodging and 10s. per week; one such employee was sentenced to six months' hard labour in 1872 for embezzling £5 12s. 6d.[9]

In 1890 and 1898 Joseph James is recorded as miller of the steam and wind mills, but he died in November 1898, aged 85.[10] This marked the end of the business, and in 1903 the third O.S. 1in. survey recorded 'Old Windmill'. Two water-colours in private possession show a Kentish waggon-shaped cap, two pairs of double-shuttered anti-clockwise patent sails, an 8-bladed fantail, and an octagonal smock frame, which stood on a single-storied brick base still in existence. Immediately east of this and sunk about six feet below the ground surface, so giving freer play to the wind, was the old slate-roofed steam mill, converted into a residence probably soon after the demolition of the

240 *West Tilbury. Undated water-colour. Mill demolished 1905*

windmill. As 'Mill Lodge' it survived until the 1970s, when it was taken down and the pit filled in.

The single known photograph of the mill offers a close view of the body and cap, but with the sails and fantail removed. A chalked inscription on the base brickwork reads: 'Pulled Down by E. James. Just Before the Battle, Mother, April 3 1905'. This must indicate the imminent demolition. Randal Bingley, Curator, Thurrock Museum, in supplying this information, states that E. James was a builder, of Stanford-le-Hope, and was unrelated to the Jameses of the windmill's working days.

Addendum

Windmill, 1561. (*Feet of Fines, Essex*, Vol. V, p. 144).

NOTES

1 E.R.O. D/DU 23/138. Probably the windmill mentioned in 1561 in a deed to effect possession to Thomas Smyth (P.R.O. CP 25(2)/259/Divers Counties/6); also probably the windmill leased by George Lambe in 1569 (E.R.O. D/A ER 11A f.51)

2 Morant: *Essex*, Vol. I, p. 232

3 Sun Pol. No. 243168 c.Feb. 1767; C.C. 26.3.1784

4 Information on rates and burials supplied by Randal Bingley, who also contributed details of Leader's will (1781): P.R.O. PROB 11/1119 f.397

5 E.S. 10.5.1834

6 Randal Bingley

7 E.R.O. D/CT 360A; *Lond. Gaz.* 1.11.1842 per H. E. S. Simmons

8 E.R.O. T/A 486/3 (from P.R.O. HO 107 1773)

9 E.W.N. 10.2.1865, 23.2.1872

10 As note 4

Tilty

Mill of unconfirmed type, but drawn as a post mill with open substructure on a map of the Maynard estates, 1730.[1] Stood at about 100 yards south of the Broxted road from a point 250 yards east of the stream flowing north eastwards, and 550 yards west of The Grange Farm. TL 589266

A DESCRIPTION[2] of the manor of Tilty in 1588 mentions Windmill Field, of 44 acres, and states: 'The yerely rent of the windmill is better worth than X[li]'. Ogilby and Morgan (1678) do not include a Tilty windmill on their map, but one is shown by Warburton, Bland and Smyth (c1724) in the area of the site identified above. The 1730 estate map also records Windmill Field, a well winded summit remote from any concentrated habitation. The mill has not been traced further.

NOTES

1 E.R.O. D/Mg P1
2 E.R.O. D/DWv M197

Tollesbury, Tolleshunt D'Arcy, Virley and Salcott

(1) Post mill in Tollesbury parish. Sampson's or Golding's Mill. Variously known also as Gynes (Guisnes) and Bourchier's Lodge Mill. Stood 220 yards south of the road to Tolleshunt D'Arcy (Chapel Road) from a point 200 yards west of the nearby T-junction with Colchester Road. The site lies 150 yards south west of Guisnes Court. TL 942116

(2) Post mill, formerly in Tollesbury; post-1888 in Tolleshunt D'Arcy at Oxley Green. Known as Oxley Green Mill, latterly Posford's Mill. Stood a few yards south west of the existing Mill House, west of the D'Arcy road and about 50 yards north west of the Plough Inn. TL 911143 (□ 241)

(3) Post mill, formerly in Tollesbury parish detached; post-1888 in Virley. Known as Virley Mill, ultimately Smith's Mill. Site lies immediately west of 'Mill Farm', a modern bungalow at the eastward bend of Virley Road, 75 yards north of the bridge over Salcott Creek. TL 948138

(4) Smock-type drainage pump. Stood on Old Hall Marshes in Tollesbury parish overlooking Salcott Channel and about 3000 yards east south east of Salcott church. TL 978130 (□ 242)

(5) Mill of unknown type. Recorded on maps by Ogilby and Morgan (1678) and Warburton, Bland and Smyth (c1724) in Tolleshunt D'Arcy parish, possibly near the present Grove Farm. No further information. Approximately TL 889140

(1) GUISNES OR BOURCHIER'S LODGE MILL

A windmill is mapped by Warburton, Bland and Smyth (c1724) a little west of 'Bourchers', and also by Chapman and André (1777) west of 'Tolesbury Lodge', which was held by Philip Bennet Esq. In the 19th century one is shown on the tithe map (1840), but not on the first O.S. 6in. map (surv. 1874), where, however, identifiable

traces of the site are included. John Ray, miller, suffered a theft at the mill in 1795.[1] In 1827 the notice of auction of the freehold manor of Tolleshunt Gynes, otherwise T. Bourchiers, included 'a capital windmill recently repaired at a considerable expense', with 24 acres of land, at about that time vacated by Charles Fitch. A comparison of this with two earlier notices indicates that the mill had been newly erected in or shortly before 1813.[2]

Simon Sampson, of Tollesbury, described as millwright in 1838,[3] but as miller and farmer in *White's* directory of 1848, was prepared to interview potential lessees in the former year, having for disposal a post mill with roundhouse, two pairs of stones, a bakehouse &c., still in the ownership of one Bennett (sic), but he remained closely connected with the mill until his death in 1854, aged 72, 'much respected'.[4] Pearson Golding appears to have been the last miller, entered in directories for 1855 and 1866, but afterwards there is no clear trace of mill or miller.

(2) OXLEY GREEN MILL: POSFORD'S

Oxley Green Mill was probably built in or a little before 1811, if the evidence in land tax records can be taken at its face value. The mill is not shown on the 1805 O.S. map, but James Brooks, miller, who sold Virley Mill c1802, advertised for an apprentice in 1811,[5] and can be traced back through the land tax returns from 1826, when he held a mill in Tollesbury in the occupation of Robert Grout.[6] Isaac Fitch was occupier in 1819. In 1836 the mill was offered for sale by private contract, and in 1837 by auction by James Brooks; it had a brick roundhouse, a cast-iron shaft, and two pairs of French stones.[7] Mention was made of Old Hall wharf, 3 miles distant, for the shipment of flour to London. The tithe apportionment (1842) gives Jeffrey Grimwood, an extensive landowner, as proprietor, and John Posford as occupier.[8] The Posfords, millers and farmers, were connected with the mill until the first world war: John Posford, father and son, and, after 1890, Stowers Posford.

241 *Tolleshunt D'Arcy: Oxley Green Mill. Demolished c 1920*

In 1851 Grimwood leased the mill and tenement for 7 years to Samuel Ely of Messing, miller, at an annual rent of £32, plus £50 yearly for each acre of ground ploughed of the total of 9 acres.[9] Two inventories were included in the indenture, one of the landlord's fixtures and going gears, including two regulators to the stones, and one of the tenant's items, subject to valuation on entry and departure and payment accordingly. These last particularly relate to chains, ropes, cords, belts and straps; also to loose items such as the stone staff and mill bills.

Samuel Ely was succeeded in 1858 by Joseph Sorrell the younger, who surrendered the lease in 1861, and in *White's* directory for 1863 a John Posford was again miller. By 1886 steam power had been added, but Stowers Posford in 1898 was using wind also, and indeed in 1917 according to *Kelly's* directory of that year. Two photographs showing Mill House and a rear view of the derelict windmill reveal a pair of single-shuttered and a pair of common sails, turning anti-clockwise, and a typically proportioned Essex post mill winded by tail pole over a single-storied roundhouse. The mill was included on the Popular O.S. 1in. map (surv. 1914-19). It was reported as 'ruinous' by Dr Turner in July 1919, and was gone by 1921. Turner was told by the last miller that the mill ceased work by wind c1914.

(3) VIRLEY, OR SMITH'S MILL

The mill house, now named Mill Cottage, stands at the junction of Virley Road and Salcott Street; hence the mill was latterly in Virley, while the miller resided in Salcott. The mill first appears on a map in the drawings for the O.S. 1in. made 1799; but a sale notice dated 1795 advertised 37 years of unexpired lease of the post mill advantageously situated for the London and country trades.[10] It was, however, Osborn May's bankruptcy which had precipitated the sale. May first appeared in the parish land tax lists in 1793, in all probability signalling the date of building of the mill, for the expiry of the lease in 1832 accorded with a 39-year term.

James Brooks of Salcott, miller, insured in 1800 the windmill with roundhouse, then in Tollesbury, for £280; the roundhouse was described as 'newly erected' in a sale notice of 1802.[11] Brooks was followed by Thomas Turnage, who 2½ years later offered to sell by private contract the mill, bakehouse and messuage.[12] In a notice to let dated 1810, the proprietor, still Turnage, engaged to lay up another pair of stones if required, the mill then having one pair only, and repeated his offer in 1820, when the diameter of the pair in use was given as 4ft. 6in.[13] Again, in 1832, Turnage advertised the lease of his one-pair mill, evidently with the same stones, and 'coming in very easy', and by 1847 had an oyster-laying in tow, but the number of stones in his windmill was then unspecified.[14]

After 1848, when Thomas Turnage last appears in *White*, directories record five farmer-millers in succes-sion: Joseph Last (1850, 55), Thomas Skipper (1859), Joseph Sorrell (1863), William Sexton (1866, 78) and Charles Henry Smith (1882, 90). Smith was the last miller, and the mill's activity may have been curtailed by his bankruptcy, resulting from which his creditors were receiving their first and final dividend of 1s. 8d. in the £ in Colchester on August 20th, 1889.[15] The mill stood unused for a while, and was just remembered in 1970 by several aged villagers, one of whom stated it was pulled down c1900. A Cornish steam boiler was latterly employed. There are thought to have been four shuttered sails. Demolition by John Foakes was effected by the removal of bricks from one of the piers.[16] The mill was marked on the second 6in. map of the O.S. (surv. 1895), but not on the third 1in. (surv. 1904).

(4) THE DRAINAGE WINDPUMP, OLD HALL MARSHES, TOLLESBURY

One of the works of the prolific writer S. Baring Gould, Rector of East Mersea, 1870-81, is entitled *Mehalah*, a melodramatic novel published in 1880, for which the Salcott Channel and Old Hall Marshes, naked to the elements, provided a harsh setting with exaggerated moods. The writer makes reference to many local landmarks known intimately to him, and calls to life the slender black-boarded windpump which stood close by the sea wall. Thus, as Mehalah and her mother were sailing up the creek to pay their rent: 'A high sea-wall hid the reclaimed land on the left. Behind it rose the gaunt black structure of a windmill used for pumping water out of the dykes in the marsh. It was working now, the

242 *Tollesbury: drainage mill on Old Hall Marshes. Collapsed probably early in 1914*

great black arms revolving in the breeze, and the pump creaking as if the engine groaned remonstrances at being called to toil on such a bright day. A little further appeared a tiled roof above the wall. "There is Red Hall", said Mehalah. . . . The house was indeed very conveniently situated for contraband trade. . . . The windmill which stood on this spit was in no favour with the coastguard, for it was thought to act the double purpose of pump and observatory.'

And, later, when fate had incarcerated Mehalah in Red Hall: 'Then she threw herself beneath the windmill, the mill that pumped the water out of the dykes, and worked day and night whenever there was wind to move the sails. The mill was now at work. The wings rushed round, and the pump painfully creaked, and after every stroke sent a dash of water into the sea over the wall'.

This mill is recorded on maps in the approximate period 1895-1920, and by chance a photograph of it, taken in 1911, was discovered by Roland Smith in an old postcard album. This shows a smock-type frame with four tapered sides, a surviving pair of shuttered sails above, and an unguarded platform at mid-height. The body could not have exceeded 25ft. to its topmost point, and the brick base and the well beneath survive today. Details of these were taken by Roland Smith in April, 1971. The base stands 2ft. high, and the four cant posts were footed roughly 9ft. apart. Below the base a brick-lined well 56in. across at the top is still intact, with a discharge pipe at a little over ground level. Mr Smith's run of luck had not yet terminated. Having found the photograph and then the remains, he returned from the lonely trek along the sea wall, and was about to drive away, when he spotted the 'ancient of days', who proved to be a Mr Buck aged 78, once employed on the local estate, including Old Hall Marshes, as far back as 1908. Mr Smith records the essentials of the interview:

'The pump was used to drain water out of the marsh and also raised water for the livestock. Mr Buck thought that the well was about 30ft. deep, into which the marsh water found its own way. Inside the mill was a lift pump worked by connecting rods from the sails. Water was expelled through a pipe which ran underground, under the ditch and through the sea wall, to discharge into the river. If the pump had not been used for some time, as would happen in the autumn, someone had to be sent first to clear the exit from the pipe and the channel over the saltings, which carried away the water. On the right hand side inside the mill door was a lever which stopped the sails and pump. From here a ladder went up inside the mill to an upper level; here could be reached 3 vertical handles which came down from works above. These were used to turn the upper part of the mill into the wind by hand when necessary. Mr Buck said it was usual to set the pump to work, then leave it unattended for 2 to 3 days. It was, he said, frequently used during the winter months. It fell over not long before the first world war, when cattle crowded against it and pushed it over, it

having become evidently very rotten at the base. The windpump was later replaced by a force pump'.

NOTES

1 C.C. 16.10.1795

2 C.C. 9.2., 31.8. & 30.11.1827; evidently also C.C. 23.4.1813, p. 2, col. 5, and 24.1.1823, p. 3, col. 4

3 I.J. 21.5. & 28.9.1838 per H. E. S. Simmons

4 P.R.O. HO 107 1778 (1851 census); E.S. 29.3.1854; see also E.R.O. D/A BR 36 p. 1107

5 C.C. 5.7.1811

6 E.R.O.; land tax and other records checked by R. Hawksley

7 C.C. 15.1.1836, 21.7.1837 per H. E. S. Simmons; E.S. 4.8.1837

8 E.R.O., examined by R. Hawksley

9 E.R.O. D/DO T895

10 C.C. 10.4.1795; *Lond. Gaz.* 2.5.1795

11 Sun Pol. No. 710660 8.11.1800; C.C. 8.1.1802

12 C.C. 21.9.1804

13 C.C. 23.2.1810 & 7.6.1820

14 C.C. 28.12.1832 per H. E. S. Simmons; E.S. 31.12.1847

15 *The Miller*, Vol. XV, 1889, p. 317. Smith is last entered in the Salcott electoral roll in 1893-4

16 Per Elijah Ponder, of Mill Cottage, April, 1970. See under Tolleshunt Major: bricks from Virley roundhouse used for engine shed built in 1903

Tolleshunt Knights (Tiptree)

(1) Post mill. Stood close to the site of the existing house 'Milldene' on the north side of Ransom Road, 190 yards south west of the tower mill. TL 893166

(2) Tower mill. Known as Tiptree Mill. Preserved and used as a residence. Stands a few yards south east of the intersection of the Maldon and Inworth roads. TL 894167 (□ 243; II 91)

(1) & (2) THE POST AND TOWER MILLS

These mills, with dwelling houses adjoining, comprised one estate; they are accordingly treated together. John Matchett, millwright, of St James' parish, Colchester, built the tower mill in 1775 and had reconstructed the post mill by the same year.[1] He took payment of £315, probably inclusive of work on the post mill, but exclusive of the erection of the brick tower.[2] The 'new re-built' post mill had one pair of French stones of 4ft. 9in. diameter and a new flour mill, also a good dwelling house 'with a conveniency for a flour-mill, to be worked by one horse.' In response to the notice of sale or lease in 1775 relating to the post mill, a lease was taken for 21 years from 28.3.1776 by Thomas Green, merchant, of Inworth, paying £10 yearly, and under obligation to keep the mill in good repair. A clause detailing liability for replacement of the mill structure in the event of loss by fire or wind proved too demanding for the syntactical dexterity of the legal hack who composed it:[3] If it shall happen that the said Post Windmill shall be Burned down, the said John Matchett his Heirs or Assigns shall within twelve Kalendar Months Build up another Post Windmill with all the going Geers and shall be of the same Size and Value and equal to the other Post Windmill in Goodness before Burned down, BUT if the said Windmill shall be Blowed down by Wind the said Thomas Green . . . shall build up another Post Windmill with all the Going Geers and shall be of the same Size and Value and equal to the other Post Windmill in goodness before Blowed down within twelve Kalendar Months after Blowed down. . .'.

George Wilbee, followed by Roger Lee, were earlier occupiers of the post mill, which had been conveyed to Matchett in October, 1764, by Byam Hewes, of Mile End, Colchester, who had taken over a new windmill erected by Matchett in that parish. Thomas Green, described as miller, insured in 1776 with the Royal Exchange Assurance the tower mill and contents for £800, and in 1802 his policy read:[4]

> Thomas Green of Tolleshunt Knights, Essex, Farmer. On his dwelling house brick and tiled situate on Tiptree Heath in the parish of Tolleshunt Knights aforesaid and called the Millhouse £150.
> On a Corn Windmill house near, brick and timber, tenant Wallis, £300. On the standing and going geers therein £100.
> On a small Corn Windmill house near, timber, tenant Brooks, £100. On the standing and going geers therein £50. On a millhouse timber and tiled near £50.
> Warranted that there be no steam engine in, adjoining or communicating with the above mills.

Green purchased the mill property in 1797 from Matchett, and by his will, proved in 1806, passed it to his son-in-law, Edward Harvey, farmer, of West Mersea. For the post mill and premises Matchett received £472. In 1812 Harvey leased the mills separately: the post mill to James Hughes and the tower mill to James Peake, in each case for 7 years, and at rentals of £55 and £63 respectively. The post mill was to be painted twice, the cost to be equally met by landlord and tenant; running repairs devolved upon the tenant. The provisions of the lease with Peake regarding the tower mill followed similar lines: the cap to be painted twice, but Harvey to repair as necessary within one month of notification: floors, joists, gurdens (sic), and other 'principal immovable timbers' and to find 'sufficient rough timber at the slab not exceeding the distance of 12 miles from the . . . premises for the reparation of the stage of the Windmill'. He was also to find timber for a new 'axle tree' should one be wanted, but Peake was to pay cartage. This is of interest in indicating that, as at the existing mills at Stansted and Stock, there was a stage, long since gone, from which the former cloth sails were set.

On the occasion of the sale of Harvey's property, following his death in 1824, both mills received brief descriptions. The post mill, valued at £650, measured 18ft. long by 10ft. wide, then having two pairs of French stones, a flour mill and a brick roundhouse, with bins on the crosstrees for the stowage of 100 quarters of corn. The 'much admired' brick tower mill was given as 36ft. in diameter, containing five lofty floors, two pairs of French stones of the best quality, and three flour mills. Both mills were then occupied by James Peake at a rent of £100.

Chapman and André (1777) represent the post mill only, their survey having pre-dated the erection of the tower mill by a short time; Greenwood (1825) shows both mills, but places the post mill at some distance to the north west of its actual site. The post mill was to be let in 1829, and again in 1837, 1843 and 1864, application to be made to T. G. Harvey on each occasion[5]. Its ultimate fate is unknown, and apparently overtook it before the survey date (1874-5) of the first O.S. 6in. map.

At the sale of 1829, the tower mill property was bought by Peake for £950, and in 1840 included a few acres of arable land.[6] In 1845 Peake became bankrupt, and his freehold estate was sold by miller-assignees.[7] A farmer at Marks Tey brought an action in January, 1846, to recover £772 for the supply of corn from 1826-39, and this being granted by the commissioner, the dividend payable to the creditors was 5s. in the £.[8] Further dividends were paid as late as 1848.[9]

243 Tolleshunt Knights: Tiptree Mill

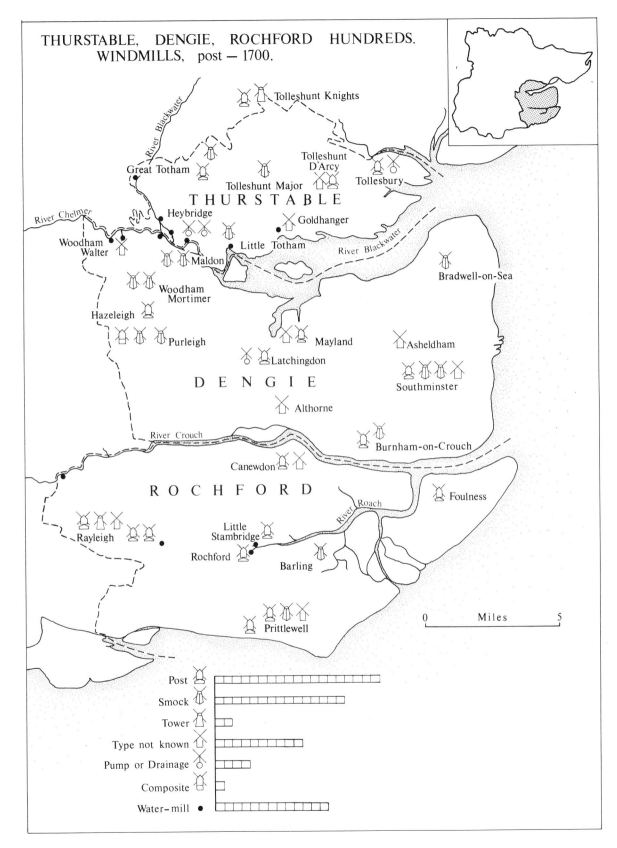

FIG. 40 *Post-1700 Windmills in the Thurstable, Dengie and Rochford Hundreds*

Peake was followed by George D. Ransom, miller and farmer (1848-84), using wind and steam power for many years, and succeeded by his widow until 1887. Henry Cattermole operated from 1898 to c1911. The use of wind probably then ceased, and the employment of power milling also, it would appear, over the war years, but the latter was resumed by Frederick King (1922-37). Stanley S. Wilkin, of jam fame, wrote in 1921 of his efforts to reduce high food prices by selling stone-ground flour from the mill in 3½ lb. bags, bearing wrappers with the words: 'Stone-ground flour, more food units, more phosphates, more digestible, more flavour, more nourishing, far nicer, and 8d. instead of 12d. per bag.'[10] The wheat was locally grown, and ground in Tiptree mill, where grain continued to be stored until the late 1960s. Wind power is said to have been used until 1921,[11] but pencilled doggerel on the upright shaft is in conflict:

> Poor old mill
> Is standing still
> Your sails are rotting fast
> Your bricks will tumble down one day
> But I'd back your stones will last
> E D 1920

Clifford Jaques acquired the mill for conversion into a residence and carried out his intentions sympathetically, but the scenario has fallen apart. Today the mill cuts a Canutian figure, with base awash in a tide of suntrap dwellings, and the naming 'Millwrights' of the close below does little to make good the loss of atmosphere.[12] The mill was advertised for sale in *The Observer*, 8th August, 1976, at a figure of about £20,000, as 'The Pick of the Week'.

NOTES

1 C.C. 13.10.1775 refers to the sale or lease of the post mill.

2 E.R.O. D/DU 491 is a bundle of documents relating to both mills during the period 1776-1839.

3 E.R.O. D/DU 491/41.

4 R.E. Pol. No. 67269 18.3.1776 & 191958 30-6-1802

5 C.C. 24.4.1829, 24.11.1837, 16.8.1839; E.S. 10.9.1841, 8.9.1843, 12.8.1864. Land tax returns (E.R.O.) give as occupiers George Bryant (1826), Thomas Green (1832).

6 E.R.O. D/CT 365A.

7 E.S. 11.7.1845

8 E.S. 16.1.1846

9 *Lond. Gaz.*, 3.3.1848, per H. E. S. Simmons

10 *Essex Chron.* 18.11.1921

11 Per an elderley resident living close to the mill. Donald Smith: *English Windmills*, Vol. 2, 1932, p. 81, states sails removed February, 1927. The middlings were, however left in position.

12 For technical review and details of preservation see relevant sections in Vol. II.

Tolleshunt Major (Beckingham)

Smock mill, probably succeeding a post mill. Stood east of Mill Lane 80 yards south of its junction with the road to Tolleshunt D'Arcy. A bungalow on raised ground marks the site. TL 902114 (□ 244)

A WINDMILL at 'Tolleshunt Beckingham Green' was mortgaged in December, 1739, by Joseph Clarke of Great Birch, miller, to John Gilson, of Colchester, baker, for £90, but four months later was sold to John Shetelworth of Great Coggeshall for £80.[1] At this date John Brown was in occupation, followed several years later by Daniel Nevill, during whose tenure, in 1751, the mill and six rods of land were sold to Robert Ludgater of Coggeshall, clothier, for £70. By 1786, Nevill and his wife Mary had assumed ownership, mortgaging the property for £200 in 1786 and leasing it to Isaac Harrison of Hatfield Peverel, farmer, in 1790, who made an absolute purchase for £260 in that year. The value in 1786, much higher than that of 1751, may be construed as resulting from a capital investment in the mill or the erection of a successor; the holding embraced an additional acre of land.

In 1799, William Smith of St Osyth, miller, paid £300 to Harrison for the mill; it remained in his family long after. Thomas Smith secured a mortgage of £400 in 1838, the premises being insured for that sum also. Smith repaid, and sold to William Larkin of Great Totham, farmer, in June, 1840, for £407 10s., who within the year resold to Simon Sampson, the occupier-miller, for £520, allowing him a mortgage of £300 on the premises at 5% interest. Sampson subsequently borrowed two further sums of £100 and one of £40 from Larkin, none of which had been repaid by Sampson's death in March, 1854. In August, at a public auction, the mill drew no bidders, and Larkin took possession. In 1856 the mill was let at £45 per annum, and this was also the sum claimed as the average spent on repairs by the landlord.

In 1874 William Frost of Inworth, miller, purchased the mill from the trustees in bankruptcy of William Larkin the younger for the sum of £330. Surridge of Kelvedon made a report on the property for Frost in October, 1880, when a mortgage was envisaged; the statement, reproduced here with a few abridgements, gives a clear idea of the milling resources available:

> The property is freehold and consists of a substantially erected brick and timber-built tower mill with patent driving sails and self-winding apparatus with two pairs of 4ft. 4in. French burr stones, flour dressing mill, jumper and four floors. Detached near the above is a brick building in which there is a pair of 4ft. French stones as fixed and fitted for steam engine driving. A brick and timber-built engine room adjoins the tower mill with a 10 horse power engine for use when required, and for which a good Cornish boiler is purchased and is about to be fixed in lieu of the present one, having more power, and near thereto a deep well has been sunk which supplies a constant flow of about 40ft. depth of water, and is carried to the boiler by a powerful force pump, driven either by the wind or steam power.

There is a brick and slate dwelling house with seven rooms and a detached kitchen and bake-office, with a 5-bushel oven; likewise a granary, stables, chaise-house ... and Mill Hill pasture, containing 2½ acres of land.

The property is advantageously situated by the roadside, is well winded, and, with steam auxiliary, is capable of doing an extensive mealing business, and with no other mills near it, has a constant and lucrative grist trade. I am of the opinion that £350 may safely be advanced upon it by way of mortgage, all the going gears, apparatus, stores and machinery being included therein, of course.

J. S. Surridge, Inworth Hall, Kelvedon.

The well alluded to in the description was very close to the mill base, the force pump being worked by a long push rod attached to an eccentric on a cranked shaft projecting from the base above head height. This shaft was operated within from a pair of fast and loose pulleys, belt-driven from a layshaft, which could be run by wind power.[2]

The mill was recorded on a number of maps, and also in trade directories: William Foster, 1848, and Christopher Scowen, 1863, in *White's*, and Henry Frost, 1890 and 1902, steam and wind, in *Kelly's*. In 1906 *Kelly* records steam only. The derelict remains of the mill in the 1920s seem to have escaped the notice of recorders of Essex windmills of that time, despite a relatively late survival.

In October, 1970, at the age of 85, Mr Hayward Henry Frost, still resident in the parish, reviewed the last years of the windmill's working life and recounted his experiences as miller.[3] He was apprenticed at 14½ years to a water miller at Codham Mill beyond Braintree, but pursued his trade only until 1913, when he turned to farming. After completing his apprenticeship he worked for the Roast brothers at White Roding in their mill which he described as 'beautiful, with floors as smooth as a billiard table'. When the wind failed, the mill was driven by belt from a portable threshing engine standing in a shed close by, but in rain it was impossible to hold the belt to the pulley. The Roasts were quiet, gentle people, but they liked their beer, which they brewed themselves. There used to be a ped of hops[4] hanging in the mill, from which they took small quantities to sell to their home-brewing customers. Mr Frost disliked the work at White Roding, because his day was continually interrupted by callers who came for coal. This he weighed out to fill their wheelbarrows and old perambulators, but for him the coal, flour and mill dust made an unappetising mixture.

After buying the mill at Tolleshunt Major, Mr H. H. Frost's grandfather, a Kelvedon miller, put his son to work in it at the age of 19. At this time there was a steam engine with a Cornish boiler; the engine was mounted in a pit about 3ft. deep which gave plenty of slack on the belt to grip the pulleys. The engine went out of commission and the mill worked by wind until 1902,

when, on a fine day, and without provocation, the wooden windshaft with iron poll end broke at the neck, and all four sails came hurtling down. Mr Frost described the shaft as very large — 'a whole tree'; there were signs of fatigue in the ironwork at the point of fracture, where the texture was crystalline. This was the end of milling by wind power; an employed miller departed, and work was not resumed until 1903, when a Crossley engine was installed in a shed made from the bricks of the demolished roundhouse of the post mill at Virley. Frost senior developed asthma and H. H. Frost and his brother succeeded him, but the first left in 1913, and the second in 1914, when called to the colours. So ended the mill's working life in a sequence of events reminiscent of many other windmills. By 1924 the sills and cant post feet were rotting badly; they were therefore sawn and the mill was thrown by a team of six or eight horses.

Mr Frost's recollections and a fine surviving photo furnish a detailed record. The mill stood on a stepped brick base and was devoid of stage or gallery. It had spring sails with coil springs near the tips, of 2½in. diameter and about 3ft. long, with heavy adjustment levers. These were operated from a mobile platform about 5ft. 6in. high and 6ft. long, and with two iron wheels of about 2ft. diameter at one end only; between the engine house and mill a fixed slatted platform gave

244 *Tolleshunt Major. Use of wind power discontinued in 1902, mill demolished 1924*

access to the sails. There was a seven-bladed fantail and a large iron wheel inside the cap for hand winding. Only once in Mr Frost's recollection was the mill exterior painted, when the workmen, apparently to amuse themselves, gave each fantail blade a different colour, perhaps to watch the effect when it span round, but all was white on completion. Equally rare were millwrights' visits — limited to the trimming of wooden cogs by Rowland of Wickham Bishops.

The smock frame, eight-sided, and basically pine, was carried on oak sills, and the internal machinery and fittings were relatively primitive in character: an all-wooden brake wheel, a massive wooden upright shaft, a large great spur wheel and stone nuts also of wood, testified against a late construction. The nuts were taken out of gear by the removal of four separate cogs in each, numbered to ensure correct replacement. Stones were limited to two pairs fed from small hoppers let into the floor above, and underdriven. The auxiliary power was applied to an iron bevel gear on the underside of the great spur by a shaft which was belt-driven outside the mill; this shaft drove, also by belt, one or other of two oat crushers. The sack-hoist bollard is remembered as painful to the hand; it was driven from below by belt from a horizontal shaft carrying a 2ft. wooden face gear meshing with a 4ft. wooden gear on the upright shaft.

Mr Frost's experiences of stone dressing seemed to be — rather aptly — firmly imprinted on his memory. The two pairs of stones, both burrs, were large; one pair took some two days to dress, but the other, of a pale yellow colour, about four, earning for themselves the testimony: 'I should think stones like that would last a lifetime'. Mr Frost could dress a pair of Derbyshire peaks in a day. When he was working in the watermill as an apprentice, his governor bought an old peak stone and had it backed with concrete. They had to change the dress on that stone, but when it was done and used as a runner on a burr bedstone, it was the best grinder of English barley he ever saw. He describes the numbing cold of stone dressing in a draughty mill in winter time and his discovery of a way to keep himself warm. This was to put a hot water bottle inside two sacks, one within the other, and then to get in himself, tying the sacks around his waist. The warmth lasted a long time, and work was suspended to repeat the operation when necessary. Mill bills were obtained from Corcoran in the City of London, and were taken at lengthy intervals to a smith at Feering for thinning and tempering, whose reputation was such that the mill bills from miles around gravitated towards him for attention. Grinding all the bills at Tolleshunt Major mill took two people one and a half hours of hard work, one being employed to turn the handle of the grindstone. Such were the demands of stone dressing.

Mr Hayward Frost could recall no personally alarming experience at his mill, but the following incident occurred when he was milling at night in a cousin's post mill at Uggeshall in Suffolk:

'While it was working the wind shifted and the sails started to slow down, and as I opened the rear door, the only light I had, a candle in a lantern, blew out. I stepped out on to the ladder in the pitch dark. In the meantime, my cousin, knowing the wind had changed, came out of the mill house, which was down in a hollow, and ran up to the mill. As I stepped on to the second or third tread, he lifted the ladder to wind the mill, but I did not know he was there, and when I felt the ladder move under me, I thought the mill was falling. Without thinking, I jumped what must have been twelve feet off the side. As my cousin said afterwards, I was lucky not to have broken my neck'.

Mr Frost's son, Percy, has two principal memories of his father's mill. One is sliding down the sack-hoist chain; the other throwing Mrs . . . What's her name's? chickens out of the fan hatch to see if they would fly. They did!

NOTES

1 About 40 deeds in private possession examined and summarised by R. W. Smith. Further references: E.R.O. D/DMb T17 (map, 1818); E.S. 26.7.1854, p. 1, col. 6; E.W.N. 22.8.1873, p. 6, col. 1; C.C. 28.11.1873, p. 4, col. 1.
2 Per R. W. Smith, as related by H. H. Frost
3 To R. W. Smith, who supplied the notes.
4 Containing about 5 cwt.

Toppesfield

(1) Post mill. Stood south of the village immediately south west of the surviving Mill House on the north side of Gainsford End Road 110 yards from the junction with Great Yeldham Road. TL 737368
(2) Smock mill. Stood 130 yards south west of the site of Hawke's Hall (variously rendered) opposite the lane which formerly led to Gainsford End until blocked by Wethersfield air base. Known as Haxell's Mill. TL 734332
(3) Post mill, replaced by tower mill. Derelict tower standing (1974) at Gainsford End, behind Houghton's Farm. TL 726351 (□ 245a, b)

(1) THE VILLAGE MILL, KNOWN AS TOPPESFIELD MILL
Like the Rock of Ages stood Toppesfield mill over the sharp declivity westwards, sanctuary of the Offords for over a century, the source of a fitful but — in the long term — dependable flow of wholesome stone-ground flour.

In 1677 Robert Smith sold to Robert Wankford 'all that messuage . . . wherein . . . Robert Smith now dwelleth and . . . the mill close (of ½ acre) . . . and one windmill upon the same close lately erected . . . situate by the king's highway leading from . . . Toppesfield towards

245a *Toppesfield: Gainsford End. Standing in ruinous condition in 1976*

Finchingfield to the east. . .'. The property had come to Smith by descent from his father, who had bought from John Overton (E.R.O. D/DO T699).

In 1720, Thomas Offord, of Wickhambrook, Suffolk, miller, bought for £116 from John Poulter, of Clare, Suffolk, gent, the cottage, mill close and windmill 'lately erected'.[1] Thomas mortgaged the property in favour of Poulter in 1734 in the sum of £130, still unrepaid in 1744, when it passed to his nephew Thomas Offord, of Great Yeldham, miller, for £200; the younger Thomas having sufficient resources to repay Poulter. This Thomas died in 1766/7, leaving the mill to his son, also Thomas, who inherited the property at an early age, and may well have been the Thomas who survived until 1836.[2] Judged by his legacies, he was a successful miller, leaving to John Eley of the same parish, farmer, a sum in excess of £1000 in trust for his grandson, and handing on the mill to his son Daniel. John Eley was also a miller, at Gainsford End.

Daniel moved to Castle Hedingham in 1847, offering the family mill on lease. In 1800 it had been specifically described as a post mill, timber-built, with no reference to a roundhouse, and in a notice to let in 1847, there seemed to be no feature of distinction worthy of another line or two of print. Daniel died in January, 1856, aged 78.[3] Ten years later his wife Ann and son William raised a mortgage of £200 on the premises; the mortgagee after one year arranged an auction and sold to the miller-occupier, George Barker, for £400. After this came the decline; Barker sold in August 1876 for £300 to George

Barker the younger, who borrowed the entire sum from the Braintree and Bocking Permanent Benefit Building Society. He died in 1879, upon which his wife sold for £250 to James Butcher of Toppesfield, shopkeeper, who was recorded as miller in a directory of 1882. Butcher was stated in land tax records to have the windmill in 1888, but not 1889, thus giving the apparent time of demolition. That no roundhouse had been added is shown by the mode of representation on the first O.S. 1:2500 map (1876 survey).

(2) HAXELL'S OR HARDY'S MILL

Hawkeswell Hall, latterly a farm, was Haxell's in the vernacular. The mill was a comparative latecomer, and was not shown on Greenwood's (1825) or earlier maps; neither was it mentioned when Edward Cory, farmer, of Hawkwell (*sic*) Hall became insolvent in 1833, complaining of bad crops and high rent, rates and tithes.[4] On the tithe apportionment (1841) we have John Hardy as owner and occupier of 'Haxels Farm' with 34 acres, and of a windmill and yard and Mill Field adjoining, together with other lands in the parish.[5]

The mill is nowhere described as of smock type, but all the evidence points in that direction. When John Hardy died in 1869, his executors auctioned at the Horn Inn, Braintree, the capital windmill, known as Hacksells, a newly-built timber and slated granary standing in the yard (to be removed), a pair of windmill sails and a pair of second-hand millstones.[6] These went, including the 'tower wind corn mill', to F. C. Hardy for £250.[7] It appears that Frederick Charles Hardy, perhaps in an attempt to keep up with John Eley, his close neighbour, who erected the fine brick tower mill at this date, over-strained his resources, for in May, 1876, his mortgagees ordered the sale[8] of the freehold of 'A Newly and Sub-stantially-Erected Brick-and-Slated Steam Mill, well situated along the high road leading to Hedingham, driving two pairs of French stones, an 8-horse-power engine, and a 10-horse-power boiler by Symington. Very ample storage and appliances. A Windmill driving two pairs of French stones, with three floors and a bricked roundhouse, with all the going gears to the said Mills, which are in full trade. The Windmill is connected with the Steam Mill by a Stage. A Miller's House, composed of five rooms'.

The auction was fixed for Wednesday, 14th June, but two days later the property was advertised to be let for a year or a term. Whatever then transpired, there is no reference to milling at this site after the following statement in the press:

East Essex and Halstead Times (8.7.1882)
    Toppesfield. Fire — On Thursday night a fire broke out at Haxell's mill, which is situate near the boundary line separating Wethersfield and this parish. We hear that the mill, which had recently been repaired, was destroyed.

Isaac Mead mentions a small place of business with a

windmill to let in Toppesfield in 1882, which he went to view, but dismissed with the comment: 'I did not like the look of the place'.[9] Both the Haxell's and the village site would seem to have merited this rejection at that date.

(3) THE GAINSFORD END MILLS

This site is recognised on 19th-century maps from the first O.S. 1in. (1805) onwards, and in 1800 it carried a post mill in the occupation of John Teader, farmer, who insured the mill for the paltry sum of £49.[10] Several years after Teader's death in 1815, the freehold estate, inclusive of 25 acres and a post windmill with a pair of 4ft. 10in. stones, was auctioned at the Horse and Groom, Bocking.[11] The land tax records show Thomas Eley senior as owner in 1826 and John Eley in 1832, the occupier throughout being Thomas Hardy. In 1841 the property, known as Houghton's Farm, was held by John Eley,[12] who is subsequently returned as miller and farmer until at least 1869, when he is said to have spent £2000 on the erection of the tower mill.[13] The keystone above the loading door on the first floor bears the inscription J E. On the left of the south entrance door,
1869
two bricks have been marked W A 1869 and L S, probably relating to the tower builders and not to the millwrights.

The mill was said to have had a short working life. Lewis Steward (1874, 98) was recorded as miller by *Kelly* as if using wind power only, followed by Joseph Chaplin (1902). Auxiliary power was certainly applied as indicated below, but the mill appears to be absent from trade directories during its last working years, and must have served local trade. Gearing was repaired in 1926, but work stopped a year or two later.

A technical review is made possible by piecing together data from photographs, from notes by Rex Wailes and others, and from an examination[14] of the considerable remains on site in 1971. At that date the stone floor was the highest level accessible. The mill was essentially a product of the last phase of windmill technology as conceived in the days of iron, wood and stone. The tower had a slight batter only, gaining thereby a little in storage space above, but losing marginally the advantage of a smaller and lighter cap. At base the internal diameter was 20ft., where the walls were only 2ft. thick (Thaxted, built 1804, 4ft. at base), and there were about 155 courses of bricks from ground to curb, a height of 40ft. By 1971, roughly vertical cracks had appeared in the brickwork, one running through 32 courses with a 1½in. gap, such as are not to be seen on the other and older remaining Essex windmill towers. No one has come forward to convert this mill into a residence.

The overall height to the top of the domed — virtually hemispherical — cap was some 50ft. There was no stage, and a single loading door was let in at first-floor level, to which the flour came down the chutes from the stones on the floor above. The floors in order of descent were dust, bin, stone, spout and ground; by 1971, after standing for years devoid of cap covering, the dust floor had collapsed and the bin floor rotted down to the main beams. Three pairs of stones — the full complement of bed and runner stones — remained *in situ*, and most of the gearing below. There were two pairs of 52in. stones and one of 54in. The brake wheel was gone — the windshaft having been taken to Finchingfield mill — but the upright shaft survived.

Most of the structural timbers were in pine, with limited use of oak. The floor beams ran alternately at right angles on succeeding floors; all were stop-chamfered on their lower edges, and, where examined, rested on oak timbers about 3ft. long bolted up and set with them into the tower over straight oak plates let edgeways into the curve of the brickwork. This was probably an original feature, intended to postpone the consequences of rot, and since they still hold after a century they served their purpose well.

There were four double-shuttered, anti-clockwise patent sails with ten bays of three canvas-covered shutters to each; they were winded by an 8-bladed fantail, the shaft from which drove through two bevel and two spur pinions to a final spur gear over the rack. This comprised segments of thin iron teeth set upwards on the outer edge of the curb. Inside the rack, the weight of the lead-covered cap and sail assembly was taken by grooved rollers which ran on a raised rail, a refinement of design considered by Denis Sanders in all probability to have had for its secondary objective the centring of the cap. This view is supported by the rather crude nature of the truck wheels in fact employed, which were probably added when the efficacy of the intended system came under question. Five short horizontal timbers, or horns, projected radially from the outside of the sheers on either side, forming the basis of the gallery, and three more were splayed out at the front from a beam passing between the sheers forward of the brake wheel; all or most of these timbers must have carried rollers beneath, as did the sheers and a tie beam between them at the rear. As per common practice, the forward rollers were larger than the remainder. Suspended below the fan stage was a wooden platform for maintenance purposes, similar to that at Patcham, Sussex.

The upright shaft is of iron, of 5in. diameter, and in two parts, with a dog-clutch coupling just over dust-floor level. Between the bin floor beams was a steady bearing for the shaft composed of two oak pieces bolted together; the same arrangement probably existed at dust floor level. The spindle beam for the upper bearing was carried between cheek pieces about 4ft. long bolted to the insides of the sheers and with mortises to allow wedge adjustment. The all-iron wallower had a wooden friction ring beneath for the sackhoist drive. The great spur wheel, also of all-iron construction, with eight arms and teeth of 2in. pitch and 4¾in. face, was 6ft. 4in. in diameter, and was positioned below the stone floor. The sprattle beam was in pine, with a 4-screw bridging box, thus the sections of the two-part upright shaft were open to find adjustment at top and bottom.

The whole weight of the stones and of the gearing beneath was borne by two sets of pine beams at right angles, with the great spur between, no stanchions or posts being employed in the manner seen at Bulmer smock mill. The stone-floor beams are 11½in. square on 64in. centres, while the lower pair, or 'box' beams, over which the ends of the sprattle (bridging beam) were halved, are of the same dimensions. Four pine posts 10½in. by 3in. are faced flat on the insides of the stone-floor beams and bolted through their long dimension to the lower pair of beams, with packing as required. The stone-floor beams carried the necessary hangers to take the bridge trees, two in wood and one in iron. The last was for the north pair of stones which could be driven by engine from outside the mill via a belt to a pulley on a shaft running to a bevel gear meshing with a bevel on the stone spindle beneath the stone nut. The driving bevel gear could be disengaged by sliding it back on the shaft and securing by a set-screwed collar. The three stone nuts could each be raised out of gear by two spindles and a ring operated by large wing nuts on the upper face of the bridgetrees. One of the three governors remains.

On the underside of the great spur, a downturned bevel gear ring was bolted to bosses cast on as originally designed; this drove auxiliary machinery. Denis Sanders

245b *Toppesfield: Gainsford End. Stone nut, with disengagement by twin-screw control and ring*

noted that most of the wooden components of the mill were made as 'stock job' parts, with sizes all but 'jig-built' in contrast to older styles where widely varying sizes were sometimes encountered for similar-purpose parts.

NOTES

1 Deeds relating to mill in private possession summarised by Roland W. Smith. Mill is shown on Warburton, Bland and Smyth (c1724). See also E.R.O. D/DO T699 (1677).
2 E.R.O. D/A BR 25, p. 545
3 Refs. in E.S. to Daniel Offord: 25.10.1844 giving evidence; 30.7.1847 letting mill; 15.2.1856 death. See also E.R.O. D/A BR 36, p. 1447: Offord's will.
4 E. & H.M. 30.7.1833.
5 E.R.O. D/CT 367A.
6 E.W.N. 23.7.1869
7 E.W.N. 6.8.1869
8 E.W.N. 26.5.1876
9 *The Life Story of an Essex Lad*, Isaac Mead, 1923, p. 46
10 Sun Pol. No. 710642 8.11.1800. Teader was miller in 1795 (E.R.O. D/DC 41/457)
11 C.C. 29.9.1815, 15.8.1817, 1.1.1819
12 E.R.O. D/CT 367A
13 E.R. Vol. XXXIX, 1930, p. 84. Article by Alfred Hills: *Four Essex Windmills*.
14 Jointly by Denis Sanders and the writer

Great and Little Totham

(1) Post mill. Brown's Mill for many years. Stood in the centre of Great Totham, north west of the church and near the Bull. The site lies east of Hall Road and opposite the junction with School Road. TL 858117 (□ 246a, b; I 52)
(2) Smock mill, preceded by post mill. Frost's, then Pulford's, then King's Mill. Stood in the north of Great Totham parish, near the Compasses. The site is east of Mill Road, midway between Brick Spring Lane and the junction with the Tiptree road. TL 869132 (□ I 50)
(3) Post, succeeded by smock mill, formerly in Little Totham. Smith's Mill; long known as Barrow Hill Mill. Stood on raised ground south of the Gold-hanger road (B1026) and immediately north east of The Millbeach P.H. TL 878078 (□ 247)

(1) GREAT TOTHAM POST MILL: BROWN'S MILL

Maps dated 1718 and c1724 mark a Totham mill at this site.[1] In 1783 William Pitt (also rendered Pett) was owner-occupier.[2] William Davey appears to have leased the mill from 1787,[3] and in the following year Robert Pett, farmer, insured it for a mere £180.[4] In 1793 the freehold was for auction and the lessee William Davey then assumed ownership, insuring the mill in his own name no steam power. James Brown had held a yearly tenancy of Henry Dixon at a rent of £25; in a sale notice of 10th August, 1876, the mill was credited with a brick round-house, patent sails and two pairs of stones, together with piggeries and one acre of arable land across the road by the gravel pits.[13] The property was bought in that year for £275, but in 1884, when in the occupation of John Cooper, it fetched £360, though a timber-built engine shed was then included,[14] and in 1882 *Kelly's* directory gave Robert Brown as miller, using steam and wind. Wind was still employed by John Cooper in 1886, but *Kelly* in 1890 omits the mill, which probably stood derelict from then onwards. The shutterless and broken single patent sails are seen in photographs taken at about the time of the mill's demolition in 1911, when a group of Edwardian figures composed of white-collared boys and bowler-hatted men forgathered to see the mill toppled. After the removal of the sail remains, the wind-shaft and a quarterbar, the body was pulled forward by Digby's steam engine, and so the mill ended its days ingloriously.[15]

246a *Great Totham post mill. Last known working date 1886*

246b *Great Totham post mill: the act of demolition, 1911*

for the reduced figure of £150.[5] Some of Davey's tenants failed in business. After the relatively stable Joseph Bridge (1796-1808) came Daniel Taylor, bankrupt in 1810, and in 1811 a successor, Samuel Unwin, absconded, hotly pursued by press notices threatening bankruptcy proceedings if he did not meet his creditors.[6] In 1812 Ralph Unwin assigned the lease to John Chopping of Finchingfield,[7] by whom it was shortly after surrendered to Davey. A later lessee was Samuel Clift, who in 1823 transferred his allegiance from tap room to spout floor, moving in from the Shoulder of Mutton and switching also his insurance cover of £500 to the contents of the mill.[8] Eventually in 1833 the mill property, with two pairs of French stones, and occupied by Reuben Cottee, was put to auction by the trustees under the will of William Davey, deceased.[9] The tithe apportionment (1843) gives Henry Dixon as owner and Thomas Goody as occupier.[10]

The business was run by James Brown through the 1860s and by Robert Brown in 1877,[11] when the mill was insured for £300 and the contents for £150.[12] There was

(2) GREAT TOTHAM SMOCK MILL: KING'S MILL

In September 1815, a freehold post mill near the Compasses was for sale, having John Patten as owner-occupier, and running two pairs of French stones.[1] This is the first milling reference known for this site, which does not carry a mill symbol on the O.S. 1in. map of 1805. In February 1817, the mill was again for auction, late the property of John Patten deceased, miller, farmer and brickmaker.[2] It was taken over by John Pitstow senior, described as bankrupt in 1822, when his new-built brick and timber tower windmill at the site under discussion and in the occupation of James Polley was for sale.[3] Like its predecessor, this mill had two pairs of stones, but what triggered the change from post to smock mill is not apparent. The new mill was stated to have been erected 'within a few years', which points to Pitstow as the builder in 1817-18. In 1826 *Pigot's* directory gave Mark Whitehead as miller and brickmaker. He was owner-occupier in 1830,[4] and the tithe apportionment in 1843 recorded Mark Whitehead as owner and James Whitehead as occupier,[5] the latter described as miller and farmer in *White's* directory for 1848. The mill was later operated by John and Benjamin Frost in succession, and finally by Arthur Pulford (1886, 98) and Alfred King (1902, 08). In 1875-6, George Sayer, millwright, of Witham, fought a battle in and out of court with John Frost, miller, of Totham, to obtain full payment for work on the gearing, which — Frost insisted — was not properly trimmed and pitched. Arbitration was sought, and the case entertainingly reported.[6]

The Frosts in 1882 were driving two pairs of French stones by wind and a third pair by a horizontal steam engine standing at least 20ft. from the mill, according to their insurance policy.[7] A photograph shows a medium-sized smock mill with no frills and furbelows, and with a fantail set on the rear overhang of the cap as at South-minster. There were two pairs of single-shuttered sails turning anti-clockwise. In the earlier days Witham and Maldon were quoted as important trading outlets for this mill.

Mr Charles King, a local resident, imparted his knowledge of the mill to Roland W. Smith in January 1970. Alfred King was his grandfather's brother. Alfred entered about 1900 and did grist work, using the steam engine to drive a pair of stones on the ground floor, and employing wind power also up to c1909. The large wooden upright shaft is thought to have been supported on the ground floor by a massive piece of York stone, which is preserved, face downwards, in Mr King's garden. It measures about 3½ft. square by 15in. deep, and contains four bolt holes. The mill was demolished in 1911 by a steam engine belonging to Digby of Braxted, who demolished also Great Totham south mill. The brickwork was broken up and sold as hardcore at 8*d*. a cubic yard for use at Heybridge New School, then under construction.

(3) BARROW HILL MILL, LATTERLY SMITH'S MILL

George Johnson, in his *History of Great Totham*, gives 1703 as the date of erection of a post mill at Barrow Hill, and records held locally (1980) give Charles Coe, of Maldon, as the entrepreneur.[1] Johnson was writing in about 1831, and so could refer to the recent destruction of that mill, which occurred in the following manner, quoted from the *Essex Chronicle* by Donald Smith in *English Windmills*, Vol. 2:

Little Totham windmill, held by Mr Green, was destroyed by a hurricane on the 30th ult. (i.e. June, 1831) about six o'clock in the evening. The miller was alone in the mill when the hurricane commenced. He was induced to leave it on account of its extraordinary motion, but had scarcely got clear of it when he observed one of the sails taken off and carried into an adjoining field. Shortly after another limb followed,.

and at last the shaft snapped and the body fell with a tremendous crash. The damage is estimated at £500. The whirlwind appears to have been confined entirely to the mill, as no damage was done to any other property in the immediate vicinity.

The post mill stood about 350 yards from the tide mill, which was in Great Totham parish, and the two were worked in conjunction. In 1795 the enterprise included a large wharf used for coals, and 16 acres of land, situated 'near to the navigable canal now making from thence to Chelmsford'.[2] In that year James Whitborn, Little Totham, miller, insured the watermill machinery and contents for £230 and £370, and the gears and stock in his windmill for £125 and £175; the windmill was 'Brick and timber and thatched', but stated to be in Great Totham.[3] Some 22 years later the output from the combined mills was estimated to be 12 to 15 loads per week, when the trustees of William Aldham put the un-expired term of a lease on the market[4]. This lease dated from 6th March, 1811, when Hannah Pigott, widow, conveyed to Joseph Finch of Little Totham, miller, the house, windmill and watermill and 10 acres of pasture and marshland, then in the occupation of James Whitborn, for 25 years at a yearly rent of £105.[5] It was, however, stipulated that Pigott could take payment in the form of 'corn rent', subject to three months' notice of this intention, the rate being £35 per load of wheat at 40 Winchester bushels per load. Several disputes had arisen between Pigott and Whitborn over the fixtures in the mills, valued at £618, an inventory of which was recorded on the conveyance. These were chargeable to the incoming tenant at a fair valuation and were ultimately to be bought back by the landlord.

The schedule throws much light on the composition of the mill, noteworthy items being the oak middlings and the single but large pair of French stones. If, as seems likely, the mill was that built in 1703, then its destruction in 1831 was not untimely, and it was in fact replaced by one of superior capacity. The schedule reads:

Wind-mill — wind-shaft, with Irons and Brasses, two Oak Midlings, four Sails and Sail Cloths, Break-wheel, Break, Break Staff and Irons, Cast Iron Nut, One pair five feet French Stones, Irons and Brasses, Vat, Ladder, Hopper and Shoe, Wheat-Bin, and Wheat-Screen, Sack Tackle, Riggers, Round Rope complete, Top Stage and Ladder, Flour Mill, Shaft Heads Rigger Iron and Brasses, Popets and Brays to Flour Mill and Shaft, Pulley Blocks, Rope and Clamps to Stones, Notch Blocks, Stone Wedges, Rolls Levers and Stone-Bearers, regulating Lighters complete, Flour-Machine with Hopper and Shoe Machine Riggers and Tackle complete, Meal Trough and Spout, Rope Shovel Brush &c., Round House Floor, Scale Beam, and Scales, four half hundred, two 28 lbs., one 14 lbs., one 7 lbs., one 4 lbs. Bloom Weights.

The inventory of the contents of the tide mill is very comprehensive and includes 50 mill bills, 5 'threfts', 8 bolting cloths and 2 pairs of 4ft. 4in. French stones.

In 1813 Finch sold the lease for £350 to Aldham, who, as outlined above, surrendered his title four years later. In November 1817, Hannah Pigott leased to Robert Green, farmer, of East Hanningfield, for a rent of £105 and 'one good fat turkey at Christmas' to be delivered to her residence in Maldon. The watermill and premises were to be insured for not less than £2000 and the windmill for £1000.

After the collapse in 1831, a smock mill was erected on the site, taking some five months to complete. The fortunate survival of the builder's specification[6] highlights the essential features of a long vanished major Essex windmill:

Specification for Erecting a Tower Windmill for C. W. Green of Little Totham
The Said Mill to be Timber built 28 feet diameter at the bottom from Out to Out and 16 feet diameter at the Curb from Out to Out, to contain Five floors as follows: the first to be 8 feet 6in. high from floor to floor, the second 8 feet do. do. the Third 10 feet do. do. the Fourth 8 feet do. do. and the Fifth 9 feet do. to the top of the Curb, to be framed with Timbers as follows:

	In.		In.
Fir Corner Posts	11	by	11
do. Girts	8	x	6
do. Kings	8	x	6
do. Braces	6	x	4
do. Quarters	4	x	3
do. Girders	12	x	12
Fir floor Joists	6	x	2½
Oak Sills	12	x	8
do. Sheer Trees	12	x	10
do. Weather beam	14	x	12
Elm Curb	12	x	10
do. Rafters	4	x	2½

To be weatherboarded with Yellow batten at 5 Inch gauge the floors to be laid with Inch yellow deal Plough'd and Tongued, the Mill to stand upon 18 Inch brickwork. Wind shaft of Cast Iron 26 Inches at the mortice and 13 Inches diameter at the Neck, Two fir Midlings 12 In. by 14 In. and 54 feet long, Two Pair of Patent Sails 12 Yards from the Center, and 8ft. 6in. wide Compleat, 4 Oak Clamps 20 feet long, Iron upright Shaft, Iron Wallower nutt and Iron cogs, Iron Spur Wheel with wood Cogs. Three Iron nutts with Iron cogs to drive with Crotch Spindles to work three Pairs of Stones; the Crown Wheel to hang under the Wallower nutt to drive one new Flour Mill and Sack Tackle Compleat, the Mill to Wind itself upon a live Curb &c compleat. The Mill to be Painted twice over in White Lead and Oil; to be properly rendered on boarding within, to be allowed the Materials of the Post Windmill to convert them as far as Sound and Useful (except those that are not used in the New Mill)

Agreeable to this Specification I Alfred Mecklenburgh Contract to Compleat the whole in a good Solid Substantial and Workmanlike Manner and Set the Same agoing for the Sum of *Six Hundred Pounds* £600

N.B. I agree to sett Two pair of Stones to Work by the 15

Jany 1832 and Complete the rest of the Wind mill in February following or forfeit the sum of Fifty Pounds.

Alfred Mecklenburgh
C W Green
Witness Robt. Francis
August 13, 1831

From 1832 the Green family continued to hold the lease, which ran to 1846, the ownership resting with Henry Coe Coape of Goldhanger. Charles W. Green employed David Kemp for twelve years from the age of 13, at the end of which, in 1837, Kemp was indicted for alleged embezzlement of 1s. from his master, resulting from an incorrect entry on a slate in the mill. The jury acquitted him.[7] Later millers included Charles Hall (1848), who employed eight men in 1851,[8] Isaac Grainger (1863) and Arthur Smith in 1890.

In September 1880, the mill was tail-winded:[9]

Maldon. Barrow Hills Mill. On Saturday morning last, during a stiff breeze, the sails of the mill at Barrow Hills, which could not have been properly secured, were set in motion by the wind. The sails were not against the wind, as is usual, but 'aback', and from their rapid motion could not be stopped, and revolved with dangerous rapidity; the slats, too, began to fly off, and were blown into the road, making it dangerous for passers-by. The man in charge, fearing the mill would catch fire from the excessive friction, and afraid to grapple with the unwieldy and dangerous mischief, called for help from a neighbouring mill, and the only expedient appeared to be to lower the top stone down on the nether stone. This rough and ready plan of course had the effect of stopping the mill, but at the cost, in broken machinery, of about £40. Mr C. Smith, the lessee of the mill, whose tenancy expires at Michaelmas, is the responsible party for making good the damage.

The windmill was taken down in 1892.[10] For a period it had worked on two sails, no doubt — like so many of

247 *Little Totham: Barrow Hill Mill. Demolished 1892*

its fellows at that time — unable to support the expense of fitting a new pair. In 1970, the last miller's son, then aged 90, recalled that his father had been apprenticed to a miller in Croydon, and that at Millbeach he employed four men in the two mills and had four horses for cartage.[11] One of the hands was Abraham Springett, whose son, aged 82 in 1970, had one recollection of the windmill — the great cloud of dust, seen from the safety of a bedroom window nearby, which rose as his father pulled it down. Auxiliary power was not used in the business, perhaps accounting for the early cessation of work at the tide mill also, which became a store for Saltcote maltsters.

John Bryant, the Colchester millwright, ascribed to the smock mill three pairs of 4ft. French stones driven from above by 7ft. long crotched quants, which proved very awkward when it came to stone dressing.[12] A surviving, rather indistinct, photograph indicates a five-floored octagonal tower in conformity with the builder's specification, with a domed cap and purpose-built fantail staging above.

NOTES

I Great Totham south (post mill)

1 E.R.O. D/DE1 p. 45; Warburton, Bland and Smyth
2 Land tax in E.R.O., where see also will of William Pett; D/A CR 18, p. 298
3 C.C. 6.4.1787
4 R.E. Pol. No. 109405 1.12.1788 per H. E. S. Simmons
5 C.C. 22.11.1793; E.R.O.: land tax; R.E. Pol. No. 137639 1.1.1794 per H. E. S. Simmons
6 C.C. 4.5.1810 & *Kentish Gazette* 24.12.1811, both per H. E. S. Simmons
7 E.R.O. D/DO T702
8 E.R.O. D/F 21/23, p. 49
9 C.C. 30.8. & 22.9.1833. See also K. & E. M. 3.4.1832, 15.1., 3.9. & 8.10.1833
10 E.R.O. D/CT 368A
11 See E.W.N. 31.10.1873: bankruptcy proceedings. Other millers (also shopkeepers): Wm. Moore, 1850, Joseph Digby, 1855
12 E.R.O. D/F 21/22, p. 280
13 E.R.O. B479
14 E.W.N. 11.8.1876, p. 5, col. 3, 15.2.1884, p. 4, col. 2
15 Demolished 1.4.1911: note per Peter Came (1970)

II Great Totham north (post and smock mills)

1 C.C. 29.9.1815
2 C.C. 7 & 14.2.1817
3 C.C. 12.4. & 9.6.1822; *Lond. Gaz.*, 8.6.1822, per H. E. S. Simmons. Re Polley see Vol. I, *Three Jolly Millers*, where Polley is stated in error to have been at the south (post) mill
4 *Essex Poll Book*, per G. W. Martin
5 E.R.O. D/CT 368A
6 E.W.N. 15.9.1875, 14.4. 16.6. & 18.8.1876. See also E.W.N. 17.10.1873, p. 8, col. 5
7 E.R.O. D/F 21/23, p. 49. See also E.W.N. 1.10.1880, p. 1

III Little Totham (post and smock mills)

1 Per Rev. D. T. Willcock, Gt. Totham, from a parish register

2 C.C. 23.1.1795
3 R.E. Pol. No. 146184 27.7.1795 per H. E. S. Simmons
4 C.C. 24.10.1817
5 E.R.O. D/DU 627/14
6 In private possession
7 E.S. 1.12.1837
8 P.R.O. HO 107 1778. (1851 census)
9 E.W.N. 24.9.1880. See also E.W.N. 13.8.1880 for auction of contents of both mills
10 *Maldon and the River Blackwater*, E. A. Fitch, 1898 edn., p. 51
11 Per Roland W. Smith
12 *Tide Mills, Part 2*, Rex Wailes, S.P.A.B., 1956, p. 27

Upminster

(1) Post mill. Known as Upminster Common Mill; for many years Pinchon's Mill. Stood immediately north of the road named Shepherds Hill leading to Harold Wood, and directly opposite the drive to Page's Farm. TQ 558904 (□ 248).

(2) Smock mill. From 1857, Abraham's Mill. Preserved. Stands 100 yards north of the Hornchurch road from a point 350 yards west of Upminster crossroads. TQ 557868 (□ 249; II 59, 84, 85, 105, 106a)

(1) UPMINSTER COMMON MILL

The site slopes down to west, south and east, and less obviously to the north; the house-name 'Windy Ridge' close by underlines the discrimination shown by the mill builders who, as stated in 1670, 'lately enclosed' a parcel of land on Gaines Common for the raising of a mill hill to carry a windmill.[1] A mill in the parish was in the occupation of Thomas Dawson until his death in 1664,[2] and

FIG. 41 *Upminster Common: MS map drawing, 1752*

this or a successor was held by John Gatwood in the years 1704 and 1725.[3] Known millers to follow were Thomas Holden (1752) and John Letch (1768), then William Pinchon (1772),[4] whose family, of strong non-conformist persuasion, was associated with the mill for a century or more, though Nathaniel Whitmore's name crops up in the period around 1850. The mill was mapped by Warburton, Bland and Smyth (c1724), and it, or a successor, persisted until after the first 6in. O.S. map (surv. 1865), on which its position is pin-pointed.

In 1775 the timber-built mill was insured for £200, the contents for £100, by William Pinchin (sic) of Upminster, miller,[5] perhaps the same Pinchon who married in 1772 and died in 1815, leaving the mill to his son James. On James' death in 1840 the freehold passed to his brother David, as recorded in the court minutes of the manor of Gaines, and so came eventually to David's son of like name.[6] The last Pinchon, on his departure, took five customers who had defaulted in payment to court, and won the day handsomely.[7]

V.C.H. *Essex*, Vol. VII, p. 152, records the demolition of the mill as taking place in July, 1880. T. L. Wilson, the late 19th-century chronicler of Upminster's history, included a sketch of the structure in his volume.[8] Though not an unobstructed view, it shows a fantail, which — according to a statement by one of the millers of the village smock mill to R. Hawksley — was over the tail pole. The last millers were A. H. Wilshire (1874), James Ewin (1878) and S. Manning, of whom Ewin would appear to have responded to the following advertisement of June, 1876:[9]

> To be let, a capital post windmill, in good working order, with patent sails and fantail, driving two pair of French stones, bake-house, granary, good dwelling house, large garden, workman's cottage and garden, two small paddocks, and suitable outbuildings; steam power mill will be added if required. Address A.B. Post Office, Upminster, near Romford.

248 *Upminster Common Mill. Sketch made in or before 1880; demolition 1882*

(2) UPMINSTER SMOCK MILL

Without doubt, more words have been written about Upminster windmill than any other in Essex, especially with regard to preservation. Anthony D. Butler's admirable booklet entitled *Upminster Mill* gives an objective account of historical and technical aspects with accuracy and clarity, and in ample detail,[10] and some of his material has been used in the brief outline of the mill's history which follows, while technical and preservational aspects are treated separately.

Strong presumptive evidence from the parish rate books indicates 1803 as the date of erection on the initiative of James Nokes, formerly of Stifford, and ultimately of Bridge House Farm, Upminster. Wilson relates an anecdote which may not be apocryphal:

'When the sails were first put up, my grandfather Andrew Wilson and my father Thomas Wilson were there with others. My father was then thirteen years old. His father got on one of the sails and walked up on to the opposite one going right to the top, when some-one called out: "Do you see Buonaparte coming?" "No", said he, "he will never come here", and again: "get over and come down the other side", but this he declined to do. A sawyer, however, named Watling, who was also there afterwards, went up, and, getting over, came down the other side. Of course, the old sails of that age were only made of battens with openings of about a foot square to be spread over with a canvas cloth; they were therefore easily climbed upon.'

The mill formed a parallel enterprise to that at the waterfront in West Thurrock, a large smock mill built a little earlier by the Nokes family, also with the London trade clearly in mind. Both these mills were distinguished by an exceptionally early introduction of steam power, thought to date from 1811-12 in the case of Upminster, as inferred from a sudden leap in the rateable value in 1812 from £50 10*s.* to £77 10*s.* Wilson gave May, 1811, as the earliest known date for the steam plant, and certainly by 1818 there is the following record in a policy register of the Essex and Suffolk Insurance Society[11] which totals £4300:

> James Nokes Sen[r] Upminster Essex
> £1990 On Wind Mill B[k] T[r] and Tiled and all the going gears attached therein
> £ 360 2 Granaries adjoining B[k] B[t] (i.e. brick-built) Slated and Meal Room adjoining B[k] B[t] & Slated
> £ 300 Steam Engine house Stokers Shed & Grinding room adjoining & all the Machinery therein all the above buildings join
> £1500 Stock and Implements in the above Buildings
> £ 150 On cottage not adjoining T[r] Slated & T[d] in the occ[n] of workmen

With regard to wind power, Nokes had an eye for landscape; the mill stands overlooking the Ingrebourne valley to the west, and would sometimes have been urged into activity by the example of Hornchurch post mill on the ridge opposite. Initially the wind-driven stones numbered three pairs, one set being added later; a

249 *Upminster Mill when active. Note the external brake rope pegged free of the door*

total of five pairs was worked by wind and steam in 1849 and six pairs in 1856.[12] James Nokes died in 1838, and his son Thomas the elder succeeded him, but was crippled by debts in 1849, and entered the pages of the *London Gazette* as a bankrupt.[13] In that year the mill and farm were auctioned as the 'Mill Estate'. The premises included two millers' cottages and a pond. The conditions of sale confirmed the title as commencing in 1803, the date of purchase of the site by James Nokes. Ambrose Colson paid £2000 for the property, but shortly after sold to James Wadeson.

By this time the Abraham family, who held the mill until 1934, were already on the scene. Thomas Abraham, born in the year of erection of the mill, and having worked for the Nokes family at West Thurrock, became foreman at Upminster in 1844 for £1 weekly, and returned in 1851 for a miserly wage of 18s., after trying his hand at farming. His dissatisfaction with the low figure must have prompted his return to farming, by which occupation he amassed enough capital to purchase the windmill and land from Wadeson in 1857 for £1,100, after having been drawn to milling again for two years at Navestock steam mill. When he died in 1882, the Upminster concern passed to John Arkell Abraham, his younger son, who lived until 1912, and who had spent many of his earlier years at Baker Street Mill, Orsett.

Wilson records a very severe thunderstorm in 1889, during which 4in. of rain fell in 7 hours, and in the course of which the mill was struck by lightning, throwing off 'thousands of sparks, like fireworks'. A newspaper report recorded the destruction of a sail and the fusing of the sack-chain links.[14] On 5th January, 1900, the *Essex Weekly News* had a worse disaster to report:

> Upminster Mill wrecked. Damage estimated at £300. During the gale on Friday afternoon, the cast iron shaft supporting the sails of the Upminster windmill snapped off at the neck and the four sails fell to the ground with a terrific crash. In their descent they carried away some 40-50 feet of the stage and smashed themselves into innumerable atoms of broken wood and ironwork, one portion lodging on the roof of the granary. Mr J. A. Abraham, the owner of the windmill, for whom much sympathy is felt, estimates his loss at not less than £300. Should the mill fail to be restored to its original state, Upminster will be deprived of one of its most picturesque landmarks. Since the erection of the mill in 1802-3, it has occasionally lost a sail or two, and in September 1889 it sustained some injury from lightning. It is not probable that the sails will be restored, steam power having been added to that of wind some 80 years ago.

The villagers rallied round in much the same way as at Bradwell-on-Sea, Bicknacre, and elsewhere, a century earlier, but from different motives, to contribute to the cost of repair. A post-mill windshaft, said to have come from a mill near Maldon, was installed in the smock mill, where it is to be seen today. John Arkell was at that time assisted by his three nephews Thomas, Alfred and Clement Abraham, all of whom were to be seen in the period around 1930, as by the present writer from the comfort of a garden swing, moving about the mill yard with slow and deliberate tread, often escorted by thirty or forty ever-ravenous hens. The mill then worked occasionally by wind, oddly anachronistic amid the sea of 'semis' to be seen ranging far and wide from the fine viewpoint of the fantail staging. Clement had latterly remarked that the mill was only kept at work for sentimental reasons, and the fact that a middling was replaced and extensive damage to the fantail was repaired in 1927 shows how deeply rooted that sentiment was. First Tom, of 'T. A. & C. Abraham' died, then Clem, the business manager, who had dealt in both corn and coal, and with his demise the working days were over. The property was sold in December, 1934. Alfred survived to the age of 95, and was a well-known figure about the town centre until well into the 1950s.

The purchase by W. H. Simmons of mill and land in 1934 for £3,400 was merely the beginning of another lengthy and stormy episode in the mill's history, during which Hector Stone, a determined and elderly Suffolk miller in retirement, made strenuous but thwarted efforts to revive the mill as a working machine. It is regrettable that the accompanying buildings remained uninhabited until their condition was beyond redemption, and that the ancient steam plant was spirited away,[15] for the chance has been lost to preserve a perfect milling complex of *c*1800 for the enjoyment of a densely populated area.

A remarkable model of the mill, standing 7ft. 6in. high, and kept in a specially constructed glass case at Romford Library, was made by the late E. W. King in the 1950s, and took about six years to complete. It is on a scale of 1:12. It was constructed with meticulous regard to detail, and is beautifully finished. The purist would not condone the use of over 6000 brass screws, the screw being so seldom encountered in windmill structures, but all can admire the application and craftsmanship which brought this model into being, and applaud the local authority for highlighting by this display the architectural treasure which survives within its boundaries.

Addendum

Clark and Wailes in 'Bell Alarms and Sack Hoists in Windmills,' *Trans. Newcomen Soc.*, Vol. XLV, 1972-3, p. 58, state: 'The bell for *each* pair of stones is hung on the end of a thin wooden rod pivoted on a beam in the ceiling. Above the bell, a cord is attached to the rod and passes up and over a pulley on the beam and down to the hopper. A wood batten is nailed to the upright shaft and, when corn runs low in the hopper, the weight of the bell allows the rod on which it is mounted to fall against this batten, which hits the rod and rings the bell.'

NOTES

1 E.R.O. D/DA T449

2 E.R.O. D/P 117/1/1 & T/P 95/1, p. 138

3 E.R.O. D/DCb 1 (1704, 1725). See also E.R.O. T/P 67/5, p. 149 (1675)

4 E.R.O. T/P 67/2

5 Sun Pol. No. 362959 27.12.1775 per H. E. S. Simmons

6 E.R.O. D/DZb2, pp. 56, 194-5, 281-4, 359, 379-82 per V.C.H. notes in MS., April, 1975

7 E.W.N. 22.1.1875, p. 3, col. 5

8 *History and Topography of Upminster*, T. L. Wilson, 1880-1, p. 196

9 E.W.N. 30.6.1876

10 *Upminster Mill*, Anthony D. Butler, Publ. Peter R. Davis, 1968

11 E.R.O. D/F 21/2, p. 165, 12.9.1818

12 E.R.O. D/DJn E1 1849; E.S. 9.5.1856: detailed sale notice, quoting rent as £210 p.a.

13 *Lond. Gaz.*, 22.1. & 16.3.1849, per H. E. S. Simmons

14 *Essex Herald* 10.9.1889 per A. D. Butler

15 See *Trans. Newcomen Soc.*, Vol. XXXI, 1958, Rex Wailes, pp. 168, 175

Saffron Walden

(1) Smock mill, known particularly as Ruse's Mill. Stood in the garden of Old Mill House, 21 Mount Pleasant Road, at the junction with South Road. TL 542377 (□ 250; I 43)

(2) Smock mill known as Middleditch's Mill. Stood 230 yards due south from a point on Peaslands Road 120 yards east of the junction with South Road. TL 543374 (□ 251)

(3) Smock mill described as Copthall Windmill. Stood in the north centre of the grounds of The Mill House, Mill Lane, off the Ashdon Road. TL 545389

(4) Post mill. Stood off the Thaxted road near Stanley's Farm Road. TL 548379

(5) Post mill at Sewards End. The site is located approximately by the bungalow 'Saffalbus' about 130 yards west of Mill House and 60 yards south of the Radwinter road. TL 566380 (□ 252a, b; I 1)

BOTH water and wind mills made formerly significant contributions to Saffron Walden's demand for flour; the former strung out along the River Cam to the west, the latter occupying the slopes on the periphery of the urban area. In the tithe apportionment of 1844,[1] field names hint at an earlier distribution of windmills more widely spread: a group of fields relating to Windmill Hill near The Vineyard off Windmill Hill to the north west; Mill Field and The Mill Close 300 yards south west of Pounce Hall on the Radwinter road; Windmill Mead 440 yards south east of Little Walden hamlet. Doubtless other sites are not so commemorated.

The 19th-century picture of the local windmills lacks clarity as a result of frequent changes in ownership and occupation, the revision of street names, and the loose association of mills with streets in directory entries. Two of the smock mills lay only 300 yards apart on the southern limits of the town, and Middleditch's mill was at various times referred to as in Mill Lane, Chalk Lane, Peaslands Road and Long Lane. Directories listing millers at Saffron Walden record chiefly the operators of windmills.

(1) RUSE'S MILL

This low-built, self-effacing mill stood on a single-storied brick base on a low mound. It had formerly a thatched cap seen in a painting and a sketch.[2] Immediately to the south west stood a two-storied miller's dwelling, commonly named the 'upside-down' cottage, since its sunken ground floor, facing north, housed the bedrooms, and its upper storey, not much above pavement level, held the living rooms, with only one window facing south. A sunken yard lies between the cottage and the site of the former windmill, where octagonal brickwork, cut off at ground level, forms a low feature in the garden (1970).

A mill is indicated here on a map of 1758[3] and later by Chapman and André (1777), but whether the smock mill

250 *Saffron Walden: Ruse's Mill, Mount Pleasant Road. Oil painting by J. M. Youngman, ante-1843. Note the thatched cap*

or an earlier post mill at those dates is not known. However, a photograph of the massive upright shaft in wood, taken during demolition in 1955, shows an imposing inscription, which may indicate the date of erection of the smock mill:

J C

R B

1785

The smock mill would seem to have been the subject of the following insurance record, dated 3rd March, 1806,[4] which perhaps also invests the J C of the inscription with a little flesh: 'James Camp of Cuckingstool End Street, of Saffron Walden in Essex, Miller. Dwelling House £80; Household Goods etc. £50; Cottage only near in tenure of Thos. Harvey Camp, Miller, £70; Barn and Stable under one roof near £30; Brewhouse and chamber only adjoining near, timber and tiled £50; Smock Wind Corn Mill only in Saffron Walden aforesaid £100; Standing and Going Gears £170. All thatched except as above. Total £550'.

The Ruse family held the property for many years. Stephen Ruse was on the electoral roll as owner-occupier in 1830, but in 1844 was recorded as occupier under William Purkis, holding less than half an acre.[5] Harvey Ruse, of Long Lane, was working the mill in 1851, but was shortly followed by James Ewin, who apparently ran the mill at Sewards End in conjunction for a few years until 1858, as indicated in rate books and directories. The Claydens, first James, then Mary (1872), worked both the Long Lane mills (sites (1) and (2)), as did later the Matthews family (1878) and James Wright in 1890 and later, but *Kelly* gives David Marsh at Mount Pleasant Road only in 1882, 86. The last directory reference to wind power comes in 1898, steam only being specified in 1902, and the windmill, probably devoid of sails, went unrecorded by the surveyors of the third O.S. 1in. map (1902). A local informant (1976) gave *c*1900 as the last date for the use of wind.

James Wright senior was able to pass on recollections of his own and of other local windmills to Donald W. Muggeridge in 1936; these form an important basis for the descriptions that follow. Wright was apparently first associated with Ruse's mill *c*1873. He stated that the mill last worked briefly on two sails after the others had been blown off in a gale. All four were double-shuttered, and each measured 8ft. 2in. and came within 2ft. of the ground. The mill had three floors only. The machinery was predominantly wooden, including the windshaft, the nearly square upright shaft and the wallower; the brake and spur wheels had iron-teeth segments attached. The two pairs of underdriven stones, on wooden bridgetrees and brays, were 4ft. 2in. for wheat and 4ft. for barley, also powered by a portable steam engine which drove via a pulley and shaft to an all-iron extra rim added to the great spur gear. Mounted on the upright shaft was an unbevelled wheel with cogs on its lower face. These meshed with a spur gear on an all-wooden shaft for sack-hoist drive, the shaft being arranged to drop at its further end in order to tighten the belt (instead of the sack bollard being forced to rise). Another shaft with a wooden cogwheel was driven from the same down-turned gear to drive an oat crusher on the first floor and a wooden countershaft on the ground floor.

The mill had been topped in its later days by a shapely metalled ogee cap behind which the fantail drove to an iron rack. The oil painting by J. M. Youngman shows the earlier domed and thatched cap with a generous extension to the rear to take the older style of winding gear.[6] The former common sails had then already been replaced by shuttered ones, and the artist indicated the vertical weatherboarding on the mill frame, as seen on mills in Cambridgeshire. This covered horizontal boarding. John Player, in his *Sketches of Saffron Walden* (1843), referred to Middleditch's 'conspicuous mill in leaden-colour dress' and to Ruse's mill, 'in virgin white, new-topped since Youngman's sketch was made, which has been presented by him to Saffron Walden Museum'. This statement appears to give an approximate date for the change of cap (but see note 2).

(2) MIDDLEDITCH'S MILL

This octagonal smock mill, standing on a single-storied brick base, was erected *c*1799,[7] and in its earlier days carried two pairs of 4ft. 9in. French stones.[8] With the 1½-2 acres of land attached, it was freehold, and when Cane, the proprietor, was selling in 1821, he claimed storage space for 100 quarters of corn in the mill, and 'breaking' capacity for a like amount weekly. Twenty years later a pair of peak stones for 'drawing trefoil' had been added; also a machine for threshing clover seed.[9] The seed business was an important sideline, there being a specially constructed shed 10½ft. by 46½ft. long described as a seed shop. For about thirty years up to 1850 William Middleditch ran this mill, or was involved in some capacity. After his death in 1850, Charles Barnard, a young master miller employing one journeyman, took over.[10] A directory for 1878 gives Mrs Jane Matthews at Chalk Lane and Walter Matthews at South Road, and the last miller, James Wright, operated both neighbouring mills, which he hired from George Gibson. In 1936 he volunteered a few details of the years of decline. The mill had five floors, including the ground, and latterly had a gallery round the cap which he had built himself. There was no stage. Two single-shuttered and two double-shuttered anti-clockwise sails had canvas on wooden frames, and these were operated by centrally placed bars as at Radwinter smock mill. Francis, millwright, of Cambridge, did work on the sails after a gale had tail-winded the mill and had broken one of the smaller pair. He restored them to working order, but the structure was weakened, and milling by wind ceased in about 1896. There was an 8-bladed fantail. The three pairs of stone last in use were 4ft. 10in. for wheat, 4ft. 6in. for barley and 3ft. for splitting beans and peas, all underdriven from an iron windshaft and wallower in combination with a brake wheel and an upright shaft of wood. Two photographs of the mill show in the one case vertical weatherboarding and in the other horizontal, the latter probably in consequence of the removal of the former. The fantail was mounted close in at the expense of a surgical operation on the cap, a large section of which was cut away to give play to the blades. Demolition followed closely on the termination of milling, probably hastened by the unsafe condition of the mill, and R. Hawksley was told that it occurred in 1898.

251 *Saffron Walden: Middleditch's Mill. Photo taken in or before 1896, shortly before demolition*

(3) COPTHALL MILL

Very little is known of this mill. It makes its début in a drawing of a tower type mill on a map dated 1828.[11] John Searle, in occupation in 1844, was in 1851 described as miller and farmer of 30 acres.[12] From 1856 to 1894 Edward Reid Brook was miller; the mill was a red painted octagonal smock on a single-storied base, with a gallery round the cap and an 8-bladed fantail. Four double-shuttered sails worked three pairs of stones, and steam was employed towards the close.[13] As at South Road, demolition followed soon after the winding up of the business in about 1896; the mill was not included in the O.S. 6in. survey of that year.

(4) THAXTED ROAD MILL

The known dates of the existence of this mill are 1799-1830. It was recorded on the preliminary drawing for the first O.S. 1in. map (1799) and on Greenwood's map (1825). In 1819 the mill, 'nearly new', containing two pairs of French stones, and held freehold with half an acre of land, was for auction at the Hoops Inn, Saffron Walden. It was then in the occupation of William Camp, the proprietor.[14] *Pigot's* directory for 1823 returns James Nicholls as miller in 'Thackstead Road', but the edition of 1826 omits him and any other title holder; however, in that year the land tax records show T. A. Catlin (late Nichols — *sic*) as owner and Stephen Ruse as occupier. From then until 1830 Ruse ran the Thaxted road mill and that at site (1) in conjunction, but after 1830 the former was not included in the land tax returns.[15]

(5) SEWARDS END MILL

In 1803 Edward Mynott of Saffron Walden, farmer and miller, insured for £30 the utensils and stock in his 'corn windmill timber built' situated at Suers (*sic*) End,[16] which mill is visible in a representation of a view from Windmill Hill executed in 1811,[17] though later omitted from Greenwood's map (1825).

In 1839 John Mynott was in occupation.[18] His post mill at Sewer's End, as then known, was realistically portrayed by Dibdin in a coloured engraving of about that date,[19] the details of which are fully confirmed in photographs taken some sixty years later. The round-house was built unusually close in, leaving half the brick piers exposed and giving the roof a very steep pitch. One pair of commons and one of double-shuttered sails were then in use; eventually all the sails were patents, struck from within the mill body. Winding was by tail pole. The weatherboarding at the front ran down at an angle from the corner posts to the prow, almost in herringbone pattern. There were two pairs of stones, arranged head and tail. Dibdin's sketch shows a wooden windshaft on the mill and another on the ground. Two side views of the mill, taken probably soon after 1900, show that the body had been extended to the rear at stone and 'stage' (roof)-floor levels, probably to accommodate a flour dresser and striking tackle. External inclined wooden supports were evidently footed on the rear sill. The millers were assuredly not sun-seekers, as is evidenced by the very small weather hatches and windows.

Millers include Richard Thompson (1850), James Ewin (1855), Alfred Thomas Matthews (1874) and Charles Kettley (1894). The last miller was George Jarvis, who, according to his two daughters living locally in 1972, used wind power only. George Patmore at the mill and Campions Farm, 1902, is the last miller noted in a directory, and it appears that the mill was

252a Saffron Walden: Sewards End. Date when ceased work uncertain; demolition probably c 1909

252b Saffron Walden: Sewards End. Note the rear extension

demolished in about 1908-9 after having stood derelict for some time. It is not recorded on the O.S. Popular 1in. map (1914-15).

NOTES

1 E.R.O. D/CT 378A
2 Oil painting by J. M. Youngman, tentatively dated *c*1845; sketch by T. C. Dibdin, 1847 (but perhaps retrospective?)
3 E.R.O. T/M 123
4 Sun Pol. No. 788270 3.3.1806
5 *Essex Poll Book*, per G. W. Martin; E.R.O. D/CT 378A
6 See note 2
7 C.C. 5.1.1821; shown on the 1799 O.S. drawings
8 C.C. 30.3.1821
9 E.S. 22.5.1840
10 E.S. 12.7.1850; P.R.O. HO 107 1786
11 E.R.O. T/M 141
12 E.R.O. D/CT 378A; P.R.O. HO 107 1786. See also *Lond. Gaz.* 26.11.1847
13 Per D. W. Muggeridge: information from J. Wright, 1936
14 *Cambridge Chron.* 19.3.1819
15 E.R.O. Q/RP1 942. Mill not shown on 1828 map (E.R.O. T/M 141)
16 R.E. Pol. No. 200334 23.5.1803 per H. E. S. Simmons
17 King's Topographical Coll., B.M. per R. Hawksley
18 *Pigot's* directory, per R. Hawksley
19 Saffron Walden Museum, E.R.O., and elsewhere

Great Waltham

(1) Post mill. Roundhouse preserved adjacent to the Windmill Inn, Chatham Green, 300 yards west of the Braintree road (A131). Formerly in Great Waltham, now in Little Waltham (1983). TL 716152 (□ 253)

(2) Post mill. Erected in or shortly before 1812 near the Spread Eagle Inn, Ford End, and offered for removal in 1813. The inn was burnt down in 1984. Approx. TL 679167

(1) CHATHAM GREEN MILL

The first references noted to Chatham Green mill dated from 1829, when it entered the land tax records, and more particularly from 1833, when on June 21st the proprietor, Thomas Child, inserted an auction notice in the *Chelmsford Chronicle*[1]:

To be sold by auction by direction of the proprietor, Mr Thomas Child, on 1st July at St Ann's Castle, Great Leighs: A capital new erected Post Windmill situate at Chatham Green, in the parish of Great Waltham, drawing 10 yards of cloth, the going gears of the best description, containing a wallower nut, spur wheel, and stone nuts, with two pair of French stones, on centre irons, cast iron stone boxes and bridging ditto, sack tackle, flour mill and jumper. Also a dwelling house. The detached buildings comprise a bake office with a new erected 5-bushel oven and patent irons complete.

A similar notice in 1835 by Child, who was then hoping to sell the mill by private contract, omits any mention of a roundhouse.[2] The mill was not shown on Greenwood's (1825) or earlier maps, which fact further strengthens the probability that the mill was built in the late 1820s.

In 1841, mill, house and yard were owned by Thomas Newman and occupied by John Bentall, who became insolvent in 1856 in Chelmsford.[3] Later occupiers were John Cottee (1863), Charles Hawkes (1866, 82) and Henry Challis, the last miller, who was present in 1886 using wind power only. In 1890 he was beer retailer also, according to *Kelly*, and continued thus to *Kelly's* 1902. Challis held house and mill in the electoral roll for 1903-4, but house alone in 1904-5. Neither living memories of the mill nor a photographic record were traceable in the 1970s.

The roundhouse is substantial, being two-floored and of 24ft. internal diameter, built entirely separate from the four brick piers, behind which it passes. It stands 12ft. high to the eaves, and is stepped inwards by $2\frac{1}{2}$in. at 7ft. over ground level. Two windows and a stable door were provided on each floor; the absence of a second door at either level suggests a tall body with sails revolving well over the ground. The four brick piers are lightly stepped on all four faces to give an upward taper and are each over 6ft. tall, so giving freedom of movement beneath the crosstrees. These are still in position, with part of the main post and small sections of the quarterbars. The lower crosstree is 14in. wide by 13in. deep, and is rebated on the sides at the junction with the post, and cut down 4in. under the upper crosstree, a gap of 1in. being left between them. The quarterbars, 11in. by 10in., are of 'boxed' heart of oak, and are secured by an iron strap and footed with double birdsmouth joints. One crosstree has been repaired by scarf jointing, the overall length of the splice being 46in., and the need for this may have hastened the addition of the roundhouse.

The presumption that it was added, based on three points of evidence implicit in the above survey, is further strengthened by the fact that the ends of the crosstrees in at least two cases were weathered with lead. The base today contains two floors, of which the ground floor has at various times served as a pigsty, a dance floor and a beer saloon.

(2) FORD END MILL

In November, 1812, Alfred and Matthew Mecklenburgh, of Chelmsford, millwrights, offered for sale a 'new-erected' post mill at Ford End, having two pairs of French stones and a roundhouse.[4] It was situated 'on an eminence by the side of a high road'. Following a notice of their bankruptcy in the following April, the sale and removal of the 'new-built' windmill was advertised in June for the benefit of creditors.[5] The mill was then stated to be at the Spread Eagle, Forth (*sic*) End. Its fate is uncertain, but there is no further note of its existence at the Spread Eagle.

'The Windmill' at Minnowmeads, a restaurant and bar of distinction, was formerly known as The Crown and Shears.[6] The justification for its renaming, if any, awaits discovery; possibly the brief appearance of a windmill as at the Spread Eagle above?

NOTES

1 Per H. E. S. Simmons
2 C.C. 21.8.1835 per H. E. S. Simmons
3 E.R.O. D/CT 379A; *Lond. Gaz.*, 1.8.1856, per H. E. S. Simmons
4 C.C. 6.11. & 11.12.1812
5 C.C. 23.4. & 11.6.1813
6 *Ages in the making: a history of two Essex villages* (Gt. & Lt. Waltham), Phillips and Bazett, p. 93. Published 1974 (n.d.)

253 *Great Waltham: Chatham Green. Roundhouse preserved; mill body presumed removed shortly after 1902*

Little Waltham

Post mill. Stood 700 yards east of the church on Wheelers Hill on the south side of the Boreham road, and 50 yards south west of Wheelers Farm. TL 718127

CHAPMAN AND ANDRÉ (1777) were the first to record the mill on a county map; it is later shown on the first O.S. 1in. map (1805) and on the tithe map (1838), but not on the first O.S. 6in. (surv. 1874). Greenwood (1825) omitted it. The mill stood on the 200ft. contour at the crest of the rise up from Little Waltham Hall and the Chelmer, and was worked in conjunction with the watermill. A crude map of a local farm *c*1760 shows the mill as of post type, and Thomas Milbank held it in 1770.[1] Joseph Milbank, miller and mealman, insured his

'Corn Windmill House timber built', viz. the windmill, in 1804 for £170.[2] His cover for the machinery was £20, and for the stock £10, suggesting a small mill with one pair of stones and without roundhouse. Daniel Harrington of Little Waltham Hall, by his will dated 1796, devised his post windmill and watermill, in the occupation of Thomas Milbank, to his nephew.[3]

The windmill was subsequently in the occupation of Charles Skill for many years. Some details of his lease of the manor estate and mills were given in a sale notice dated 18th July, 1823, though the windmill was not described beyond the fact that it stood on one rood of land.[4] According to the tithe map (1838) and apportionment (1839), Windmill Field lay directly west of the site and Mill Field to the south. Wheelers Farm, opposite, was held by Skill.[5] The last known appearance of the windmill is on the Essex and Suffolk Railway plan of 1845, which records Joshua Mallett as lessee under Charles Skill as owner.[6]

Faden's map (1804) places a windmill symbol just north of Croxton's watermill, but finds no substantiation from other sources.

NOTES

1 *Ages in the making: a history of two Essex villages* (Gt. & Lt. Waltham) Phillips and Bazett, p. 49. See also Sun Pol. No. 534209 10.8.1787. Map c1760: E.R.O. T/M 459

2 R.E. Pol. No. 209150 11.8.1804

3 E.R.O. D/DSm T23

4 C.C. 18.7.1823. Land tax (E.R.O.) 1826-32: owner Jas. Skill, occupier Chas. Skill.

5 E.R.O. D/CT 380A

6 E.R.O. per R. Hawksley

Waltham Holy Cross

Post mill. Known as Honey Lane Windmill. Stood about 120 yards south of the Epping road (A121) from a point 550 yards east of the turning to Upshire. The site is now approached by Windmill Close and occupied by housing of recent date. TL 394003 (□ 254; I 30)

STATED to have been built between 1811 and 1826,[1] the mill is not shown by Greenwood's map (1825), or by the parish map by Crawter,[2] surveyed in 1823-4, in which the site area, owned by John Raine, carries no distinctive features. It first appears on the revised first O.S. 1in. map (1844). Directories record the Websters at Sun Street from 1839 onwards, and specifically at Honey Lane in 1902. Most of what is known of the mill comes from the memory of Ralph Pettit, aged 80 in 1972, son of the last miller, and from a news item headed 'Collapse of the Windmill at Waltham Abbey' in the *Weekly Telegraph* of 1st September, 1911. The latter is worth quoting as a succinct and contemporary statement of the event:

> The mill has been in the Webster family all along the line of years, and was still owned by Mr Harry Webster, who carried on the business of corn merchant, etc., there. The collapse came almost without warning. Mr Webster and the miller (Mr Pettit) were in the mill about 4.45 (Friday, 25th August) and they had scarcely been out three minutes, when with a great noise, the mill collapsed and fell to the ground, a complete wreck. Buried beneath the debris is about three tons of corn.
>
> The cause of its falling is attributed to the great hurricane and thunderstorm which visited Waltham Abbey on Friday, July 28th, and it is thought on that occasion that it was struck by lightning at the top of one of its main supports. Mr Pettit, who has lived at the mill for over 20 years, states that the hurricane was one such as he has never experienced before, and since then he has noticed that the mill did not appear so firm as it previously had done. The centre main oak post was put in new about eight years ago by Mr Webster, and at great expense. Besides, of course, removing a familiar landmark, the loss to Mr Webster is a heavy one.
>
> The old mill — a dreary wreck lay she — was visited by hundreds of inhabitants of, and visitors to, Waltham Abbey during last week-end.

254 *Waltham Holy Cross: Honey Lane Mill after the collapse in August, 1911*

Decimus Pettit, the last miller, entered the property c1890, and rented it from Harry Webster.[3] Pettit was named Decimus as the tenth of seventeen children, who were reared in the existing timbered Mill House in Little Sampford on the road to Great Sampford from Finchingfield. Decimus married twice, but appropriately drew the line at ten children. He is seen in photographs of the wrecked mill, looking, indeed, the great character he is said to have been by his descendants.

Several views of the mill in working order are also preserved. It had a plain weatherboarded body, with neat sash windows on the stone and spout floors, standing over a capacious roundhouse, evidently two-floored. The rear ladder stringers rose to mid-door level as at Birch, and a 6-bladed fan set well down over the ladder turned the mill to wind. It would appear from a photograph of the wreck that the mill never had a tail pole. The centre post, though reportedly new, snapped at the quarterbar junction, a vulnerable point. An unusual feature for an Essex mill is indistinctly seen immediately below the sheers. Here, it would appear, a circular iron plate was bolted up carrying small inset rollers to run on a track, presumably set on the upper surface of a collar, not visible in the photographs. At Topcroft, Norfolk, and Bledlow Ridge, Bucks., among others, there were comparable arrangements. Nothing is revealed of the drive to the stones. In one photograph the sails are seen to be double-shuttered anti-clockwise patents, well clamped over the canister, with nine bays of three shutters in each, and set from within the mill, but in 1907 there were four sails with single canvas-covered shutters. Although details of the mill's machinery are not available, it is thought that there were two pairs of stones in the head, which is most likely correct.

NOTES

1 *The Mercury* (Herts.), Friday, 13.10.1972. Article on mill relating details supplied by Ralph Pettit, son of former miller.

2 In possession of Mrs R. M. Huggins, Waltham Abbey (1970). Also E.R.O. D/DHf P. 19-27

3 Family details supplied by Miss Eileen Savery, as related by her mother, Christma Pettit, daughter of Decimus, Feb., 1975

Walthamstow and Woodford

(1) Post mill. Stood in Woodford parish approximately at the junction of Bunce's (formerly Windmill) Lane with Woodford New Road. TQ 398913

(2) Post mill. Stood in Walthamstow parish a few yards west of the Napier Arms near the junction of Oak Hill with Woodford New Road. The open space bears the name (Upper) Mill Plain. TQ 395910 (□ 255)

(1) WOODFORD MILL

Three windmills in these adjoining parishes responded to the breezes of the 17th century, and in the closing decades at least two of the mills co-existed. A map of the Foresters' Walks c1640[1] places a windmill in the vicinity of the Mill Lane of today on the west side of the High Road near the present Woodford Green United Free Church (TQ 400920), and it is evidently to this mill the manor of Higham court rolls refer in 1628 when locating a cottage 'on the Lord's waste adjoining a windmill called Woodford windmill'.[2] Verifiable records of this mill after c1640 have not come to notice, and it is therefore omitted from the post-1700 sites listed above.

Although it might be thought to feature in a print of Warner's Pond, Woodford, dated 1774[3] — and has been so interpreted — this northerly Woodford mill is not indicated on three or four intervening maps which would have been likely to show it. The illustrator may have taken the liberty of slipping Walthamstow mill into his picture as an embellishment.

The southern mill, at site (1), is shown on the map by Ogilby and Morgan (1678) and on a map of c1700.[4] This was evidently the Woodford Hall manor mill which is stated to have survived until 1710, when the manor was sold.[5] It was presumably the mill 'near Woodford' to which Daniel Defoe made reference in stating that a group of refugees from the plague in London had gift corn ground there about September, 1665, for the Walthamstow mill had not yet been erected.[6] In 1677 the low sweep of the mill sails led the justices to record[7]: 'Item we present the windmill at Woodford to be fenced in by John Smyth because it is not only dangerous for cattle but for passengers also'.

Richard Clarke, miller, of Walthamstow, was prosecuted at the Quarter Sessions in 1699 for conspiring with Henry Wilkinson, blacksmith, of the same parish, to set fire to the windmill belonging to the Lady 'Therowgood', but the mill was spared destruction.[8]

There is no ground for supposing that the mill survived after 1710. Its absence from the map by Warburton, Bland and Smyth (c1724) and from the map of turnpike roads dated 1728[9] is very strong evidence for its disappearance. The tithe map (1840) records Windmill Lane for what is now Bunce's Lane.[10]

(2) WALTHAMSTOW MILL

This has often been referred to as Woodford mill, and is better known than the windmills which truly lay within that parish. Walthamstow mill was built by John Hawkes, millwright, of Whitechapel, and was approached by Windmill Lane (now Fullers Road) from the east. Land belonging to William Maynard was enclosed in 1676 for the purpose of erecting the windmill, which appears on the map of c1700 which shows additionally the mill at site (1).[11] It is further recorded — in the nick of time — by a symbol on the preliminary drawings (1799) for the first O.S. 1in. map of 1805. An entry dated 12th January, 1801, in the Wanstead vestry book records a proposal to build a parish mill to be worked by 'Mr Fitch ye occupier of ye mill lately blown down at Woodford,'[12] and mention of millers in the rate books ceases in 1800. The Greenwood map (1825) places a windmill symbol at the site, for which no corroborative evidence has emerged. A perambulation of the parish boundary in 1812 refers to the site where the windmill formerly stood,[13] and Coe's parish map (1822) bears no sign of a windmill, though clearly marking the mill enclosure and the cottage.[14]

There are a number of recorded references and an engraving. The miller, John Hanes, was selling beer

*255 Walthamstow Mill, near the Napier Arms. Engraving stated to date
from 1781. Mill blown down c1800*

without licence in 1745-7, for which he was presented at
the court of Walthamstow Toni, but in 1750 held a
licence.[15] In 1753 his weights were found to be
deficient.[16] Later millers were Gibson (1759-62),
Hantler (1762-84), Shaw (1784-9), Smith (1790), Fitch
(1791-1800). In 1778 and 1781, Hantler, described as of
Woodford, miller, insured his granary and house
situated opposite the church, and in 1784, on his death,
these and the mill were advertised to be let.[17] The ample
house had been newly erected and possessed a forecourt
'defended by pallisadoes'. The windmill then had two
pairs of stones, and was claimed to be in substantial
repair. A print said to have been published in October,
1781,[18] shows it with broken sail frames and weatherboarding. It is portrayed as a post mill of orthodox build
for an 18th-century mill, with single-storied
roundhouse, and four common sails turning anti-clockwise. The mill house, known as Mill Cottage, survived
until 1909/10.[19]

Addendum

1571: mill, etc., in manor of Walthamstow Tony.
(*Feet of Fines, Essex*, Vol. V, p. 267).

NOTES

1 Reproduced in E.R. Vol. XIV, p. 193

2 *The Walthamstow Windmill & Essex Windmills Today*, A. D. Law,
Walthamstow Antiquarian Soc., 1970, p. 4

3 Per Ernest A. Fulcher, of South Woodford, who also drew attention to the Bunce's Lane site and supplied many details. Print: in
Mint Portfolio, E.R.O.

4 E.R.O. D/DCw P 1.

5 V.C.H. *Essex*, Vol. VI, 1973, which contains many references to
the mills in both parishes

6 *Journal of the Plague Year*, O.U.P. edition, 1969, p. 146

7 E.R.O. Q/SR 436/15

8 E.R.O. Q/SR 500/2, 5, 6

9 Per R. Hawksley

10 E.R.O. D/CT 408

11 See notes 2 & 5. Map *c*1700: E.R.O. D/DCw p. 1

12 Stated Woodford, but in fact Walthamstow. E.R.O. D/P 292/8/9 per R. Hawksley

13 Per Mrs M. J. Hamilton-Bradbury, of Hammersmith

14 Note 2 above, op. cit. p. 10, on which are figured reproductions of the mill site at Walthamstow as seen on maps dated 1699, 1781 & 1822

15 See note 5

16 E.R.O. Q/SBb 195/12

17 Sun Pol. Nos. 403024 28.9.1778, 451182 13.11.1781; C.C. 16.4.1784

18 Booklet: *Fifty Pictures of Old Woodford*, publ. 1935, p. 32, and in Notes at end

19 Per Mrs M. J. Hamilton-Bradbury, from an examination of the poor rate records in the Vestry House Museum archives

Walton-on-the-Naze

(1) Mill of unknown type of 18th-century date. Stood about 260 yards south of the former tide mill and at the north end of Mill Lane. The site is at or close to the modern bungalow 'White Cottage'. TM 253219

(2) Post mill of 19th-century date. Stood about 200 yards north north west of the tide mill; the site is now occupied by the Walton and Frinton Yacht Club House. TM 252223 (□ 256; I 35)

(1) THE FIRST MILL: SAVAGE'S

The Essex Notebook (1884) records that Richard Savage built the Walton watermill in 1770, after having suffered greatly in 1767 from a dreadful tide[1]. If this was so, he was singularly unfortunate, for he had evidently taken over the mills in answer to the following advertisement only two years before the disaster:

Chelmsford Chronicle, 15th March, 1765:
To be sold immediately and entered upon next mid-summer at Walton in the Naze, in Essex, a water-mill and a wind-mill, near each other, with a pair of French stones, a bolting mill with scales and weights in each mill, also the quays and wharfs belonging to the said mill and a privilege of a bridge, also a very good bricked house, with a granary, a convenient brewhouse and cellars, stable, orchard and garden, now in the occupation of William Stone . . . The mills are situated near the open ocean, very convenient for water carriage to London.

William Stone had been admitted to a watermill in Walton in 1740 according to the records of Walton manor,[2] and in 1747 held also a windmill 'new erected'.

The proprietor in 1765 was one Choat, of Barnston, who planned to spend all of Friday, 22nd March, at the Black Boy in Chelmsford to treat with prospective buyers and doubtless seal the bargain as befitted the venue. Perhaps Savage appeared on that very day. In June 1784, he in turn was advertising the property for sale 'as buyer and seller can agree', but possibly tried to

drive too hard a bargain, for the premises remained on offer for two or three years more.[3] Combined output was 8 to 10 loads weekly, and a coal yard had been added. Savage, from Kirby, re-advertised the mills in March 1785, and in August of that year, as an alternative to sale, invited 'a steady married man', with £200 to £300 to invest, to enter into partnership, closing his notice peremptorily thus: 'This mill will be advertised no more in this paper.' Eating his words after a lengthy silence, Savage renewed his appeal in the newspaper columns in September 1786, with a footnote: 'N.B. This will be advertised no more.' Again it appeared in July 1787, reinforced by the claim that the nearest watermill was 11 miles away. Yet another notice appeared in August 1787, allowing a two-thirds mortgage on the purchase price;[4] this apparently had the desired effect. Savage had in 1785 insured his watermill with contents for £350 and the windmill for £100.[5]

256 *Walton-on-the-Naze. From an old picture postcard. Probably disused from 1897. Taken down 1921*

The windmill is shown on an Admiralty chart dated 1804, and was evidently standing in 1808 when Thomas Pattrick entered, but had gone by 1820.[6] A court entry of 1824 specifically stated that the mill had been pulled down.[7]

(2) THE SECOND MILL: ARCHER'S

In 1841 Thomas Pattrick held the premises with 38 acres of land and mill pond, and John Archer worked the tide mill as tenant.[8] Archer built the second windmill to work in conjunction with the tide mill in 1846,[9] and the business remained in the hands of his family until 1897. An Admiralty chart (1844-9) records 'New Mill (Wind)' at Walton.[10] A word of appreciation of the John Archer of mid-century, who had moved south from Yorkshire, was recorded in *The Miller* at about the turn of the century. Archer believed in teaching by example, it was stated, and expanded his business with enterprise and energy, being one of the first to introduce the silk reel into his mills. Much of his flour moved on to London, and during the Crimean War the mills' capacity was stretched to the utmost.[11] John Archer's personal estate was assessed at £48,000 in 1892, following his decease.[12]

The mills, standing conspicuously on the saltings in a much frequented resort, prompted unrestrained comment in print. One note gives 19 pairs of stones as the maximum used and mentions a reciprocal trade in flour and coal with northern England carried in Archer's boats.[13] One doubts the claim to 19 pairs, as steam is never coupled with Archer's name in the directories which specified its use. Two independent notes ascribe 8 pairs of stones to the tide mill in its latter days, but the number driven by the windmill — probably 2 or 3 pairs — is not known.[14] One writer credits the windmill with six pairs of stones[15] — conceivably the unwitting petrifaction of the miller's six sons, all of whom are said to have been apprenticed to the trade, a legendary touch unhappily too late for the pen of the Reverend Baring-Gould.

The mills were bought in 1897 by Col. R. P. Davis, the local squire, but they stood in idleness with little hope of further employment until 1921, when both were demolished.[16] Here again, reports are in conflict. One has it that the windmill fell down in a strong wind on the very day that the demolition of the tide mill was completed — an unhappy ending to the unwritten romance.[17] Another version is best quoted, for it is perhaps penned by the hand that felled the mill:[18]

> It may interest you to know that the . . . windmill . . . was not blown down as stated; the circumstances are as follows:
>
> In 1921 the spit of land on which the mill stood, with a small area of saltings, was bought by a few friends so as to erect thereon a clubhouse for a newly formed yacht club. They were then confronted with the problem of taking down the ruinous structure, which promised to cost far more than was at first expected. The mill was one with a tail pole, and to the lower end of the pole an iron rod was fitted, attached above to the top of the mill post, and owing to the whole structure being out of balance, this iron rod was as taut as a fiddle string.
>
> Selecting a perfectly windless afternoon, two of our number, by means of a hacksaw, cut through this tie rod and within a few minutes the mill collapsed in a great cloud of dust. The only casualty was one rowing boat on which one of the millstones fell.

The tie rod mentioned is seen in photographs; it braced the tail pole, not to the centre post, but to the rear transverse member, or thereabouts, at the base of the roof rafters. To explain how its severance caused the mill to capsize is left as an exercise to the student of post-mill anatomy.

Many photographs and some paintings of the windmill exist, mostly dating from the days of dereliction. One view, however, shows the mill in full working order, complete with the external tackle so quickly removed once the stones have ground their last.[19] From these pictures the approximate dimensions given below are taken, and must be treated with some reserve. An unusual feature was the 16-sided, weatherboarded roundhouse standing about 2ft. 6in. over the sloping ground level which may occasionally have been awash. The doors were entered by a short flight of steps. Hector Stone reported that during spring tides the mill could sometimes be reached by boat alone.[20] The brick piers, remnants of which remain in situ, nominally contributing to the support of the clubhouse, were some 8 to 9 feet high, their buttressed rears visible. The roundhouse was therefore perched up high, the base of the roof being about 12ft. from the ground. The mill body, 20ft. by 12ft. in plan, and 28ft. to the roof ridge, rose to an overall height of approximately 45ft., carrying the sails of 65ft. span which swept 5ft. from ground level.

There is no known record of a fatality at this mill caused by the sails, but Archer — a family man — was perhaps responsible for the notice painted on a brick pier: 'Beware of the Sails'. A movable platform, about 2ft. 6in. high, and 3ft. 6in. square, was pushed round the mill on four rollers, slightly toed in to run crab-fashion around the mill base for tending the mill sails. It would also have reduced accident risk if kept under the revolving sails. There were two commons on the outside middling and two double-shuttered patents on the inside, turning anti-clockwise seen from the front. The vanes were controlled by — to all appearances — a rocking lever at the rear instead of a Y-wheel, a pull on the striking rod rearwards having the effect of closing them. There were no leading boards. The patents had 9 bays with 3 shutters each on the leading side, complemented by 7 bays with 3 of full width, one bay of 3 shorter shutters, and an innermost bay boarded over on the trailing side.

The mill was winded by manual pressure on the tail pole, for which a lever to raise the steps with a 7 to 1 advantage and a yoke at the rear were employed. The yoke consisted simply of two battens let vertically down through the tail-pole extremity, spaced to take the miller's shoulders.

Little is now to be discovered of the internal arrangements. A fragment of a 6-cant clasp-arm brake wheel is preserved, estimated to have been about 10ft. in diameter.[21] Exposed side framing in later pictures reveals an orthodox pattern, seemingly with main rear corner posts at the extremities of the body, suggesting, therefore, all-through side girts.

NOTES

1 Per G. W. Martin

2 E.R.O. D/DBm M239

3 I.J. 12.6.1784

4 I.J. 12.3. & 20.8.1785, 9.9.1786, 28.7. & 4.8.1787

5 R.E. Pol. No. 95250 14.11.1785 per H. E. S. Simmons

6 E.R.O. D/DBm M240, D/DU 5/19

7 E.R.O. D/DU 5/24

8 E.R.O. D/CT 383A

9 *White's* directory, Essex, 1848, p. 477, per R. Hawksley. See also E.C.S. 16.10.1897. E.S. 19. & 26.6.1846 advertise the watermill to be sold, in the occupation of John Archer

10 In B.M. Note by R. Hawksley

11 *The Miller*, Vol. XXV, 1899-1900, p. 690

12 E.W.N. 24.6.1892

13 Per B. H. Stone, 1947. See: *Tide Mills, Part II*, S.P.A.B. publ., Rex Wailes, p. 29

14 Ibid.: *Tide Mills, Part II*; per W. C. Horsnail, 1943; also as per note 8

15 E.C. No. 78, July, 1963, p. 376. Article by M. V. A. Wilkinson

16 E.A.T., Vol. XIX, 1930, p. 337

17 Ibid.

18 E.C. No. 13, Autumn, 1955, p. 38. Letter from W. H. Chadwick, O.B.E.

19 Castle Museum, Colchester. A painting of the mill by Ford Madox Brown (1821-1893), dated 1860, is held by the City Museum and Art Gallery, Birmingham (per Charles Skilton)

20 *Essex Windmills*, Rex Wailes, *Trans. Newcomen Soc.*, Vol. XXXI, p. 174, per D. Sanders

21 In Walton-on-the-Naze Record Office

Little Warley

Smock mill. Stood by a group of farm buildings, demolished in recent years, close to the modern residence 'Mill House', a few dozen yards east of the junction of Magpie and Bird Lanes. TQ 596903

THIS ill-fated mill was operated for most of its brief existence by the Bennett family. Its date of erection has not been established, but William Bennett was given as miller by a directory for 1832, and was entered in the highway rate book for 1835 as holding 'Mill and Premises'.[1] The mill appears on the revised edition of the O.S. 1in. map (revision of *c*1840). In 1848 William Bennett was styled miller and baker at Little Warley in *White's* directory, and, in 1851, the same, aged 43 and resident at Mill House, had the services of one of his sons, also William, as miller.[2]

Following — as the rate books indicate — Bennett senior's death in 1854 or 5, which apparently coincided with his bankruptcy,[3] the freehold estate was put to auction in Romford.[4] It comprised a smock mill (so described) driving three pairs of stones, with a residence, miller's cottage, barn and outbuildings. The mill was subsequently held by William Bloomfield (1856), Grove and Stollery (1858) and William Bennett (1860-66).[5] *The Essex Standard* recorded the mill's demise in unexpansive mood:[6] 'Windmill Blown Down — During the gale on Monday (8th January, 1866), Little Warley Mill, near Warley Gap, was blown over, and, of course, made a complete wreck. Providentially no one was working in it at the time'. The mill makes a posthumous appearance on the revised second O.S. 1in. map (1893).

The enterprise appears to have been launched *c*1830 during the period when smock mills were still confidently appearing in mid-Essex, as at Shenfield, Willingale and Mashbury. Steam milling at Brentwood and deliveries of flour by railway would have subjected

the business, not well placed for outlets, to slow strangulation, and the destructive gale could be said to have effected a merciful release.

NOTES

1 Notes on highway rates (E.R.O. D/P 66/20 1835-63) supplied by David Ransome (V.C.H. *Essex*)

2 P.R.O. HO 107 1774 (1851 census)

3 *Lond. Gaz.*, 9.11.1855, per H. E. S. Simmons

4 E.S. 17.8.1855

5 See note 1

6 E.S. 12.1.1866

South Weald

(1) Post mill, known as Warley Mill. Stood near the surviving mill house about 100 yards west of the Horse and Groom public house on the south side of Mascalls Lane. TQ 587917

(2) Post, succeeded by tower mill, both bearers of the title 'Bentley Mill'. Stood west of Cecil Lodge on the north side of Mores Lane and in the western angle of the road triangle. The mill buildings stood to the south on the site occupied by Greenways. TQ 568968 (□ 257)

(3) Post mill named Rush Mill (1848) or Brook Street Mill. Stood on a rise 80 yards south of the former main Colchester road opposite Vicarage Close. TQ 571925 (□ 258)

(1) WARLEY MILL

This mill appears as a red disc on a parish map dated 1788-9, and the schedule has an undated entry 'James Hurst' altered in pencil to his widow.[1] The mill is absent from Chapman and André's map (1777), but is on the first O.S. 1in. (1805). Thomas Wadsworth of Great Warley, at his death in 1805, held for a rental of £35 per annum the lease of a 32-acre farm and premises, described as situated on Warley Common.[2] These buildings included a dwelling house, mill, granary and stabling for twelve horses. By 1817, when the windmill, stated to be of post type, was to be let or sold by private contract, its marketability appears to have reached its nadir.[3] In the absence of the positive information usually supplied, we may infer that it was a one-pair mill without roundhouse. A bake-office was in use, the barracks were near, and there was a good 'private' trade; nevertheless in 1820 an auctioneer was preparing to sell 'peremptorily' the premises lately known as Warley Mill, well adapted for a hunting box in a good sporting country, with extensive views, abounding in game and having several packs of hounds at the ready.[4] To be sold in lots were 'the brick piers that supported the mill, together with the mill sails, middling, timbers, burr stones, ironwork, &c.' A vicar's division tithe map, using the parish map of 1788-9 for the purpose of the tithe apportionment in 1839, records two Mill Fields, one to the north and one to the south of the lane, close to this site.[5]

In 1829 was advertised the auction on the premises near the Thatchers' Arms, Great Warley, of the entire erection of a corn mill of two horse-power, including one pair of French stones and going gears, nearly new.[6] Here, the horse-power rating may be taken at its face value.

(2) BENTLEY MILL

A mill symbol is placed at the Bentley site by Warburton, Bland and Smyth on their map of c1724. This mill was possibly the forerunner of the post mill moved from this site to Chadwell Heath c1820.[7] A small watermill was also in existence in the parish at Brook Street c1775,[8] and is marked on the map of Chapman and André (1777), who also place a windmill at Bentley Heath, but not at Brook Street. Milling in South Weald from 1794, or earlier, was largely in the hands of the Moss family, who operated at sites (2) and (3), and later also ran a steam mill at Brentwood. Thomas Moss in 1794 held the copyhold of the Brook Street property, including a windmill, and the freehold of Bentley Mill.[9]

Careful study gives some reason to suppose that the ex-Bentley post mill could be the subject of photographs taken at Chadwell Heath after 1900, which recorded the last of the trio of post mills still active there in the early 1890's. The departed (thought c1820) Bentley mill was replaced by a tower mill, and Henry Moss, then lately deceased,[10] was succeeded by another Henry, no doubt the son. The widow died in 1833 aged 80, 'justly esteemed for her benevolence and extensive charities'.[11] At 47 years in 1841, the reigning Henry Moss, for no known reason, committed suicide by shooting himself through the head in one of his stables, leaving a widow and four children.[12] As a consequence his estate was offered for sale. Bentley mill was described as brick-built, with five floors, and driving six pairs of stones with the combined power of wind and a 10 h.p. steam engine.

257 *South Weald: Bentley (tower) Mill. Machinery for sale and removal in 1884, and no further record*

The freehold mill was stated to have been erected without regard to expense and to be proverbial as the best building of its kind in the county.[13] A few cottages and a small farm of 12 acres were also held. The miller in 1850 was still a Henry Moss, much respected by the poor, whose premises, nevertheless, were at risk from incendiary activity. His mill and house were saved from fire by a favourably directed wind when one of his barns nearby was ignited.[14]

The 1851 census records Moss at the age of 32 as miller and farmer of 44 acres employing eight men.[15] He was unmarried. He continued the charitable activities of his forebears, fitting up an adult school room adjoining his house and 'contributing to the intellectual gratification of his neighbours' by arranging concerts and other functions. The miller at Bentley Mill in 1863 and 1874 was Frederick Moss, though in the former year Henry Moss was still proprietor.[16]

In 1884, C. J. H. Tower Esq., then owner, announced the forthcoming sale by auction on 17th April of 'the entire going gear in the large tower mill . . . from the sails to the ground floor in one lot; also stables, granaries, and other buildings, as standing, for removal'. A reason advanced was the departure of Moss to Brentwood. This notice was printed in *The Miller* as well as the local press,[17] and apparently drew a response from the mill-wrighting firm of Hunts of Soham. Writing in 1957, T. C. Hunt gave his father's recollections of sending their man John Darnell to take down the sails of Bentley Mill, which were subsequently fitted to Stoke Ferry Mill, Norfolk.[18] They were said to contain 39 shutters, all of wood, but with one bay shortened at the centre. This agrees with a photograph of the South Weald windmill showing four double-shuttered anti-clockwise patent sails with 13 bays on the leading and 12 on the trailing side of the whips, the mill itself being of such height and girth as to carry these heavy sails comfortably aloft, well above ground level. The massive cap descended in a graceful parabolic curve from front to rear, behind which was set a six-bladed fantail. There was a walk-way round the cap, but no stage below. This mill doubtless justified its good reputation, and the stone floor can be presumed to have accommodated four pairs of stones with ease.

(3) BROOK STREET MILL

Though absent from Greenwood's map (1825), Brook Street mill appears in company with the other two South Weald windmills on the preparatory drawing for the O.S. 1in. map (1799). Its date of erection can be put tentatively at a little before October, 1778, in which year Thomas Moss, miller, insured his windmill situated at Brook Street for £300 and the contents for £200, figures suggesting the launching of a substantial new post mill; the death of presumably the same Thomas — of Brook Street mill — was reported in 1816.[19] In July, 1823, a young employee was caught by the cogs of 'the large wheel' by which he was 'literally crushed to atoms'.[20] In

1839 the windmill, with houses and 23 acres of land, was held by a Thomas Moss,[21] and in 1851 a very junior Thomas Moss, aged eight years, orphan, was unusually described as head of house, in which lived his uncle, William Moss, a farmer, as guardian.[22] The mill came shortly after into the hands of George Cole (1853), who remained miller until after 1882, using wind only, to be succeeded, according to trade directories, by Ephraim Rowland, who had been his foreman (1886, 1902). A local informant states (1980) that the mill stopped work c1905. *Kelly's* directory for 1906 does not include a Brook Street miller, and Dr Turner gives the date of demolition as 1913.

258 *South Weald: Brook Street Mill, from an old picture postcard. Year of demolition said to be 1913*

There are two known photographic views.[23] One of the rear of the structure shows four single-shuttered anti-clockwise sails, which an indistinct front view appears to indicate as patents. Winding was by tail pole. The body, with a plain rear face and a single-floored roundhouse, was of unexceptional appearance. The sail-circle is seen to reach almost to the ground, inviting, and indeed realising, another fatality at the mill. Jane Wilkinson, aged ten years, a local girl, was sent to the mill for some barley meal in April, 1880, as on many an occasion.[24] Ephraim Rowland, foreman, described at an inquest at the Nag's Head Inn what transpired after he had served the girl; the report reads: 'Shortly after she left, witness went down the steps for the purpose of stopping the mill, then believing the child was gone away. As he was going down the mill steps, he heard a noise as if one of the vanes of the sails has dropped out. He walked round the mill with a view to examining the sails, and found the deceased lying on the ground away from the path, with a little water lying on her temple. He said "You foolish girl, how did you come here?", but finding he could not obtain an answer from her, he ran for assistance and medical help and she was removed into the house.' After consultation three surgeons removed some bone pressing on the brain, but the child

died within the week after apparently making a little progress. A verdict of accidental death was returned, and it was agreed that the victim had strayed from the path in a thoughtless manner, the revolving sails being fully visible in the daylight conditions.

NOTES

1 E.R.O. D/DTw P 3 (map), D/DLa M60 (schedule, 1780-90)
2 C.C. 20.9.1805
3 C.C. 8.8.1817
4 C.C. 18.8.1820; see also C.C. 3.7. & 30.10.1818
5 E.R.O. D/CT 388/1 & 2
6 C.C. 18.12.1829
7 See under Dagenham, Vol. III, p. 108; also Vol. I, p. 59, 'Windmills in Transit'
8 C.C. 5.9.1777
9 E.R.O. D/A ER 35, p. 225
10 C.C. 6.7.1821
11 E.S. 24.8.1833
12 E.S. 2.4.1841
13 E.S. 16.7. & 13.8.1841
14 E.S. 5.4.1850
15 P.R.O. HO 107 1774
16 E.S. 8.5.1863
17 E.W.N. 4.1.1884; *The Miller*, Vol. X, p. 83
18 *Essex Windmills*, Rex Wailes, *Trans. Newcomen Soc.*, Vol. XXXI, 1957-9, p. 179
19 Sun Pol. No. 404272 19.10.1778 per H. E. S. Simmons; C.C. 23.8.1816
20 C.C. 18.7.1823
21 See note 5
22 See note 15
23 Excluding distant shots
24 E.W.N. 30.4. & 7.5.1880

Weeley

Post mill. Stood a few yards south east of 'The Mill House' on the south side of Mill Lane leading west from the Colchester road. TM 153205 (□ 259)

FOR an impending auction Weeley post mill was advertised on 1st May, 1847, as an excellent windmill, with bricked roundhouse, 3 pairs of French stones, a flour machine, and self-adjusting wind tackle.[1] It was well winded, 'durably built', and had been erected about three years previously. There were two acres of land attached. In the 1970s, two authorities on the former windmills of the region agreed that Weeley mill bore a genuine Suffolk stamp.[2] Documents indicate John Whitmore of Wickham Market, millwright, as a likely builder, as he was at least financially involved, but Brooks, the last miller at Ramsey, would have it that the mill was moved from Melton, near Woodbridge, having been built by Collins.[3] If the latter is true, Weeley mill could have been one of the two post mills allegedly exported to Essex, as noted in 'Windmills in Transit' in Volume I. Indentures of 1842 record the purchase of land and messuages in Weeley by Whitmore, and his immediate mortgage to James May, miller, of Lawford, the whole being sold in 1846 with the mill 'late erected and now standing' to the Rev. Thomas W. Mercer of Weeley. Following Edward Kidby, William Balls was tenant at will in 1847 at the windmill for £50 annually.

Thomas Grimwood, who was miller in 1850, and probably entered in 1847,[4] bought the mill from Charles Daines for £800 in 1855. He or another Thomas continued until his death in 1902,[5] after which the steady prosecution of the business was no longer sustained. S. N. Disney, after a short term in 1906, went bankrupt;[6] as a consequence the mill was sold by private contract after first being withdrawn at an auction at a figure between £500 and £600.[7] Disney's improbable successor was a petal dust maker named S. M. Seward, who ran a scent works in London. He employed George T. Godbold as miller at Weeley in the period around 1910. Mr Godbold, aged 87 in 1973, with justifiable pride was able to produce the testimonial received on his master's departure:

> Mr George Godbold has been in my employ for two years during which he has had the entire management of my wind and power mills.
> During this period I have always found him to be honest, sober, industrious and trustworthy.
> I consider him very intelligent, a keen buyer, and in all duties allotted to him he is most reliable.
> Having disposed of the Mills and my successor wishing to retain his services is the only reason for parting with him and which I very much regret.
> In his future he carries my best wishes.

Weeley Mills   S. M. Seward
September 5th, 1910

Seward was succeeded by E. H. Borneman, thought to be a German, whose presence and activities came under some suspicion, and Godbold preferred to move to Tendring Mills, which, however, one of the Borneman family bought up after a few weeks, causing his fugitive employee to remove to Ipswich. Like many old millers who have dressed stones innumerable, and often continuously for a working week, George Godbold could show the blue discolorations on the backs of his hands where metal particles had lodged, some of which had worked themselves out over the years. They cause no pain on entry, or subsequently, but the skin had formerly been dark with them.

In Godbold's day the windmill drove three pairs of stones, all overdrift: two pairs of four-foot stones in the head and one in the tail, using double-shuttered anti-clockwise patent sails in an iron windshaft. To close the shutters the striking rod was pushed forward. The miller had sometimes to turn out in the middle of the night, if a contrary wind arose, to ensure that the sails headed into it to prevent the dreaded tail-winding. These sails swung above head height, but it was prudent to stop them when a horse and cart approached. The fan tackle over the rear steps kept the mill to wind in normal circumstances, driving the carriage wheels over a wooden track.

259 *Weeley. Working up to 1914. Body removed shortly after 1920; roundhouse demolished in 1935*

The steam mill was a product of Whitmore and Binyon. There was a separate round boiler, and from the engine the crankshaft rose vertically, driving a large flywheel with a bevel gear from which a long shaft drove the stones in the steam mill, two pairs in all. Seward spent much time and money in renovating the windmill, which was in excellent order at the outset of hostilities in 1914. Borneman was interned, and the mill is said to have been ill-treated by troops.[8] It was demolished in the early 1920s, save for the two-storied roundhouse, which was removed in 1935 — strange to relate — by a Mr Weeley, who in 1971 stated that when the church was rebuilt in 1881, bones disturbed in the graveyard were given their second burial in the miller's sacks. He also stated (1981) that Borneman was able to prove that he was American and was deported to the United States.

NOTES

1 E.R.O. D/DEt T43: abstract of title up to 1855
2 Jesse Wightman and George Godbold
3 See note 1. Brooks' observations per Donald W. Muggeridge. Rex Wailes, in his *Source Book of Windmills and Watermills*, Ward Lock, 1979, p. 18, asserts that the move took place. R. Hawksley claims that his researches prove that it did not
4 1848 directory: Thomas Greenwood *(sic)*
5 *The Miller*, 1.9.1902: Thos. Grimwood, late of Weeley Mills, per H. E. S. Simmons
6 *The Miller*, 29.7.1907, per H. E. S. Simmons
7 *The Miller*, 6.1.1908 & 7.10.1907, per H. E. S. Simmons
8 *English Windmills*, Vol. 2, Donald Smith, 1932, p. 57. An exterior photo by Edwin Smith taken May, 1922, shows the badly damaged sails and evidence of wanton destruction (Passmore Edwards Museum Coll., West Ham)

Wenden Lofts

Post mill. Stood 100 yards north of Mill House, at a point 300 yards north of the Chishill road and opposite the turning to Duddenhoe End. TL 461380 (□ 260)

LOFTS MILL, as sometimes described, was distinguished on many maps, including those of Ogilby and Morgan (1678), Warburton, Bland and Smyth (c1724), Chapman and André (1777) and Greenwood (1825). Recorded references to it have proved scanty. It was part of the estate of Lofts Hall, and is thought to have survived until c1920;[1] it was included on the Popular edition of the O.S. 1in. map as 'Old Windmill', and appeared also on the third 6in. (1919).

The mill was mentioned in the millers' invasion returns of 1798 as capable of grinding 12 sacks of flour daily.[2] In 1848 Herbert Hamster was miller, in 1855 Charles Smith, and from 1863-90 George Nottage, in the latter year using wind and steam. The last miller named in directories was Henry A. Eldridge (1895, 98), and after 1899-1900 he is not in the electoral register.

260 *Wenden Lofts, c 1896. Demolished probably c 1920*

There is a tale current that the mill parts were numbered and taken to America for re-erection, but no confirmation has emerged.[3] There are several photographs, one of which is a particularly good record of the mill, which appears to have stood on slightly raised ground. Both the mill and the roundhouse were boarded and painted white, the latter being octagonal and having a ground floor only. The weatherboarding of the body was brought down on all sides to within inches of the roof below, giving a neat and trim appearance. No tail pole was visible, and the mill was winded by an 8-bladed fantail over the rear of the tail ladder. There were

four single-shuttered anti-clockwise patent sails struck from within the mill, leaving a plain rear face without porch or platform below. The roof was less rounded than usual, and carried 'blisters' to accommodate the brake wheel and brake.

NOTES

1 Per B. J. P. Palmer, of Mill House, as per his informants. For 1695 ref. see E.R.O. D/DHf E101
2 E.R.O. L/R 1/1
3 See note 1 above

Wethersfield

(1) Mill of unconfirmed type. Stood 175 yards west of the Braintree road, about 700 yards south east of the village centre to the north of 'Parkside'. TL 713306
(2) Smock mill, succeeding a mill probably of post type. Stood at Blackmore End on the south side of the existing Mill House. TL 738311 (□ 261)
(3) Post mill. Stood west of the Finchingfield road about 100 yards from the parish boundary. Approximately TL 706313
(4) Smock mill. Stood close to and south east of Mill House on the south side of the Finchingfield road, 350 yards west of the church. TL 708312

THERE were two watermills and apparently four contemporary windmills in Wethersfield in the early 19th century. Warburton, Bland and Smyth (c1724) give only the south mill, placed closer to the river than the corresponding symbols on Chapman and André (1777) and on the O.S. 1in. map of 1805; the 1777 map shows in addition a mill at Blackmore End. Greenwood (1825) seems to have focused his attention solely on the south windmill, though there is documentary and map evidence for the existence of two others in the parish at that time.

(1) THE SOUTH MILL

Greenwood's symbol provides the last noted indication of this mill, which survived only in the name Mill Field (plot 171) on the tithe map (1840-41).[1] The field on which it stood is edged by hachures on Chapman and André and on the 1805 O.S. map, and it offered a well-winded position overlooking falling ground on three sides. The mill was marked by Ogilby and Morgan (1678), and is drawn as a post mill with open trestle on a detailed plan of 1741.[2] This plan covers the later known windmill sites in the parish, but leaves them blank. Matthias Davey senior was miller in the parish for at least the years 1782 to 1811, operating Wethersfield (water)mill.[3] He is also credited in rate returns with a windmill in 1793, and by implication in other years.[4] This may have been the windmill 'burglariously entered' in 1810, when in the occupation of Charles Davey, who offered 10 guineas reward for the apprehension and conviction of the thieves.[5] In 1818, Thomas White, the lord of the two local manors, held Mill Field, and presumably also the windmill, Davey having by then acquired his own windmill.[6] Nothing more is known of the south mill beyond the fact of its inclusion on Greenwood's map (1825), but failure to mark two existing windmills in the parish could be complemented by the non-deletion of a vanished mill shown by earlier cartographers.

(2) THE EAST MILL AT BLACKMORE END, LATTERLY BRAND'S MILL

From the survey dates of Chapman and André (1772-4) until 1815, little more can be gleaned from the incomplete records available than that Thomas Brown held the mill 1790-5.[7]

The freehold dwelling house and windmill, in the ownership and occupation of George Jennings, were for sale in 1815.[8] The property had previously been bought by Jennings for £450 from James Percival, and was now conveyed to Thomas Butcher of Shalford, miller, who secured a loan of £300 from his brother-in-law, but died in 1825 leaving both mill and debt to his son Thomas, having appointed Charles Davey of the rival windmill as trustee for the sale of his property should his son default

261 *Wethersfield: Blackmore End Mill. Water-colour by Arthur Legge. Undated. Mill demolished c 1918*

in repayment.[9] The mill was indeed sold, for in 1827 William Rayner, the then proprietor, offered for auction his 'capital new-built tower windmill', having four floors and two pairs of French stones.[10] It had new machinery, was 'well-winded', could average eight loads weekly, and carried patent sails. Despite these attractions and the compelling 'winds herself upon an improved principle', the mill was seemingly not sold, or remained, at least, in the same family; later in the year it was to be let, and in 1839 was to be sold by Joseph Rayner.[11]

The mill was run for many years by John Mansfield, owner-occupier in 1842, who died in 1858 aged 68.[12] In 1876, on the death of Frederick Mansfield, the freehold mill and premises, still with no more than two pairs of stones, was auctioned at Braintree and sold to Robert Brand for £400, £50 less than the sale price of pre-1815.[13] John Brand (1886) and Robert William Brand (1890 1910) are recorded by directories as using wind power only; Robert was recorded as farmer only in 1912. The mill is seen on the Popular edition of the O.S. 1in. map (1914-19), and land tax records show that it was taken down in 1917-18. No satisfactory photograph has been found. Those available show four double-shuttered anti-clockwise patent sails and a fantail fore and aft of a domed cap, but the base of the mill is not in view.

(3) THE NORTH-WEST MILL: LIVERMORE'S POST MILL

John Livermore, farmer, of Wethersfield, insured a windmill, 'timber-built', for £200 in 1806,[14] and this betokens its initial appearance. It was freehold, and stood in Rainbow Field.[15] Matthias Davey, having an established milling business in the parish, as mentioned under site (1) above, was much displeased at having to meet a farmer's competition. Livermore had built the windmill to set up one of his sons as a miller. In August, 1807, at Great Bardfield, resentment was translated into violence in the Market Room of the Vine inn. Livermore was offered by a gentleman farmer a sample of wheat for grinding, whereupon Davey allegedly exclaimed 'Damn you! It's of no use for you to buy wheat, you can't grind it! . . . I've got an old sow and a jackass at home that can eat more than you can grind!' A brief verbal exchange was followed by blows from Davey — 'a stout strong fellow', but Livermore, described as of small stature and a valetudinarian, was spared further assault by the intervention of a witness, who interposed his person and pleaded with Davey to be merciful.[16]

After his decease, John Livermore's executors offered for sale in 1814 the 'new-built post windmill' having two pairs of stones but evidently no roundhouse.[17] It was acquired by Charles Davey,[18] presumably to buy out the competition, for no more is known of it, and a removal is likely to have occurred.

(4) THE WEST OR JOYCE'S MILL

This 'dazzling white windmill', as Barrett described it in his *Essex Byways*, c1893, is likely to have taken shape in or soon after 1807, when Charles Davey bought the copyhold site from John Legerton[19] — situated provocatively close to Livermore's mill. Davey's mill was assessed at £8 for the poor rate continuously from 1818 to 1831.[20] At the time of his death in 1850, at the age of 75 years, Davey held wind and water mills and a brick kiln.[21]

William Joyce was in possession in 1875, when the windmill claimed a human life in a particularly grievous manner, as described in *Essex Weekly News* 11th June, 1875:

> On Wednesday, the 2nd inst., the family of Mr Walter Halls, of Wethersfield, were plunged into deep sorrow in consequence of a fatal accident occurring to their boy Harry, a little over two years old: — On Saturday, the 5th inst., an inquest was held before W. Codd Esq., coroner. Mr Halls occupies the Mill House, belonging to Mr W. Joyce, and from the evidence of Mary Ann Harrington, the servant, it appeared that after the child had been missed for about ten minutes, between three and four o'clock in the afternoon, she saw it lying on the stage under the windmill sails — the mill going at the time. She called to the miller, who stopped the mill, and the child was taken in by its mother in a state of insensibility, with a wound on its head. — Mr Rust, surgeon, of Wethersfield, stated that he saw the child shortly before four o'clock, with every symptom of concussion of the brain. The skull was fractured on the right side, from which blood was flowing, caused apparently by a blow from the corner of the windmill sail. He attended the child up to the time of its death, but it never rallied. The cause of death, which took place about midnight, he had no doubt was from an effusion of blood on the brain, the result of an injury. The Jury, in accordance with the evidence, returned a verdict of 'Accidental Death'. The 'stage' is ascended by five steps, and by these the poor little fellow evidently reached the top. At the suggestion of the Jury, three of these steps will be removed, thus preventing, it is hoped, the recurrence of so sad an accident.

The stage could have been akin to that seen in a photograph of Stambourne mill, built to be pushed round the mill base for attending to the sails, which are said to have been of the spring variety.[22]

William Joyce was milling by wind and steam until his death in the mid 1890s, after which another of the same name continued until precisely the 10th April, 1911. That night he dropped his lantern while aloft in the mill and the escaping oil caught fire. The whole mill was rapidly engulfed in flames, and although the brigade was called from Finchingfield, a lack of water rendered their efforts fruitless.[23] The mill's foundations are still traceable (1969) at ground level, forming a rough octagon about 25ft. across the flats.

The upper part of the mill is barely visible in an old picture postcard entitled 'The Green Wethersfield', but a domed cap with finial winded by an 8-bladed fantail can be discerned.

NOTES

1 E.R.O. D/CT 393
2 E.R.O. D/DFy Pl
3 E.R.O. D/P 119/25/119-121 per R. Hawksley
4 E.R.O. D/P 119/21/1 per R. Hawksley
5 C.C. 12.1.1810
6 E.R.O. D/P 119/11/1 per R. Hawksley
7 See note 4
8 C.C. 19.5.1815
9 E.R.O. D/DO T790/14 & D/A BR 32 p. 472
10 C.C. 2.11.1827
11 C.C. 3.5.1839 per H. E. S. Simmons
12 Per G. W. Martin
13 E.W.N. 10.11., 24.11. & 1.12.1876
14 R.E. Pol. No. 228168 24.12.1806 per H. E. S. Simmons
15 E.R.O. D/DFy M46 per R. Hawksley
16 E.R.O. D/DO B24/36
17 C.C. 4.3.1814; also C.C. 30.7.1813
18 E.R.O. D/A MR 14 p. 375
19 E.R.O. D/DFy M45 p. 158 per R. Hawksley
20 E.R.O. D/P 119/11/1
21 E.S. 27.9.1850
22 Per H. E. S. Simmons. R. Hawksley states that local informants recall a fixed stage
23 *The Miller*, 1.5.1911, per S. Freese

Wicken Bonhunt

Smock mill. Stood north of the village at the end of a track about 170 yards from Mill House, which stands 350 yards east of the church. TL 501335 (□ 262)

CHAPMAN AND ANDRÉ (1777) do not include the mill in their map survey, but John Headland of Wicking (*sic*), yeoman, insured in 1765 a windmill standing in the parish, in the tenure of Thomas Wyman, miller, for £100, and the contents for £40, possibly in reference to the known windmill as above, which retained the primitive feature of hand winding until the end.[1] Certainly there was a 'substantial smock windmill', with two pairs of French stones and a flour mill, in 1786, when the freehold was for sale by private contract, enquiries to Debden Wright, of Newport.[2] In 1796 the mill contents were insured for £60 by Thomas Nottage of Clavering, shopkeeper, farmer and miller, who also ran a windmill in Clavering. He was succeeded by James Pavitt, who insured stock and utensils for £30 in 1800.[3] These low figures suggest that most of the mill's contents belonged to the landlord. In the Nottage insurance entry, the windmill is described as 'timber boarded and thatched' and in Pavitt's 'Timber built and thatched'; in neither case is a reference to brickwork included, as was usual when there was a brick base. Photographs of the mill show a substantial brick base of two storeys with a short and strongly battered octagonal smock frame set above, somewhat akin to the style of the Manuden smock mill. The possible raising of the mill in the last century by the insertion of brickwork below is readily suggested, as occurred, for instance, at Boxford, Suffolk c1850, where the wooden frame was bodily raised 16ft. for the insertion of two lower floors.[4]

262 Wicken Bonhunt. Photo perhaps c 1910. Last worked c 1905; standing 1921, but demolished not long after

There were numerous millers. After Joseph Thurgood (1832) came Samuel, bankrupt in 1840,[5] to be succeeded by James Osborne.[6] Others included Frederick Miller (1848), John Grayston (1863, 66) and George Moore (1874, 94). During the Moores' tenure (George and John), Herbert John Ruse, miller, using wind power, is also returned under Wicken Bonhunt in *Kelly's* directory (1890, 1902), presumably as a partner or subtenant. The windmill was offered for sale as part of the Shortgrove estate in 1889, when let to George Moore on a yearly tenancy at £20 annually.[7] It was then described as part brick and part timber built, having two plain sails, two patent spring sails, and two pairs of stones. These sails are seen in an oil painting dated 1885 in the possession of a member of the Ruse family, and a photograph shows the 'plain' or common sails in an iron windshaft.

The cap was straight-ridged, apparently covered with sheet metal, and minimally rounded near the base to follow the curb; it carried a petticoat at the sides, with a rear overhang to shelter the large winding wheel. When Dr Turner called in 1921, he found the mill sadly derelict, having last worked c1905, according to his informant, the last miller at Henham windmill.[8] The latter was surprised by Dr Turner's wish to photograph the mill: 'What's the use now that they are no longer used?' The mill was taken down during the 1920s.

NOTES
1 Sun Pol. No. 222598 24.7.1765
2 C.C. 6.10.1786
3 R.E. Pol. Nos. 151203 27.5.1796 & 179324 14.11.1800
4 *The Miller*, Vol. VIII, 1882-3, p. 93
5 *London Gazette*, 7.7.1840, per H. E. S. Simmons. Land tax records (1826): Isaac Thurgood occupier, Wm. Smith owner (E.R.O.)
6 E.R.O. D/CT 394A
7 E.R.O. B1574, 25.6.1889
8 Southend R.L. Notes on Essex windmills, p. 83

Wickham St Paul

(1) Post mill, latterly Ruffle's. Stood on the south side of the Hedingham road 80 yards east of Mill House and 300 yards north west of the church. TL 824373

(2) Mill of unknown type. Stood in a field about 180 yards south south west of the T-junction south of the village centre made by the roads leading to Nether House and Park Farms. TL 831361

(1) RUFFLE'S MILL

The maps of Warburton, Bland and Smyth (c1724) and Chapman and André (1777) both record a mill in the neighbourhood of the last known site, but the latter map appears to represent the mill as much nearer the turning leading to the Hall, and does not mark the present Mill House. This house occupies a shallow depression. The site is on a flat tableland on which the winds enjoy full freedom.

Despite the lengthy milling activity, no press notices advertising for new owners or lessees have been found. In 1839 Isaac King was occupier under the Trustees of Earls Colne Charity, and his mill-tenant was Isaac Marsh,[1] followed by John Marsh (1845, 55), Josiah Marsh (1856), Robert Ruffle (1858), William Gooding (1870, 74) and William Bull (1878), who was replaced by Richard C. Ruffle in 1898, the last miller to work the mill by wind.

Gooding gave evidence at an inquest held in December, 1872, a few hours after a fatal accident had befallen a youth, Henry Cooper, in his employment. The details appeared in the *Essex Weekly News* and in the *Halstead Times*:[2]

The deceased was in my service, and was sixteen years of age. The last time I saw him alive was this morning, about five minutes past twelve, when I called him to go up to the mill, telling him I should be there in a few minutes. I told him to put the wheat stones in. In the course of about a quarter-of-an-hour I went to the mill, and on going in, I said "All right, Harry?", but I got no answer. I then went up on to the stone floor and there I saw him, hanging from the cog wheels by his neck, which was crushed between them; he was quite dead. As I was attempting to release him the wind blew the window out, and put out my light. On my return with a light, having called up Frederick Parmenter, we tried to release the deceased, but were unable to do so, and we then reversed the mill, and the body dropped on to the stone. My opinion is that as the deceased was attempting to fix the stone nut into the spur wheel ready for work, a gust of wind must have caused the mill to draw back, and have drawn the deceased into the cog wheels. I cannot account for the accident in any other way. The deceased was in the habit of setting the mill going; the wind was very strong at the time. — Frederick Parmenter, farm bailiff, of Wickham St Paul's, gave corroborative evidence, and the Jury returned a verdict of 'Accidental Death'.

About a fortnight later, the vacant post was thus advertised:[3]

To Millers. — Wanted, a single man to work in a windmill; to live in the house; an improver not objected to. — Apply to William Gooding, Miller, &c. . . .

Mr Ernest Pilgrim, a local resident born in 1897, was able to give details of the mill.[4] It was of post type, painted white, and had a porch and landing. A fantail was mounted over the rear ladder and there was a bricked roundhouse with two floors. The four spring sails drove two pairs of stones in the mill breast; these were overdriven, as the account of the fatality makes clear. Another informant stated[5] that by 1911 the mill was not working by wind power. Steam drive appears to have been introduced in the years a little before 1910.

The mill appeared as 'Old Windmill' on the O.S. Popular 1in. edition (1914-15), but was cleared away before the outbreak of war, according to a member of the Nott family. Richard Ruffle (1898, 1914) was succeeded at the steam mill by William J. Ruffle (1917, 29); today only the engine block remains.

(2) OAK FARM MILL (RUFFLE'S)

This windmill had a short life and was worked by the Ruffle family of Oak Farm. Robert Ruffle was described as miller and farmer in the directories of 1859-66,[6] and the mill figures as a red disc, as does also the other parish windmill, on the first O.S. 1:2500 map of 1876.[7] It is not distinguished on the tithe map (1839) or on the revised second O.S. 1in. map (1893). The last known reference to the mill is in the land tax records for 1878-80, having the entry 'Oak Farm and mill'.

William Gooding, of the north mill, inserted the following in the *Essex Weekly News* in February, 1873:[8]

To Millers and Millwrights. To be sold cheap, two good deal middlings, 44 feet long, 13in. by 10½in. at poll; one pair of spring sails in good repair; a good break wheel; one pair of French stones, 4ft. 8ins., with irons and brasses; a thorough good iron tail wheel, 6ft. di, to take in halves, with cogs nearly new, an iron stone nut to same, sack tackling, riggers, &c for a post mill; also flour mill real (sic) and beaters, very good. Address, Wm. Gooding, Miller, Wickham St Paul's, Essex.

Possibly this had some connection with the Ruffles' property, for which there may have been no immediate buyer. It is said[9] that the machinery for the dismantled Foxearth post mill, which had two pairs of stones in the head, was taken to Wickham St Paul in or soon after 1868, and Gooding may have traded in mill parts as a sideline.

Addendum

A most notable 'worthy', known as 'The Handy Handless Man', was Henry Cook, who worked for the Ruffles of Belchamp Walter and Wickham St Paul mills. In 1912 he was featured in cinematograph pictures at the Sudbury Picture Hall. The secretary of the Halstead and District Local History Society (Adrian Corder-Birch) writes (1985): 'Henry Cook lost one hand in a chaff-cutter and the other in a reaper. He had wagered he could run round a field twice to the reaper's once, being rather proud of his running. He had lapped the machine, but, cutting the corner in front of it, had slipped and lost his other hand in the machine. Despite this, it was little of a disability to him: he could steer a traction engine by slipping his ringle over the steering handle. During threshing he was on the straw stack and had a special short pitch fork with a leather thong. For eating he had knife and fork that screwed into his attachments and he lived a fairly normal life. One is forced to admire the courage he exhibited in making so light of his disability.'

NOTES
1 E.R.O. D/CT 397A
2 E.W.N. 13.12.1872; *Halstead Times* 14.12.1872
3 E.W.N. 3.1.1873
4 Enquiries by R. Hawksley, Oct., 1979
5 Mr Howard, of Earls Colne, to R. Hawksley
6 But possibly at the north site (land tax returns)
7 Per R. Hawksley
8 E.W.N. 14.2.1873
9 Per H. E. S. Simmons

Widdington

Post mill. Stood in the south-west angle of the intersection of bridleways about ¼ mile south of Ringers Farm. TL 532332 (□ 263)

PASTOR A. D. ROBERTSON, born in the mill cottage in 1878, and son of one of the last millers of Widdington, stated in a letter dated June, 1970; 'The mill according to the cuttings on the post was very ancient, built 1660'. He further stated that the roundhouse was added in 1761 and that the mill was in full use until 1895. This last date may be presumed to mark the end of milling by his own family — grandfather and father, for *Kelly* gives Ralph Iredale as milling by wind in 1898.

A plan of 1633 (ERO D/DAb E5) shows a windmill apparently at this site, where Warburton, Bland and Smyth (*c*1724) and later cartographers record a mill symbol. In 1749 Matthew Stanes was miller.[1] In 1799 the freehold of the mill, in the tenure of William Barker, came under the hammer at The Hoops in Saffron Walden, four miles distant by the turnpike road.[2] Following this, George Rayment, miller, insured the mill for £200, the standing and going gears for £60 and the stock and utensils for £40 — low figures suggesting a one-pair mill.[3] In 1821 the freehold was again for sale, comprising a post mill with 'one pair of good French stones, dressing machine and other conveniences complete', a lime kiln, dwelling house and land, all in the occupation of Adam Howard at a rent of £25 yearly.[4] In 1840 William Howard was tenant to George Wright, but was under notice to quit, the property being again for disposal.[5]

263 *Widdington, 1907. Disused from c 1902, taken down c 1910*

For a lengthy period the mill was run by William and later George Woodcock Perry of Widdington Hall, farmers, until eventually the younger became bankrupt. The Robertsons were in their employ as millers. Iredale assumed ownership for a short period, but the date when the mill ceased work is not reliably known. It was probably about 1900, for it is not listed in 1902 by *Kelly*.

Photographs of the derelict mill and old memories contribute a few details. The mill had a single-storied roundhouse and tail-pole winding and the plain weatherboarded body with small square hatches was topped by a mansard roof. The single-shuttered sails turned clockwise; they had nine bays with the heel close in to the canister and swung low. A. D. Robertson explicitly describes the brake wheel as driving two pairs of stones: 'The two pairs of stones were laid side by side behind the crowntree and were empowered from the brake wheel which was geared on the face (not the edge) which drove an upright shaft carrying two sections, the lower one cast steel called the waller, which received the power, the top of the shaft carried a finer cog wheel called spur section which drove two steel cone heads of spindles communicating with the bearing of the stones'. Another source gives an iron windshaft driving head and tail stones.[6] Steam power was not applied, but Perry used a portable steam engine at his farm to drive a pair of stones when the wind failed.

The mill was taken down *c*1910, some ten years after it had fallen into disuse, but the machinery and substructure lay about for some years. In the early 1920s the main post was sawn and used to make a staircase in Widdington. Today nothing remains and there is no mill mound, though a low one may have existed. The main approach to the mill site was by a rough but hard-surfaced cart track from Widdington Road to the south. There are fine vistas to west and south and a free air flow from other quarters, the type of elevated position much favoured by the earlier windmill builders.

Addendum

Edward Ebrington by his will of 1578 left to his children: 'Widdington windmill in lease at 53/4'. (*Elizabethan Life: Essex Gentry's Wills*, Emmison, p. 81).

NOTES

1 E.R.O. D/A BR 24, p. 39
2 C.C. 4.1.1799
3 Sun Pol. No. 696587 12.12.1799. E.R.O. D/A BR 30, p. 569: George Rayment's will, made and proved 1812 — mill and lime kiln to son George.
4 C.C. 23.11.1821. In 1832, Adam Howard still occupier under ownership of Debden Wright (E.R.O. land tax returns)
5 E.R.O. D/CT 398A; E.S. 1.5.1840
6 D. W. Muggeridge, as per his informant

Willingale Doe

Smock mill, succeeding an earlier — presumed post — mill. Stood behind the mill house, renamed Mount Cottage, on the north side of the Roxwell road 300 yards west of Shellow Bowells church. TL 604079

HERE stood two or more mills in succession on a mound, one being shown in the maps of Warburton, Bland and Smyth (c1724) and Chapman and André (1777). Reginald Terry was evidently the miller in late 1677.[1] In 1792, Francis Marriage, of Willingale Doe, farmer and miller, was proprietor; he insured the windmill and machinery for £150 and his thatched dwelling for £50.[2]

By 1830 a smock mill was in being, still described as 'recently erected' in 1841.[3] It had two pairs of stones. For a decade or more it was owned by John Harris, nurseryman, of Broomfield, whose trustees under his will advertised the sale of the freehold in 1841. The mill was stated to have an iron sheet covering and patent sails, and was occupied by John Maylen at a rent of £42 10s. annually. Maylen was both farmer and miller, employing two men in the milling and twelve on his 89 acres. The 1851 census records him at the windmill in Torrells Hall hamlet, aged 44, born in South Ockendon, married, and with seven sons and four daughters all below the age of fifteen.[4] Shortly after the census one of his very young daughters climbed upon the stool used for shifting the sail cloths — as reported, sustained a fractured skull, and died a few hours later.[5] This implies that the patent sails of the sale notice comprised one pair only, but it is more likely that the description 'patent' was loosely used in reference to spring sails. In its last years the mill is stated to have carried four spring sails.[6]

Maylen was later succeeded by his eldest son, also John, who was miller in 1863, when he married.[7] Later, Charles Maylen ran the business, became insolvent in 1882, and put up the mill to be let or sold in February, 1884.[8] It was again on the market in 1889,[9] when occupied by Thomas Yeomans, and yet again in April, 1891, application to be made to F.B. Roast, of White Roding mill.[10] *Kelly* records Charles Martin as milling by wind only in 1890.

The mill was withdrawn, unsold, at an auction in Chelmsford on September 18th, 1896, despite the 'low upset price' of £200 to 'ensure a sale' of the dwelling house with eight rooms and lean-to brewhouse, out-buildings, and 'smock tower windmill, with two pairs of stones, wind and steam driving gears . . . as lately used'.[11] The last miller was William Chapman, recorded in the electoral registers for 1892-3 and 1893-4 only.

The mill stood on a single-storied brick base and had a fantail. It was demolished piece by piece by a local man, Arthur Lucking, before the date of the third O.S. 1in. map, c1903. There is no illustration to hand.

NOTES

1 E.R.O. D/A BR 10, p. 105. E.R.O. Q/SBb 189/22 (1752) gives Wm. Hockley, miller, at Torrells Hall Hamlet
2 R.E. Pol. No. 127688 24.4.1792 per H. E. S. Simmons
3 E.S. 17.9. & 8.10.1841; see also C.C. 14.4.1837: auction of freehold, Samuel Dawson tenant at will, per H. E. S. Simmons
4 P.R.O. HO 107 1771
5 E.S. 13.6.1851
6 Per Donald W. Muggeridge from two informants
7 E.S. 11.9.1863
8 E.W.N. 19.5.1882, 1.2.1884; see also *The Miller*, 5.6.1882 & 5.5.1884, per H. E. S. Simmons
9 E.W.N. 20.9.1889
10 *The Miller*, 6.4.1891, per H. E. S. Simmons
11 Sale notice in possession of J. M. Welch, Chartered Surveyors, Great Dunmow

Wimbish

(1) Smock mill, succeeding an earlier mill. Base survives at Tye Green 1000 yards east of the Thaxted road from Saffron Walden (B184) on the north side of Mill Road (left fork at Howlett End). TL 589353 (□ 264)

(2) Smock mill. Base stands with 'Old Mill House' built on at Wimbish Lower Green. Stated to have stood earlier 200 yards to the east at the T-junction, where there was a windmill c1840. TL 605350 from its alleged former location at TL 607352 (□ I 42)

(1) TYE GREEN MILL (MUNSON'S)

The site is given a mill symbol by Chapman and André (1777) and Greenwood (1825), as well as by later maps. In 1757 Charles Wymondesold, lord of the manor of Wimbish Hall, leased for 99 years to William Butcher, of Finchingfield, a piece of ground described as 'Mill-hill', Butcher having lately erected a windmill upon it at his own cost.[1] A covenant for removal of the windmill at any time was included in the deed. John Giblin, yeoman, purchased the mill and premises from Butcher for £255 in 1791, and in 1794, when described as farmer and miller, insured the windmill for £80 and the contents for £100.[2] In 1802, however, Frederick Giblin insured his 'corn windmill brick and timber' for £280 and the contents for a further £100,[3] possibly reflecting the addition of a second pair of stones and fittings.

In 1817 the property was sold to James Leonard, of Castle Camps, Cambs., yeoman, who evidently had the existing mill pulled down, for in 1819 he advertised for sale by private contract his 'newly-erected' tower windmill to be removed, being brick and timber built, with one pair of stones and convenience for another.[4] It had been built by Reuben Hunt, millwright, late of Thaxted, some time after February, 1818, for £400.[5]

Leonard's invitation in 1819 to move the mill was declined, and by his will made in 1828 and proved in

April, 1830, the mill passed to his son Walter.[6] The tithe map (1841) puts a tower mill drawing at the same site, the apportionment (also 1841) describing the property as in the ownership and occupation of Walter Leonard, who owned Westley's Farm.[7] By 1844 Leonard had removed to London, putting the mill up for sale, now fully fledged with patent sails driving three pairs of stones, and with a 'bake office' attached.[8] A plan of the

264 *Wimbish: Tye Green Mill. Use of wind last recorded 1912. Body said removed in same year. Base preserved as living quarters*

London to Norwich Direct Railway in 1844 describes William Giblin as occupier.[9] A sale was again advertised in 1847,[10] when the mill was in the occupation of one Munson, and John Townsend came forward as purchaser for £205. George Munson, miller (1874, 90, 1902), was succeeded by R. Munson as tenant, milling by wind only in 1912 according to *Kelly*. Robert Saville Munson bought in 1910 the (by that date) freehold mill from Emily Townsend for £25, and sold to Capt. W. Glynes Bruty for £50 in 1917. It seems that by the date of the latter conveyance there were in operation stones in the mill base only, driven by a Petter oil engine, the power being incorrectly given as petrol by *Kelly*. The windmill does not feature as such on the Popular edition of the O.S. 1in. map (surv. 1914-15), and several local informants have stated that it was taken down to the brick base in 1912 after having last worked by wind with two sails only.

There are two undated photographs of the mill, one showing a degree of dereliction and taken pre-1910, to judge by the attire of young children in the foreground; the other is of the mill in working order. This shows four double-shuttered clockwise patent sails, a domed cap with ball finial and gallery, and an 8-bladed fantail correctly matched to the sails. The body was of sturdy build, having only some 35 lines of weatherboarding over the single-storied brick base in contrast with as many as 80 at Upminster, but able to house three pairs of stones. Unusually, the eight corners of the base, all vertical, were strengthened externally by brick buttresses. These remain today to support the converted base made suitable for habitation.

(2) LOWER GREEN MILL (MYNOTT'S)

The surviving base is hexagonal in plan and obscurely situated. The first map-related clue to the existence of a mill at Lower Green is provided by the tithe records (1841), according to which it was part of plot 877 (Mill and Cottage) containing 20 rods, in the ownership and occupation of William Mynott. He, or the same, junior, also held plot 871a corresponding with the present position of the mill base. Plot 877 lay at the east end of the lane running past the present Old Mill House, where stands today at the T-junction the cottage named 'Joe on the Donkey', once a beerhouse. In 1850 and 1863 the Mynotts, senior and junior, were styled millers and beer retailers. At neither site is a mill marked on the tithe map, in contrast with the site at Tye Green, but there was a Mill Field adjacent to the eastern plot, and in the latter the schedule number may have usurped the space occupied by the mill. These observations lead one to question whether the mill was moved from east to west for 200 yards, so making its appearance on the first O.S. 6in. map of survey date 1877 at the position where the base now stands. W. H. Mynott asserted in 1975 that his great-grandfather William Mynott junior (c1795-1867) lived at what is now 'Joe on the Donkey' and moved the mill on rollers to the west site, the operation (date not known) taking a fortnight. An abstract of title in reference to the east plot, dated 1910, states 'wherein a windmill was formerly standing'. The probability of a move seems therefore to be well founded, but the discovery of a brick clearly inscribed with the date 1828 in the present mill base during cleaning operations in 1976 has also to be taken into account.[11]

The electoral register for 1832 and the records of the manor of Wimbish Hall[12] throw a little more light on the obscurities outlined above. The register lists William Mynott as holding a freehold house and mill at the Lower Green, Wimbish. The court records state, in an entry dated 14th November, 1835, that Sarah Allen, for £25 received, had conveyed 20 rods of land at the east end of Wimbish Green to William Mynott 'as the same has been lately staked out and divided from the residue...', and in Mynott's will, dated 23rd August, 1856, reference was made to the 'twenty rods on which a windmill formerly stood but since pulled down . . . together with the cottage . . . recently erected and built thereon.' The sequence of events may therefore have been:

1828:   Windmill erected at the east site (not recorded in the court rolls, probably because the principal tenant continued in occupation).

1832:   William Mynott entered in the electoral register as holding 'freehold house and mill' at Lower Green.

1835: Copyhold land at the east site, on which the mill was standing, conveyed from Sarah Allen to William Mynott.

Between 1841 and 1856: Windmill moved to west site; new brick base inscribed 1828 casually without the use of a proper date stone.

In *Kelly's* directory for 1886, William H. Mynott is given as using wind power, but in 1894 steam only, and the second O.S. 6in. map (surv. 1896) describes the windmill as disused. The gale of Sunday, 30th October, 1887, severely damaged the sails of both Wimbish mills, as well as wreaking havoc on the mills at Clavering, Debden, Lindsell and Stansted near Elsenham, and it is probable that this marked the end of milling by wind at Wimbish Lower Green.[13] Edgar Mynott was the last miller, using steam power up to 1906 according to *Kelly*. The smock body is thought to have been removed *c*1912.

There is one known photograph, undated, showing the mill to its cap, and with one well-clamped middling in position. The cap was domed and had a ball finial and gallery, as at Tye Green, and the sails were probably patents. The remains of the fantail staging are visible. Nothing is known of the mill interior, but it was small — the base measures only 13ft. 5in. across the flats internally — and probably held two pairs of stones.

NOTES

1 E.R.O. D/DU 875/1. Bundle of deeds covering 1757-1917
2 R.E. Pol. No. 142832 2.12.1794
3 R.E. Pol. No. 191519 5.6.1802
4 C.C. 19.11.1819
5 E.R.O. D/DAd 134: Court Baron, manor of Wimbish Hall
6 See note 1 above
7 E.R.O. D/CT 404
8 E.S. 5.7.1844
9 Per R. Hawksley, examined at E.R.O.
10 E.S. 12 & 19.2.1847
11 Enquiries by George W. Ingram, who has established Wm. Mynott's dates as *c*1795-1867. Mr Ingram also states that, contrary to the information given in Vol. I, p. 70, the eastern premises, first a cottage, later became an off-licence, being then named 'Joey and Donkey'
12 As note 5
13 *Herts. & Essex Observer* 5.11.1887 per R. Hawksley, who was told locally (1976) that the portable engine did not drive the windmill

Witham

Smock mill. Stood about 90 yards from Bridge Street (the Colchester road) and 25 yards east of Howbridge Road, approximately at the junction with Maidment Crescent. TL 818139

INFORMATION on this mill is singularly meagre. A 'new-built Tower Windmill' with two pairs of French stones &c complete, and standing as above described, was for sale by auction in November, 1819,[1] and was recorded on Greenwood's map (1825), as also subsequently on the tithe map (1839).[2] It featured also in sale notices dated April, 1830, and February, 1845.[3] In the latter, the mill was to be let and was described as a smock mill, still with two pairs of stones. By this date the description 'smock' mill was well established in reference to wooden tower-type mills, and this mill can be accepted as such for the record.

In 1842 John Cutts was owner and Thomas Hoffgood (*sic*) Shoobridge occupier at 'Tower Mill and Close', embracing a little over 1 acre. Shoobridge was long after returned as miller at Town (water) mill, and one of the family had insured a watermill in Witham in 1801.[4] In October, 1844, poor rate records give John Cutts as owner of the windmill with John Mecklenburgh as occupier.[5] The mill and premises may be further traced under Bridge Street in the poor rate for October, 1847, as occupied by John Tatum and owned by John Granger, but the church rate of July, 1848, gives no such entry.[6] Granger's will, proved in February, 1847, leaves his real property on trust for sale, and a garden owned by his executors in 1849 was possibly the mill site without mill.[7]

Dr Turner stated that a lifelong Witham resident, presumably elderly, could (*c*1920) recall no windmill in the town,[8] and the mill is not to be seen on the O.S. 6in. map surveyed in 1874.

NOTES

1 C.C. 22.10.1819
2 E.R.O. D/CT 405
3 C.C. 23.4.1830; 28.2.1845 per L. Smith, Witham
4 Sun Pol. No. 716311 21.2.1801
5 Per R. Hawksley: E.R.O. D/P 30/11/23-4
6 Ditto: 30/11/31 (1847), 30/5/2 (1848)
7 E.R.O. per R. Hawksley
8 Notes on Essex Windmills, Southend R. L.

Wivenhoe and Elmstead

(1) Post mill. Stood in Elmstead above the valley on the east side of the stream 400 yards south west of the lane to Alresford, in the area of the modern Dene Park housing estate. Approximately TM 043220

(2) Post mill. Stood in the angle of Belle Vue and Rectory Roads, opposite and west of the rectory. TM 043223

(1) ELMSTEAD MILL

In a document dated 8th December, 1660, there is a reference to a windmill lately erected on Cold Hall Field, in Elmstead, late in the tenure of John Dawbee.[1] This was doubtless the mill shown by Ogilby and Morgan

(1678); for greater precision as to site one may refer to Warburton, Bland and Smyth (*c*1724), Chapman and André (1777) and the first O.S. 1in. map (1805). In 1793 the windmill at Elmstead was mentioned in the will of Edward Stammers of Fingringhoe, miller, who named John Smith as tenant,[2] and in the following year the executors put the windmill, together with Butt mill, Colchester, to auction.[3] The Elmstead mill was then stated to be of post type with roundhouse. In 1801 the structure, machinery and stock were each insured for £100 by Manister (or Manester) Cooper,[4] who was in occupation when the mill was repeatedly advertised to be let or sold in the years 1806-10.[5] It was driving one pair of stones. If by analogy with the horse's teeth the count of mill bills may be taken to indicate a windmill's age, then the 51 included in Manester Cooper's stock in trade in 1810 disclosed a very old nag indeed. No further reference has been found, but the emergence of a post mill nearby in Wivenhoe may have some relevance to the demise of Elmstead mill.

The tithe apportionment for Elmstead (1844) lists six fields designated 'mill' in some form, all situated on the periphery.[6] A group of three lay in the east centre by the stream nearly opposite Great Bromley windmill; two were against the boundary with Wivenhoe in the area of the post mill located above, and one was in the south-east corner of the parish adjoining the Frating brook. Of these, Mill Field, No. 594, in the west, corresponds most closely with site (1).

(2) WIVENHOE OR MORTLOCK'S MILL[1]

This post mill may have been erected in 1816 when John Smith, miller, was admitted to the plot on the road to Elmstead where Greenwood (1825) places a mill symbol.[7] It received a press mention in 1833.[8] It stood some 400 yards from the Elmstead mill site on land held copyhold of the manor of Wivenhoe. A deed of mortgage[9] dated 1859 lists the occupiers of the premises from 1805, John Smith the elder, (1816), being later succeeded by Robert Beckwith and John Smith the younger. The first John Smith held the mill for many years; in 1826 he was described as miller and maltster,[10] and he was returned in 1848 as corn miller in *White's* directory, in which year, however, the premises were to be let, and Beckwith entered.[11] In 1859 the two residences, malting, and copyhold post windmill in the ownership of John Smith the younger were for sale.[12] The mill, complete with roundhouse, drove two pairs of French stones, and these and the ten-bushel oven in the bakery were the basis of a well-established flour and bread trade. The premises were bought by Cooper, of Messrs Daniel and Cooper, the occupiers, for £490. Further millers were Joseph Francis (1863) and Charles Mortlock (1874), after which milling continued under the direction of the Mortlocks until the second world war, the last of the millers of that name dying in about 1950.

The windmill's activity terminated, however, in the early 1880s. In 1833 it had been struck by lightning, a brief account of which misadventure implied a tiled and plastered roundhouse, and referred to a ten-foot splinter of wood torn off one of the sails.[13] The final disaster of November, 1882, occurred after the mill had been running for a time on two sails.[14]

> On Friday morning (17th November, 1882) a fire was discovered at the mill, Wivenhoe, the property of Mr Charles Mortlock. The discovery was made by Mr Mortlock's brother, who lives in a house near by. Seeing a strong light through his bed-room window, and hearing a crackling noise, he hurried out, and finding the mill was on fire, he alarmed the inmates. His brother soon came down, and with the assistance of several neighbours who were on the spot, a quantity of corn, which was stored in sacks in the roundhouse of the mill, was removed in safety. The mill, being very old and dry, burnt like matchwood, and was soon reduced to ashes. It is stated that about 12 months ago two of the sails were blown off, and since that time the bearings have occasionally got very hot, and it has been necessary to apply water to cool them; frequent oiling has also been necessary. It is thought this overheating must have occurred, and that a change of wind after the mill was closed at ten o'clock, brought about the ignition of the premises.

Another press account[15] refers to the total destruction of all but the roundhouse, and comments that the wind fortunately drove the flames away from the house and steam mill adjoining.

Steam milling continued at the site long after the fire. A descendant of the millers writes that Charles Mortlock, who died in 1887, had the windmill moved from a point on higher ground further east.[16] Taken literally, this does not readily match the known facts. Possibly there was a move from a distance of about 500 yards where 'Old Mill Field' is recorded on the south side of the Alresford road on the tithe map (1844).[17] This lies to the east, but probably relates to the mill which stood at site (1), from which a move may have occurred. Greenwood (1825) marks a mill at the known site in Wivenhoe, opposite the rectory, much earlier than Mortlock's associations with the mill, so that if a mill was brought to the site in his time it must have replaced an existing one. Greenwood does not mark the Elmstead mill, and there is no evidence to suggest that the two mills co-existed. Both known sites were levelled by bulldozers in preparation for building in 1972.

NOTES

1 E.R.O. D/DHt F 45
2 E.R.O. D/A BR 28 p. 433
3 C.C 14.3.1794
4 R.E. Pol. No. 180982 9.1.1801 per H. E. S. Simmons
5 e.g. C.C. 24.1.1806, I.J. 15.2.1806, C.C. 21.10.1808, I.J. 2.9.1809, C.C. 7.9.1810
6 E.R.O. D/CT 129A
7 E.R.O. D/DEt M20 (court minutes)

8 E.S. 29.6.1833
9 E.R.O. D/DE1 T173
10 *Pigot's* directory
11 E.S. 4.2.1848
12 E.R.O. B1925; E.S. 4.2.1859
13 See note 8
14 *East Essex and Halstead Times* 25.11.1882
15 E.S. 18.11.1882
16 Information from Miss E. D. Sparling of Wivenhoe, 1972
17 Old Mill Field was centred on TM 048222

Wix

(1) Map symbol placed east of Wix Green by Warburton, Bland and Smyth (*c*1724) at approximately TM 180280. Mill Farm on first O.S. 1in. (1805).

(2) Post mill. Stood 220 yards south of the Harwich road to the south of the existing 'Old Mill House', both reached by a track leading off from a point 440 yards east of Wix crossroads. TM 166283

(1) THE MILL FARM MILL

This site was probably already occupied in 1622, when Henry Wodward (*sic*) of Wix, miller, by his will, left to his son the tackle of the windmill which he held in that parish.[1] No further information is to hand.

(2) SOUTHGATE'S, LATER KINDRED'S MILL

Francis Josselyn of Great Oakley, miller, bought a house and land in Wix in September, 1808, and had the post mill erected. The property was sold to Benjamin Skipper in 1814 for £650, and in 1821 was bought by Henry Beckwith of Wix, miller.[2] The mill duly appeared on Greenwood's map (1825). It was latterly described by Brooks, of Ramsey windmill, as low built, driving one pair of stones from the brake wheel, and having no tail wheel.[3] If this was so, some of the machinery would seem to have been removed after 1864, for in that year, following the death of John Southgate, the mill was for auction with patent sails and two pairs of stones. Two acres of pasture and a residence with a bakery attached, copyhold of the manor of Wix Park Hall, were then in the occupation of John Kindred at a rent of £35 per annum.[4] Brooks recollected the fantail on the rear steps, and a brick roundhouse roofed with tiles. He gave the last miller as Grimwood; according to *Kelly's* directory, Thomas Grimwood was at Weeley in 1894, which leads one to conclude that Wix was taken under Weeley's wing before the final abandonment in about 1896. The mill must have been taken down soon after.

A few references to the mill in its earlier years have been noted. An odd theft occurred in 1836 when the irons from the mill ladder were taken and passed on to an ironfounder at Manningtree, for which crime the thief received six weeks hard labour.[5] In the 1840s the mill, stated to be owned by Henry Beckwith, miller, was worked by John Southgate.[6] Southgate had the distressing experience in September, 1841, of finding the mangled corpse of his 15-year old apprentice — who had been left in charge of the working mill — held in the jaws of the machinery. There was no witness.[7]

William Southgate as miller (1848, 55) was followed by John Kindred (1863, 82) and Mrs Sarah Kindred (1886). The mill apparently never graduated to the use of auxiliary power. It was shown in the revised second O.S. 1in. map (surv. 1893), and finally on the second 6in. (1896), there described as 'Old Windmill', indicating inactivity. It probably disappeared shortly after, as it is not remembered (1979) by a local man who was born in 1885.

NOTES

1 E.R.O. D/A BR 5, p. 546. See also Vol. I, p. 100
2 E.R.O. D/DLy M49 pp. 40-41 per R. Hawksley
3 Per Donald W. Muggeridge, noted at Easter, 1936
4 E.S. 5.2. & 10.6.1864
5 E.S. 26.2.1836
6 E.R.O. D/CT 407A
7 E.S. 10.9.1841

Woodham Ferrers

Post mill, known as Bicknacre Mill. Stood 80 yards from Mill House (or Mill Farm) on the south side of Mill Lane about 200 yards west of the Maldon road (B1418). TL 785022

AS A POINTER to the relative antiquity of its site, Bicknacre mill stood on a mill mound, still moated on its northern side at the time of the tithe survey (1843).[1] The remains of the mound, which were to be seen for many years after the disappearance of the mill, were bulldozed away in recent times. The mill is distinguished on maps from Warburton, Bland and Smyth (*c*1724) onwards, and is mentioned in papers relating to the Barrington estates in 1684, 1778 and 1780.[2] In 1780 John Pitt was

FIG. 42 *MS map drawing, 1693*

lessee for a term expiring in 1792 of mill, dwelling house and buildings 'well situated for country business' at a rent of £21 per annum.[3] In 1787 he insured the utensils and stock-in-trade in the 'Windmill and Roundhouse adjoining timber built' for £300, and additionally covered the structure in 1790, also, for £300.[4] He renewed his lease, but in November, 1800, met a severe reversal of fortune when his mill was felled in a storm. The insurance cover was inadequate to meet the cost of replacement. A report in the *Chelmsford Chronicle* read:[5]

> That which is not the least lamentable we have to record is of a windmill being blown down on Bicknacre Common, occupied by Mr Pitt, a very industrious and respectable man, who within the last nine years, having obtained a new lease, had expended upwards of £700 upon it. The estate is the property of J. Strutt Esq., of Terling, who we have no doubt, from his known benevolent disposition, will render Mr Pitt, who has a large family, every assistance that he can expect, as the mill is let, subjecting the tenant to repair every damage whether from high wind or otherwise. The centre post was decayed and which was unobserved by the mill-wright when particularly desired by Mr Pitt to inspect the same. A person was in the mill when the violent gust of wind came, but threw himself out, providentially on the contrary side to which it fell. Mr Pitt is also a considerable sufferer in the loss of his meal and grain, which the wind scattered in such a manner as to preclude all hopes of the recovery of it.

A public subscription was raised in aid of Pitt, for which he recorded his thanks 18 months later.[6] The mill was rebuilt, together with a timbered roundhouse. Pitt died in 1805, leaving the lease to Ann, his widow, who in 1813 disposed of the mill with 6 acres of land to William Bright, who had bought Rettendon windmill shortly before, and who died in 1822.[7] In that year an inventory and valuation of the fixtures and utensils in Bicknacre mill was made by Abraham Mays and Thomas Merryfield, millwrights.[8] The floors were named stage, stone and grinding in order of descent, and the stone floor housed two pairs of French stones arranged head and tail. These were 4ft. 10in. at the front and 4ft. 4in. at the rear, and were separately governed below. The stone floor also held a bolter and a 'three-wired jumper' driven from it. Miscellaneous items included a writing desk on the grinding floor and a sack brand, pitch pen and two kettles in the roundhouse. The total value, excluding windshaft, brake wheel and front bedstone, was put at £99 7s. 6d.

James Riley, miller and farmer, followed as lessee to James Holden Strutt,[9] remaining until about 1851, when John Hymas, for long a miller at Springfield, was in occupation. He supported a family running into double figures, from which the sons were recruited into milling on attaining 14 years of age.[10] Robert Keeble followed in the 1860s. The last miller was Thomas Doe, for whom William Baker of Danbury, millwright, did work on the sails and stones in 1884 for a bill of some £40.[11] Doe is listed as milling by wind in *Kelly's* directory for 1898, and is last included in the electoral lists for 1900-1, by which time the mill may have been out of commission. It was gone by 1904 (third O.S. 1in. survey). The *Chelmsford Chronicle* for 17th July, 1896, records the destruction by fire of the steam mill belonging to Thomas Doe.

NOTES

1 E.R.O. D/CT 409
2 E.R.O. D/DRa T20-30
3 Ibid. T30
4 R.E. Pol. Nos. 104628 20.12.1787 & 119297 29.12.1790; see also No. 138527 25.2.1794 per H. E. S. Simmons
5 C.C. 14.11.1800
6 C.C. 30.4.1802
7 After rebuilding: R.E. Pol. No. 187536 14.9.1801 per H. E. S. Simmons; Pitt's will: E.R.O. D/A BR 30 p. 12; C.C. 29.1.1813; Wm. Bright: E.R.O. D/DO B2 (see also under Rettendon), C.C. 8.2.1822
8 E.R.O. D/DO B2
9 C.C. 7.5.1824; E.S. 5.2. & 26.11.1841; E.R.O. D/CT 409A (1843)
10 P.R.O. HO 107 1775
11 Record in possession of Baker & Sons (Danbury) Ltd

Woodham Mortimer

A pair of smock mills on the hilltop east of Old Mill House, i.e. just east of the junction of the lane to Hazeleigh Hall with the Bicknacre road. TL 832044

A MAP dated 1759 depicts a post mill with roundhouse at this site,[1] but in view of later references it would seem that a smock mill should have been represented. Chapman and André (1777) record two windmill symbols as 'Woodham Mills'. Today, the breezy summit, commanding extensive views towards the Blackwater, is pock-marked by a depression or two, evidently connected with the former mill buildings.

The mills were not destined to operate for long as a pair. In September 1768, they were to be let with Bacon's Farm for a term of years, and were described as 'two large Dutch Windmills', lately built, with four pairs of French stones and four bolting mills, two of the latter being driven either by wind or by horse. The miller was offered a house and a modest plot of land to be held independently of the farm.[2] The wisdom of setting up two new windmills in this relatively isolated position may even at that date have been questioned, but the well-winded site and the short haul of two miles to Maldon could have been the deciding factors. In the event, insolvency was in the air, and in June 1785, the assignee of the estate of William Pain, a bankrupt meal-man, was advertising the premises to be let containing 'two capital smock mills . . . from Maldon two miles . . . where sloops are daily going to London; eight miles from Chelmsford; seven from Witham, and eleven from

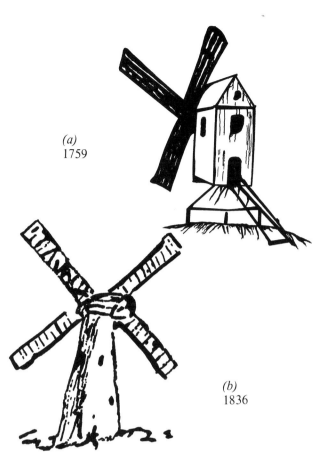

(a)
1759

(b)
1836

FIG. 43 *Woodham Mortimer, MS map drawings*

Coggeshall, all plentiful markets'. A year and a half later the two mills were similarly advertised.[3]

Three insurance registrations in the period 1789-91 refer to the mills. In September 1789, James Whitborn, of Woodham Mortimer, mealman, insured 'two Wind Corn Mills adjoining and communicating' for £400, and in December 1790 John Muggeridge, of the same parish, miller, insured the 'utensils and trade' in his 'Smock Windmill called the Great Mill' for £300, and those in 'another Smock Windmill called the Old Mill situate near' for £100 only. Both mills were described as timber built.[4] A further insurance entry relates to John Royce, of Woodham Walter, who on 14th November, 1791, covered his 'new windmill' for £300 and the 'old' for £200 (in the occupation of 'Muckeridge and Company').[5] The 1785 sale notice suggests lavish improvements to the dwelling house shortly before the lessee's departure. The preliminary drawings (1799) for the first O.S. 1in. map show one mill only.

In 1803, Abraham Ling, miller, was in quest of a helping hand for a single mill, which in 1804 was insured for £200 by Mary Royce, and subsequently neither maps nor other records disclose a pair.[6] In 1823 the surviving mill is credited with two pairs of French stones, and a home trade, embracing Chelmsford, sufficient to

employ it. William Brewster Cozens, of Woodham Mortimer Lodge, was the head tenant, as recorded later in the tithe records, the mill being leased from 1823 for 7 years by Daniel Spight from Jeffrey Grimwood of Cressing.[7] The tithe map (1838), drawn to a large scale, shows the mill approached by a track spiralling up the contours from west and south. The mill property at this time was still owned by Grimwood and occupied by Spight.[8] Spight was followed by Stephen Cox, who in 1844 paid an annual rent of £36. A counterpart lease records the landlord's fixtures, which included the principal gearing and shafts. Among the tenant's fixtures and utensils were the brake rope, sack rope and chain listed under the heading 'Stage Floor'. There were 21 mill bills weighing 44 lb., and 9 furrow splines to the stones, with the usual series of weights, headed by 4 at 56 lb.[9]

In 1852 Grimwood, described as of Woodham Mortimer Lodge, leased the mill to Robert Munson, as yearly tenant, for £30. Owners and millers were many during the next forty years, including Miss C. Marriage, of Chelmsford, who owned the mill in 1865, with Messrs. Garrett in occupation. The Garretts were succeeded by Aaron Middleditch, spanning at least 1869-86, rendered Earn Middleditch in the church rates (1869-81), and later came Walter Henry Nicholls (wind and steam, 1890). Middleditch probably introduced the steam power, for an insurance note dated 1869 stated that the mill was *now* sometimes worked by steam power and that there was a stove on the lower floor with a pipe running through the brickwork. The engine was portable.[10]

From the evidence of the electoral registers it seems that the mill last worked in 1890-91. The second edition of the O.S. 6in. map (surv. 1895) records the mill as disused. It was presumably taken down soon after, and was gone by c1900. There is no known illustration, but a sale notice (1857) states that the mill had patent sails, a wind-fan and two pairs of 4ft. French stones.[11]

NOTES

1 E.R.O. D/D BR P 1

2 C.C. 9.9.1768. Lease for 7 years taken by John Crozier. See *Essex People*, A. F. J. Brown, p. 14. Publ. 1972 by E.C.C

3 I.J. 9.7.1785, 24.2.1787

4 Sun Pol. No. 561046 24.9.1789; R.E. Pol. No. 119289 29.12.1790 per H. E. S. Simmons

5 R.E. Pol. No. 124646 14.11.1791 per H. E. S. Simmons

6 C.C. 18.11.1803; R. E. Pol. No. 213554 24.12.1804 per H. E. S. Simmons. R. Hawksley, from the amount of the insurance and from a comparison of the 1759 plan, C & A (1777) and the first O.S. 6in., believes the mill that survived to have been the older

7 C.C. 22.8.1823; E.R.O. D/DO T777

8 E.R.O. D/CT 410A. D/DO E15 also contains references to the property

9 E.R.O. D/DO T915

10 E.R.O. D/F 21/18 p. 146

11 E.S. 9.10.1857

Woodham Walter

Windmill of unknown construction, formerly situated adjacent to the watermill known as Blue Mills, which has been converted into a house. TL 813077

HERE, as so often elsewhere, the wind was pressed into service when the last poundal of power had been wrung from the water: Maldon lay conveniently near. The watermill was new-built in 1810, using large gears and two pairs of French stones.[1] There are references to the windmill in mid-century during the long tenure of the Riley family (John Riley 1823, Joseph Riley 1863).[2] In 1856 the freehold water and wind mills drove respectively three pairs and one pair of stones, but the windmill was deemed capable of driving two.[3] The mills were let to a 'good' tenant, yearly, at £120, presumably to Joseph Riley, who in 1857 insured a granary and engine house with windmill attached for £500.[4] He also insured the steam machinery for £200, probably on the occasion of its installation, since it is not mentioned in the preceding year in a notice of sale.

In 1875 Miss Benton ordered the sale of her wind, water and steam mills and premises, and the whole was again for auction in May, 1878.[5] Three months later, a grim evaluation of the wind and steam adjuncts appeared: 'To Farmers, Millers &c. — For Sale, a good substantial Windmill with iron shafts and new machinery, including one pair of stones; will drive two pairs; cash £60. Also a Second Hand 8 h.p. Beam Engine, with 10 feet driving wheel; cash £20. Apply, A. Gozzett, Blue Mills, Woodham Walter, near Maldon.'

No further reference to this windmill has been noted, and there appears to be no directory entry for any of these mills after 1866. Three buildings stood in line abreast from west to east: the mill house, the watermill, and a building which must have carried the windmill, and which evidently became the engine house. All three are shown on the tithe map (1845) and the first O.S. 6in. map (1873-4); today the first two survive, much modified, and there are some remains, only, of the third.

NOTES

1 I.J. 10.9.1810
2 E.R.O. D/F 21/4 27.12.1823; *White's* directory
3 E.S. 15.2.1856
4 E.R.O. D/F 21/14, p. 14, 30.7.1857
5 E.W.N. 6.8.1875, 30.8.1878

Writtle

(1) Post mill on a long occupied site. Latterly Warren's Mill. Stood in the north west angle of the T-junction formed by the turning to Cooksmill Green and Roxwell off the main Chelmsford road (A414). Site in Highwood (1976). TL 639053

(2) Post mill. Southgate's Mill. The last of a presumed long succession of post mills standing on the existing mound 150 yards north of the Chelmsford road behind Mill House, and 650 yards east of the bridge over the Wid. TL 687063 (□ 265)

(1) WARREN'S MILL, COOKSMILL GREEN

Ogilby and Morgan (1678) and Warburton, Bland and Smyth (c1724) place a post mill symbol at both the Writtle sites. A symbol also appears at Cooksmill Green on a survey of Bennet Oats Farm (1774-6).[1] The mill was insured by Henry Moss in 1778 for £300 and the contents for £100, and, since it was described as 'timber and tiled', a post mill with roundhouse is suggested.[2] In 1789 Moss switched his insurance from the Sun to the Royal Exchange, increasing the sums insured to £400 on the 'windmill and roundhouse under timber built' and £200 on the contents.[3] The ownership of the mill passed to the Luckings, Joseph and William, who further increased the sums insured in 1808 to £500 and £300.[4] At the Luckings' mill a young woman of 18 years was killed by the sails in 1807 when setting off with flour just purchased.[5] The accident was not witnessed, but it was thought that the girl had attempted to pass between the moving sails, a most dangerous action which in 1853 had fatal consequences at Rettendon mill.

A mortgage deed dated 1815 recites previous title holders as Thomas Overill, Henry Moss senior and junior, and three Luckings in the order: Joseph, William and Thomas;[6] the owner in 1830 and 1843 was Joseph Cliff,[7] who appeared as mortgagee in 1815. One of the Lucking family was described as a 'reduced miller' in 1841, his daughter being sent to a foundation school by the St. Ann's Society.[8] William Fitch ran the mill from the 1840s to c1863; then came William Warren, last mentioned in a directory in 1890 and in an electoral roll of 1892-3. During Warren's occupation in 1867, the mill was offered for auction as a post windmill fitted with spring sails and two pairs of French stones, the rental for the mill and premises being £32 10s. annually.[9] The mill was omitted from the revised second O.S. 1in. map (1893).

There was a conspicuous mound approached by a ramp from the east, seen to be occupied by the mill on the first O.S. 6in. map (1874), but not the second, surveyed about five years after the date (c1890) when the mill is thought to have been destroyed by fire.[10] The moat afforded good skating in its time. The last remains of the mound were obliterated in 1974 by a road-straightening scheme.

(2) SOUTHGATE'S MILL, WRITTLE EAST

This mill, together with Ropers Farm, was owned by New College, Oxford, and leased to a succession of tenants.[11] It stood on a pronounced mound with ditch, and features on most windmill-bearing maps of Essex from Ogilby and Morgan (1678) onwards.

A list of lessees after 1800, with dates of entry or renewal, runs: Joseph Edwards (from 1800), Daniel Blythe (1807), Daniel Blythe and William Boosey, yeoman (1814, 21, 28), Jeremiah Pledger (1835), John Attwood (1842).[12] In 1805 Daniel Blyth (*sic*), of New Lodge Farm, Writtle, insured the mill, in the occupation of John Luskin (*sic*), for £120 and the contents for £80.[13] In 1868 New College contracted to sell an estate in Writtle, including Ropers Farm and the windmill, to Arthur Pryor of Hylands Park, Essex.[14]

Robert Crush succeeded William Boosey as the active miller in 1816, hoping by 'strict attention' to 'merit future favours';[15] Elizabeth Crush, widow, continued the business *c*1845. Her son Robert took it over, but eventually concentrated on farming (*Kelly's* 1855). The last millers were the Southgates; a sample of directory entries gives Ashford Southgate in 1874-8, Mrs Susannah Margaret Southgate in 1890, 98 (wind and water), and Southgate Bros. as late as 1937, the last still using water power. Ashford Southgate came to the mill in 1872, but died at the early age of 31 years from tuberculosis, for which the inhaling of flour dust was thought in part responsible.[16] He was succeeded by Herbert Southgate and two brothers. A note on a water-colour of the windmill states that it was blown down in 1897, and this is said to have resulted from the 'Essex Tornado' of 24th June, which did much damage in the Writtle area. *Kelly's* directory of 1898 appears to record the continued use of wind at this site. The roundhouse stood on in use as a store until it was burnt down, evidently by youthful vandals, on 3rd March, 1970.

265 *Writtle: Southgate's Mill. Water-colour, undated. Mill blown down in 1897*

The post mill with roundhouse is seen in several paintings. One, dated 1865, shows four single-shuttered anti-clockwise sails and tail-pole winding, but in the later days double-shuttered sails and a 6-bladed fantail mounted over the rear steps were employed. Baker of Danbury, millwright, did work at the wind and water mills in the 1880s.[17] For taking down a broken middling

and sails he charged 15*s*. 6*d*. for his own and two men's labour for one day, his rate being 6*d*. an hour. The new middling measured 43ft. Other sizeable items were, in 1883, a new weatherbeam 10ft. 6in. by 18in. by 13in. and a new shaft by Christy (type unspecified) for £7 5*s*. 6*d*. The sails required heavy maintenance costs, being often in need of repair or renewal of levers, backstays, uplongs, canvas shutters, and the like; all four were to be taken down and thoroughly overhauled in 1890. Details of the internal arrangements are not known.

Addendum

By her will of 1599, Mrs Rose Pinchon left her lease of — inter alia — the windmill (687063) to her son Edward. (*Elizabethan Life: Essex Gentry's Wills*, Emmison, p. 120).

NOTES

1 E.R.O. T/M 313
2 Sun Pol. No. 405197 3.11.1778 (All insurance references in this section per H. E. S. Simmons)
3 R.E. Pol. No. 110233 23.1.1789
4 R.E. Pol. No. 239146 28.7.1808
5 C.C. 4.12.1807
6 E.R.O. D/DE T156. See also D/DU 45/35 (1814)
7 *Essex Poll Book* per G. W. Martin (1830); E.R.O. D/CT 414A (1843)
8 E.S. 7.5.1841
9 C.C. 27.9.1867 per R. Hawksley
10 Per Dr Turner: Notes on Essex windmills, Southend R.L.
11 K. & E.M. 6.12.1831; E.R.O. D/DHi T44
12 E.R.O. D/DHi T44 (1868, but includes leases after 1800)
13 R.E. Pol. No. 216074 8.6.1805
14 See note 12
15 C.C. 17.5.1816. See also E.R.O. D/DDy T3, including will of Wm. Boosey dated April, 1831
16 Later history per Mrs Ambrose, *née* Southgate, of Mill House, Writtle
17 Ledgers in possession of Baker & Sons (Danbury) Ltd

Great Yeldham

Post mill. Stood 180 yards south of the drive to Spencer Grange on the west side of the road to Tilbury juxta Clare. TL 762394

THE MILL SITE, on a rise above the Colne, is today occupied by a small wood. It lies almost opposite and slightly south west of the entrance to the narrow lane marked 'Cart Track' which leads to Little Yeldham parish. The mill appears on all the county maps from Ogilby and Morgan (1678) to Greenwood (1825), and the description of the plot in the tithe apportionment (1842) is 'Windmill Meadow &c' in the occupation of John Offord and ownership of Caroline E. Way.[1] Although a helpful comma is lacking between the words

'Windmill' and 'Meadow', the land tax records for 1844 confirm that the mill was standing at that date. John Pasley Offord, miller and corn dealer, of Great Yeldham, was involved in bankruptcy proceedings in and after 1844, and no further mention of the windmill occurs.[2]

There are a number of 18th-century references. George Pollard, of Great Yeldham, miller, by his will of 1709, proved in 1710, left his freehold mill to his son John, and John, in his turn, directed (will: 1727, proof: 1729) that the windmill be sold after his death.[3] It was later bequeathed by Daniel Stammers, of Sible Heding-ham, miller, to his son Daniel, in accordance with his will proved in 1733.[4] In 1774 Jacob Firmin, miller, of Great Yeldham, insured the windmill 'part timber built' for £280, goods and utensils for £120 and the roundhouse for £30,[5] while in 1785 William Tomlinson, miller, insured the mill and contents for an overall figure of £500, the policy now describing it as 'a windmill and warehouse under it brick and timber built and tiled'.[6] As 'tiled' must refer to the roundhouse roof, we may accept this as a description of a post mill. The only news item located in reference to the windmill comes from 1798, when a thief unwittingly laid a trail of flour from the mill to his retreat, with, for him, regrettable results.[7]

NOTES

1 E.R.O. D/CT 415A. Land tax 1826-32: owned Rev. Lewis Way, occupied 1826 Robt. Eley, 1832 Thos. Stansfield
2 *Lond. Gaz.*, 2.8.1844, 29.4.1845, 15.9.1846, per H. E. S. Simmons
3 E.R.O. D/A MR 8, p. 300, & MR 10, p. 282
4 E.R.O. D/A BR 21, p. 197
5 R.E. Pol. No. 63605 4.8.1744 per H. E. S. Simmons
6 Ibid. No. 95183 9.11.1785. See also E.R.O. D/DU 204/79, 80 (1815)
7 C.C. 25.2.1798

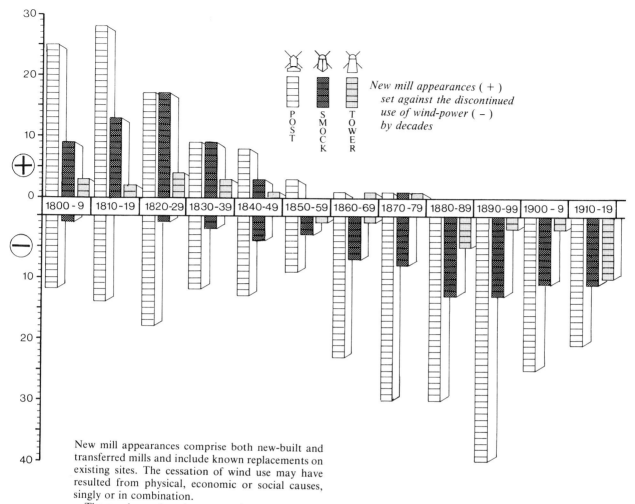

New mill appearances (+)
set against the discontinued
use of wind-power (–)
by decades

New mill appearances comprise both new-built and transferred mills and include known replacements on existing sites. The cessation of wind use may have resulted from physical, economic or social causes, singly or in combination.

The graphs are based on approximate figures and seek to convey an overall impression. The data relate to a closely estimated windmill establishment in 1800 of post: 172; smock: 25; tower: 10; unknown type: 8 (total 215), and in 1900 of 50; 20; 18; 0, respectively (total 88). Note also that the 1900 figures relate to active mills, not derelicts.

Excluded from the graphs are 18 mills of unknown type and non-corn grinding mills. A further 8 mills are excluded from the positive bar graphs as their decade of origin is unknown; in some cases they were replacements on existing sites. Little Laver composite mill is included with the post mills.

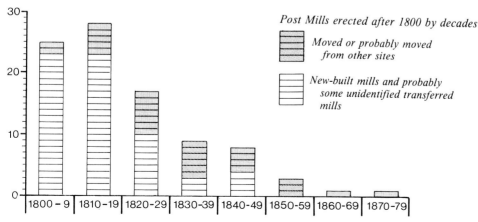

Post Mills erected after 1800 by decades

Moved or probably moved
from other sites

New-built mills and probably
some unidentified transferred
mills

FIG. 44 *Essex Windmills 1800-1920: The Decline*

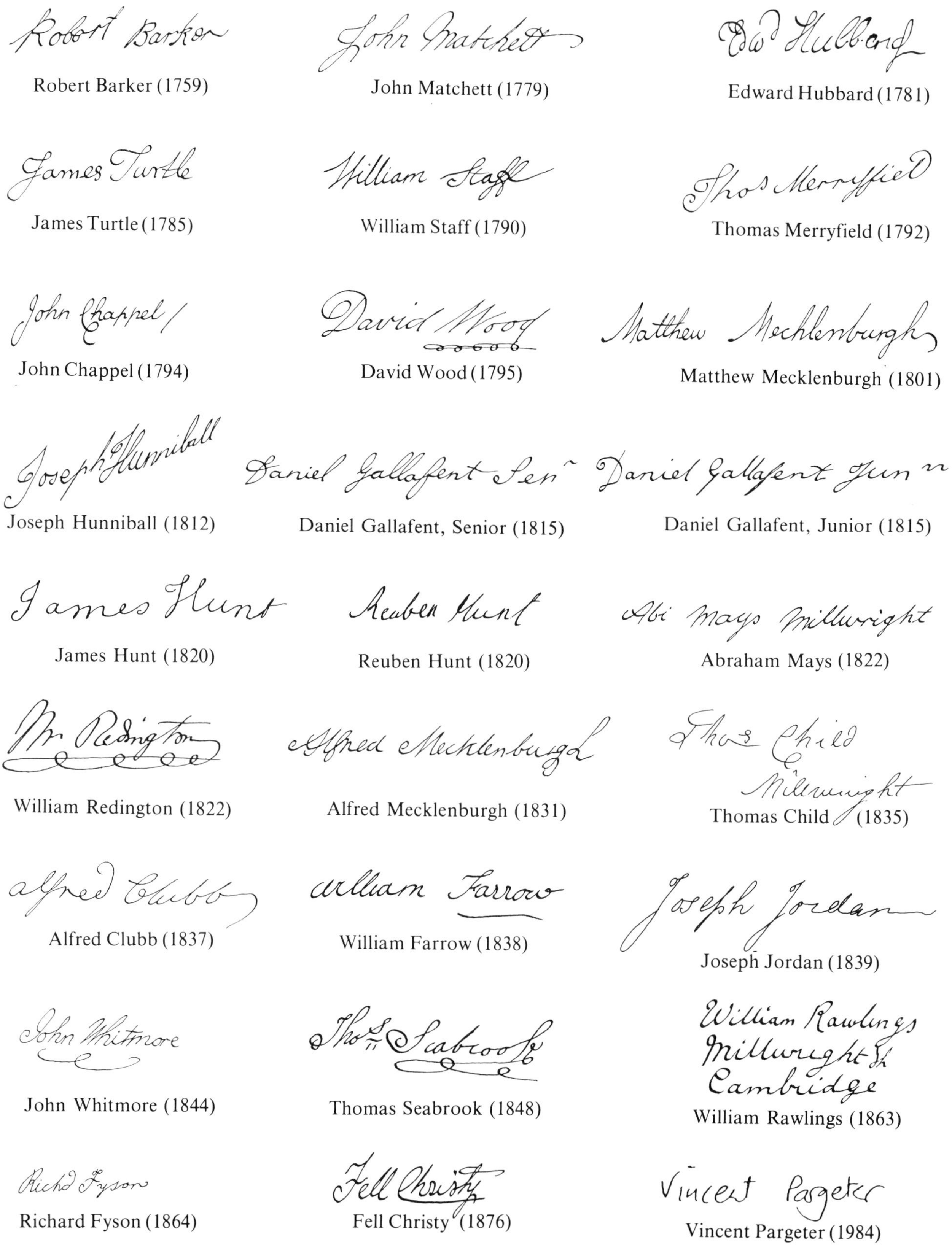

Robert Barker (1759)

John Matchett (1779)

Edward Hubbard (1781)

James Turtle (1785)

William Staff (1790)

Thomas Merryfield (1792)

John Chappel (1794)

David Wood (1795)

Matthew Mecklenburgh (1801)

Joseph Hunniball (1812)

Daniel Gallafent, Senior (1815)

Daniel Gallafent, Junior (1815)

James Hunt (1820)

Reuben Hunt (1820)

Abraham Mays (1822)

William Redington (1822)

Alfred Mecklenburgh (1831)

Thomas Child (1835)

Alfred Clubb (1837)

William Farrow (1838)

Joseph Jordan (1839)

John Whitmore (1844)

Thomas Seabrook (1848)

William Rawlings (1863)

Richard Fyson (1864)

Fell Christy (1876)

Vincent Pargeter (1984)

FIG. 45 *Millwrights' signatures*

APPENDIX G

ESSEX WINDMILLS AFTER 1700:

SIGNIFICANT DATES

c 1700   Evident smock mill standing over the Abbey Mill watermill at West Ham — the first noted smock mill in Essex.

1704   Probable date of erection of Great Bardfield mill, evidently in the form of a brick-built tower mill, and, if so, the first known in Essex.

*c*1724   Map of Middlesex, Essex and Herts. by Warburton, Bland and Smyth records 130 windmills in Essex.

1734   Great Dunmow post mill (at the former Stowles Green) recorded as having two pairs of stones and a roundhouse, in both respects the first such record known for the county of Essex.

*c*1741   Smock mill evidently erected over a watermill which stood on the Roding several hundred yards below Passingford Bridge, in Stapleford Abbots parish.

Mid-18*c*   John Smeaton, engineer, active in introducing improvements in windmill construction and machinery and the use of cast iron in the country at large.

1745   The fantail was invented by Edmund Lee, but was introduced tardily in Essex, winding of mills in the 18*c* being generally effected by tail pole: or by a wheel with chain or rope.

*c*1760   Barling smock mill erected, an early smock mill in S. E. Essex.

1762   Alleged date of erection of Manuden smock mill: perhaps the first known smock mill in N. W. Essex if dating accurate.

1765-70   John Milne patents wire machines for dressing flour — convenient for installation in windmills, and, as also the bolter, widely adopted.

1772   Belchamp Otten post mill recorded as having 2 pairs of stones in the head on the lower floor and 2 flour dressers in the tail.

1772   Spring sails patented by Andrew Meikle, a Scottish millwright.

1777   Map survey of Essex (1772-4) by Chapman and André records 180 windmills: an almost complete representation of those existing.

1784   Albion Steam Mills, Blackfriars, set up (burnt down 1791) — a landmark in milling technology.

1787   Thomas Mead introduces and patents the governor principle for regulating the gap between the stones in relation to wind, and therefore stone, speed.

1788   Earliest known reference in Essex to bevelled gearing in mills.

1795   Approximate peak year for Essex post-mill construction.

1800-1   Movement to institute parish mills for the relief of the poor, e.g. at Great Dunmow.

1805   First 1 in. O.S. map (surv. 1799) records windmills, but with many omissions.

1807   Sir William Cubitt, engineer, introduces his newly invented 'patent sail', an important labour-saving improvement in sail control.

1809   Rayleigh tower mill built with cast-iron wind and upright shafts.

1810   Approximate peak year for Essex smock mill construction.

1812   Approximate peak year for Essex tower mill construction.

1815   Bulmer smock mill described as self-winding.

1815   (from —) Regulators (governors) for control of the gap between the millstones frequently mentioned in sale notices.

1817-18   Introduction of steam by these years at West Thurrock, West Ham (Abbey Mills) and Upminster.

1822   Turnpike Roads Act, Section 127: 'No person shall hereafter erect or cause any windmill to be erected within the distance of 200 yards from any part of any turnpike road.'

1824   First known reference in Essex to three pairs of stones in a post mill (Little Bentley).

1825   Greenwood's map (surv. 1824) marks 224 windmills, but omits approximately one-fifth of those standing.

1830-40:   Standing Essex windmills reach a maximum of some 280.

1835   Highway Act, Section 70; Forbidden to erect 'any windmill within 50 yards from any part of any carriageway.'

1839   First steam railway in Essex: Bethnal Green to Romford.

1840s   Independent steam mills built, e.g. at Great Coggeshall *c* 1842.

1846   Repeal of the Corn Laws has long term repercussions on milling: as the industry expanded at major ports using cheap imported grain, country mills succumbed to the competition.

*c*1850-3   Two composite mills constructed: Little Laver and Purleigh Barns, one certainly and the other apparently adaptations from pre-existing structures.

1859   Introduction at Roxwell of Zahn's 'Patent self-Regulating Wind Engine' for pumping water.

1862-77 survey: First O.S. 6in. records 239 windmills in Essex (see I, 45, & III, 38: West Bergholt).

1866 By 1866 a 'wheel' (annular) sail was in use by Chopping at his post mill in Roxwell (Chopping's own invention). It was stated to drive four pairs of stones — the only record in Essex of four pairs in a post mill.

c 1872 Last corn smock mill in Essex erected at Little Bardfield.

1875 Last post mill erected in Essex at Little Dunmow (on removal from another site).

1875 Trade journal *The Miller* first published.

1877 Last corn-grinding tower mill in Essex erected at White Roding to replace a destroyed post mill.

1877 Formation of the Millers' Benevolent Association.

1877 T. D. Ridley & Sons, Chelmsford (steam) buy 4 patent porcelain rolls, invented by Wegmann of Naples, for turning middlings into flour (*The Miller* 3.12.1877). Stated first sold in England that year (per R. Hawksley).

1878 Inaugural meeting of the Colchester Millers' Association.

1880 Post-1880 mill owners loath to repair windmills suffering extensive storm damage.

1880 Last brick 'tower mill' in Essex (strictly a 'wind-engine') erected at Colne Engaine for pumping sewage.

1880 onwards: gradual introduction of roller milling, but not in windmills.

1886 *Kelly's* directories first specify the use of wind power where relevant against millers' names.

1890-1900 Peak decade for the abandonment of wind power.

1891 Messrs. O. D. & L. Belshams' new roller mill at Maldon described (*The Miller*).

c 1896 Second O.S. 6in. map records 155 windmills.

c 1900 The demise of some windmills, resulting in the loss of a valued landscape feature, arouses publicly expressed regret, backed in a few cases by financial assistance towards reinstatement.

1919-22 Survey by Dr J. Turner of Rochford, of Essex windmills: MS deposited with Southend Reference Library. The first such mill survey known in Essex.

1928 Bocking Church Street post mill preserved by the local council.

1931 The Society for the Protection of Ancient Buildings (founded 1877) establishes a Windmill Section, fostering thereby interest in the preservation of surviving mills.

1932 Publication by the S.P.A.B. of *English Windmills*, Vol. II. The author, Donald Smith, included a major section on Essex windmills.

1935 Stansted windmill given to the care of the local council.

1937-8 Essex County Council assumed responsibility for the upkeep of five windmills of varying character.

1949 Last working windmill in Essex (Terling) stopped turning.

1975 Establishment by Essex County Council of the post of County Millwright.

1983, 30th April: official opening to the public of Aythorpe Roding post mill by Kenneth G. Farries, following restoration to working order by Vincent Pargeter, county millwright.

1983, 13th November: official opening to the public of Mountnessing post mill by Hervey Benham, following restoration to working order by Vincent Pargeter, county millwright, incorporating, also, work by Peter Stenning, of Sussex.

1985 Inaugural meeting of the Essex Mills Group.

APPENDIX H

LIST OF ESSEX WATERMILL SITES

(Research by R. Hawksley)

AUTHOR'S NOTE: Research into windmills inevitably turns up references to watermills, especially in a county such as Essex where both were numerous, and R. Hawksley has additionally investigated Essex watermill sites by documentary study, field research, and reference to the work of other investigators. The last includes the files of the late H. E. S. Simmons, Hervey Benham's publication *Some Essex Watermills* (1976 and 1983), and the standard works of reference on Essex history. Contributions have also been received from Paul Tritton of Great Leighs.

I list all the Essex sites identified by Mr Hawksley; it is arranged in two sections with 1700 as the dividing date, as adopted in the case of the windmills. The sites are given in order proceeding downstream, following first the main river, then the tributaries. Grid references are added when known. Evidence for obscure sites and other brief notes are included where desirable. Hylands Mill, Chelmsford, being turbine-built, is omitted. Domesday mills are included in a separate list.

* indicates that the mill building survives in some form (1981)
** indicates that it contains substantial machinery
Mills known to have been tidal are named in italics

Writtle Mill, Essex, 1931
From Kenneth C. Reid's 2-volume work
" Watermills of the London Countryside"
(Charles Skilton Ltd)

ESSEX WATERMILLS, POST-1700

CAM

GREAT WENDEN. TL 520364
LITTLEBURY. Audley End Mill. TL 523384
SAFFRON WALDEN. Audley End Pumping Mill**. TL 523385
LITTLEBURY*. TL 518395
GREAT CHESTERFORD. (Replaced by turbine mill) TL 504427
ASHDON*. (On a tributary). TL 586412

STOUR

BIRDBROOK. Baythorn(e) Mill*. TL 723430
ASHEN. TL 763443
PENTLOW*. TL 808463
FOXEARTH. Weston Mill. TL 831463
LISTON. TL 856449
BORLEY*. TL 858430
BRUNDON*. TL 864422
GREAT HENNY. TL 880383

WORMINGFORD. TL 933339
BOXTED. TM 012344
LANGHAM. TM 025345
DEDHAM. TM 057334

STOUR (Tributaries)

STURMER. TL 693445
BELCHAMP WALTER*. TL 827404
LAWFORD. Two mills (Shirburn Mills) on map by Warburton, Bland and Smyth (*c.* 1724); buildings of both on 1st, 2nd & 3rd 6in. O.S. maps:
Upper TM 077316
Lower* TM 078317

STORT AND LEA

CLAVERING. Insured in 1791 (R.E.Pol. No. 123657). Site unknown
STANSTED. Bentfield Mill. TL 500246
LITTLE HALLINGBURY**. TL 495169

SHEERING. TL 488144
HARLOW. TL 471128
LATTON. TL 460121
NETTESWELL. Burnt Mill. TL 445113
LITTLE PARNDON. (Replaced by turbine mill). TL 439111
ROYDON*. TL 402102
WALTHAM HOLY CROSS. Two powder mills in series separated by main road:
Upper**. approx. TL 375020
Lower. TQ 377997
WALTHAM HOLY CROSS. Pin Mill. TL 380008
WALTHAM HOLY CROSS. Corn Mill. TL 380007
WALTHAM HOLY CROSS. Blue Mill, Sewardstone TQ 377969

CHINGFORD. TQ 363925
WALTHAMSTOW*. Oil, later copper, last used for pumping. TQ 357885
LEYTON. Temple Mills. TQ 376855
WEST HAM. St Thomas'. TQ 380834
Spillman's, two in parallel after being operated as one mill, latterly single mill for chemicals. TQ 381835
Saines, later *Waterworks:* divided into industrial then corn, on east, and pumping on west. TQ 383837
West Ham, Abbey Mills. TQ 388833
Three Mills: House Mill**, *Clock Mill*** (3rd mill stood after 1700). TQ 384827

STORT AND LEA (Tributaries)

ELSENHAM. TL 533258
BIRCHANGER. TL 517223
HATFIELD BROAD OAK. Insured in 1790 (Sun Pol. No. 571465) Probably TL 543166

RODING

MARGARET RODING. Waples Mill. TL 593104
FYFIELD*. TL 572066
STANFORD RIVERS. Littlebury Mill*. TL 552012
NAVESTOCK. Shonks Mill. TQ 528982
STAPLEFORD ABBOTS. Passingford Bridge Mill* (Turbine). TQ 502975
STAPLEFORD ABBOTS. Lower (18th century) mill. TQ 500975
WOODFORD. Artificial slate factory (above Woodford Bridge) Approx. TQ 420917
WOODFORD. Watermill E.S.E. of church on map *c* 1724 by Warburton, Bland and Smyth. Probably TQ 412901
LITTLE ILFORD. Greenwood's map (1825). TQ 432861
BARKING. TQ 437841

CHELMER

THAXTED. Folly Mill. TL 608288
LITTLE EASTON. Elmbridge Mill*. TL 618239
GREAT DUNMOW. Shown on map by Warburton, Bland and Smyth (*c* 1724) south east of church. TL 631221
FELSTED. Formerly Abchill, now Felsted Mill*. TL 671196
FELSTED. Hartford End Mill*, partly in Gt. Waltham TL 685174
GREAT WALTHAM. Howe Street. TL 695151
GREAT WALTHAM. Langleys Mill (name of manor). TL 698138

LITTLE WALTHAM. TL 709125
LITTLE WALTHAM. Croxton's Mill*. TL 712115
BROOMFIELD. TL 713103
CHELMSFORD. Bishop's Hall Mill. TL 709078
CHELMSFORD. Moulsham Mill*. TL 715062
SPRINGFIELD** (partly in Chelmsford). TL 713071
SPRINGFIELD. Barnes Mill*. TL 726065
SPRINGFIELD. Sandford Mill. TL 740061
LITTLE BADDOW. TL 758084
LITTLE BADDOW. Paper Mill (in Dengie Hundred). TL 775090
WOODHAM WALTER. Hoe Mill. TL 807081
MALDON. Beeleigh Mill. TL 840082

CHELMER (Tributaries)

TILTY**. TL 600267
LITTLE EASTON. Pumping Mill. TL 603237
ROXWELL*. TL 641084
WRITTLE*. TL 687060
WRITTLE. Much Mill. TL 690072
BOREHAM. TL 740093
DANBURY. Overshot Mill (destroyed by fire, 1710: E.R.O. Q/SBb 49). TL 702035
TERLING**. Pumping mill on corn mill site. TL 771147
TERLING. Little Mill (shown on map of *c*1774 — E.R.O. T/P 87 — on a tributary of a tributary). TL 771143
HATFIELD PEVEREL. TL 783115
WOODHAM WALTER. Blue Mills*. TL 812076
STEBBING. Bran End Mill*. TL 652251
STEBBING. Town Mill**. TL 659240

BLACKWATER

LITTLE BARDFIELD. On 1755 plan (E.R.O. T/M 253). TL 671311
GREAT BARDFIELD**. TL 680311
WETHERSFIELD. Wethersfield Mill** with Overshot Mill in parallel. TL 720296
WETHERSFIELD. Codham Mill**. TL 734282
BOCKING. Church Street Mill. TL 756256
Bradford Mill*. TL 763244
Strait's Mill. TL 770244
STISTED**. TL 791245
PATTISWICK. Blackwater Mill. TL 808230
LITTLE COGGESHALL. West Mill (two occupations at one time: woollen and corn). TL 830221
GREAT COGGESHALL. Tye Mill. TL 849225
LITTLE COGGESHALL. Abbey Mill**. TL 856222
LITTLE COGGESHALL. Pointwell Mill*. TL 854214
FEERING. Feeringbury Mill (Old Mill on first O.S. 6in.). TL 865211
FEERING. Rye Mill. TL 868199
KELVEDON. Easterford Mill**. TL 866191
KELVEDON. Grey's Mill*. TL 861182
GREAT BRAXTED. TL 851169
LITTLE BRAXTED*. TL 833148
WITHAM. Blue Mill**. TL 830131
WICKHAM BISHOPS. TL 824117
LANGFORD*. TL 857091
HEYBRIDGE. TL 855081

BLACKWATER (Tributaries)

FINCHINGFIELD. Mill on Warburton, Bland and Smyth (c 1724) on way to Spains Hall from village. Probably TL 683335

FINCHINGFIELD. Near Brook Hall, which is shown on 1st O.S. 6in. map. Was a tannery. TL 686327

BRADWELL-NEXT-COGGESHALL. TL 818223

GREAT COGGESHALL. Mill building* marked 'Brewery' on 1st. O.S. 6in. map. TL 847227

GREAT COGGESHALL. Gravel Factory (Pigot, 1839). TL 849226

GREAT COGGESHALL. Squitt Mill. TL 857224

RIVENHALL. TL 820189

GREAT TOTHAM. On 1790 map stating 'mill now disused' (E.R.O. D/DU 123/39/2). TL 855113

BRAIN

RAYNE. Rayne Mill. TL 728240

BRAINTREE. On Greenwood's map (1825). TL 758226

BRAINTREE. Meg's Mill. TL 765227

CRESSING. Bulford Mill*. TL 773204

WITHAM. Chipping Hill Mill. TL 816154

WITHAM. Town Mill or Newland Mill. TL 816146

BRAIN (Tributaries)

BLACK NOTLEY. TL 767208

WHITE NOTLEY. TL 785184. The wheel is still there.

COLNE

SIBLE HEDINGHAM. Alderford Mill**. TL 784339

SIBLE HEDINGHAM. Hull's Mill.* TL 793332

HALSTEAD. Box Mill. TL 809313

HALSTEAD. Town Mill*. TL 813303

HALSTEAD. Langley Mill*. TL 834298

COLNE ENGAINE. Ford Mill. TL 846298

COLNE ENGAINE. Name not known but was 'middle' mill. TL 855298

EARLS COLNE. Colne Ford Mill (Priory Mill). TL 866289

EARLS COLNE. Chalkney Mill*. TL 875284

WAKES COLNE. Wakes Colne Mill**. TL 892284

ALDHAM. Ford Street Mill. TL 919271

FORDHAM. Fordham or Lower Mill. TL 928272

WEST BERGHOLT. Cooksbridge Mill. TL 948271. There were once two in parallel.

WEST BERGHOLT. Newbridge Mill. TL 958267

LEXDEN. Oil Mill. TL 973255

COLCHESTER. Middle Mill. TL 998257

COLCHESTER. East Mill*. TM 007253

COLCHESTER. Hythe Mill. Existed 1707. (E.R.O. D/DE1 T357). TM 016247

COLNE (Tributaries)

HALSTEAD. Greenstead Green. TL 825277

HALSTEAD. Bullock Mill. TL 836282

PEBMARSH. TL 853331

COLNE ENGAINE. Overshot Mill**. TL 860299

LEXDEN. A fulling mill, converted to corn. TL 973255

ARDLEIGH. Spring Valley Mill**. TM 038278

ARDLEIGH. Wallswood Mill. TM 035270

COLCHESTER. Crockleford Mill*. TM 031262

COLCHESTER. Bourne or Bourne Pond Mill**. TM 005239

COLCHESTER. Cannock Mill*. TM 011239

COLCHESTER. Hull Mill. TM 016239

COLCHESTER. A fulling mill on the south boundary. TM 023219

ALRESFORD. Mill marked on revised first O.S. 1in. only. TM 072200

ELMSTEAD. Mill shown on Greenwood's map (1825). TM 041219

ROMAN RIVER

LITTLE STANWAY. Stood on the Copford boundary TL 936239

GREAT STANWAY. TL 955215

LITTLE BIRCH. On a tributary of Roman River TL 956212

LAYER-DE-LA-HAYE*. TL 980206

FINGRINGHOE. Roman River Mill*. TM 030205

GREAT BENTLEY. TM 109188

THORRINGTON**. TM 082194

ST OSYTH. TM 115155

MISCELLANEOUS SITES

SOUTH WEALD. Brook Street TQ 579930

SOUTH OCKENDON. Under windmill TQ 604831

PURFLEET (West Thurrock parish). Stood 9 chains above Mardyke estuary E. of main stream TQ 548786

CORRINGHAM. Western site, but not known precisely

CORRINGHAM. Formerly Fobbing, when Fobbing Old Mill. On Chapman and André (1777) as 'Island Mill' TQ 740825

RAYLEIGH. On Greenwood's map (1825) TQ 805910

ROCHFORD. Fresh water site TQ 874905

LITTLE STAMBRIDGE. TQ 888902

BATTLESBRIDGE. In Rawreth parish TQ 781946

GREAT TOTHAM. On Blackwater estuary: Barrow Hill Mill TL 875078

GOLDHANGER. Pumping Mill. Shown on 1805 O.S. 1in. map TL 912093

PELDON: Strood Mill TM 016153

TENDRING. Crow Mill TM 151232

WALTON-ON-THE-NAZE. TM 255226

RAMSEY. TM 212298

MISTLEY. TM 615315

ESSEX WATERMILLS, PRE-1700
Tithe dates refer to the apportionment

CAM

NEWPORT. Mill in 1271 (Cal. Inquis. Vol. I, No. 808). Approx. TL 520360

SAFFRON WALDEN. Abbey Mill, c1142. (E.R. Vol. XLV, p. 76). See also in E.R.O.: Saffron Walden and its Environs, D. Monteith, 1958. (Typescript thesis)

SAFFRON WALDEN. Tithe, 1844: includes part of Mill Hole (Field) which adjoins in Littlebury, evidently the mill in Manhall manor (mediaeval). (Thesis as above, in E.R.O.) Approx. TL 519405

LITTLE CHESTERFORD. Mill, etc., 1531. (Feet of Fines, Vol. IV, p. 180)

STOUR

LAWFORD. Site of mill named Crick Mill mentioned in 1750. (E.R.O. D/DU 479)

STOUR (Tributaries)

BELCHAMP WATER. Tithe, 1847: Mill Meadow TL 815395
GREAT HENNY, Loshes Mill. On plan, 1600. (E.R.O. D/DU 372/9a) TL 872370
ALPHAMSTONE. Reference in 1303. (Cal. Inquis. Vol. IV, No. 154). Tithe, 1840: Gt. & Lt. Mill Fields TL 883357
BURES HAMLET. Reference on plan c1600. (E.R.O. T/M 59) TL 897338

STORT AND LEA

FARNHAM. Reference in 1500. (Morant, Vol. II, p. 625). Tithe, 1842: Mill Field Approx. TL 485241
BIRCHANGER. Mill existed 1324. (B.M. Add. MS. 6164, p, 188). Tithe, 1840: Gt. & Lt. Mill Fields TL 500233
GREAT HALLINGBURY. Wallbury Mill, 1555. (Feet of Fines, Vol. V, p. 79)
SHEERING. Lower Mill, in Sheering Hall manor. Apparently burnt down c1401, later rebuilt; in 1431 ruinous. (V.C.H. Vol. VIII, p. 246)
LITTLE PARNDON. Upper Mill. 'early in 13c. Rt. of Parndon agreed with Waltham Abbey, owner of Netteswell manor mill, to move his own mill 41 perches further west.' (V.C.H. Vol. VIII, p. 225) Approx. TL 443113
WEST HAM. Stratford: a mill above Abbey Mill. Reference in the 12c. (V.C.H. Vol. VI, p. 89)

STORT AND LEA (Tributaries)

STANSTED. Stansted Hall manor (Uttlesford Hundred). Mill in 1293. (Morant Vol. II, p. 557)
GREAT HALLINGBURY. Mill of manor of that name, 1275. Fulling mill in 1571. Probably at site of Gt. & Lt. Mill Fields on tithe, 1840. (V.C.H. Vol. VIII. p. 121)
HATFIELD BROAD OAK. Place name on 1624 plan: Mill Stanes 7 fur. N. of church. (E.R.O. D/DQ 14/191) TL 545180

RODING

LITTLE CANFIELD. Disused mill pond on N. side of Stane Street on 1590 plan (E.R.O. D/Ht M20) TL 586213
GREAT CANFIELD. Watermill ruinous, 1386 (Cal. Inquis. Vol. V, No. 17). Tithe, 1847: Mill Mead TL 595178
HIGH RODING. Mill, 1562 (Morant Vol. II, p. 466) Tithe, 1841: Plot 359, Mill Field TL 582162
AYTHORPE RODING. Tithe, 1846: Plot 255, Mill Mead TL 582152
BEAUCHAMP RODING. Tithe, 1843: Mills Mead S. of bridge on boundary TL 589087
CHIPPING ONGAR. Mill, 1372 (V.C.H. Vol. IV, p. 166)
GREENSTEAD near Ongar. Mill, 1349 (V.C.H. Vol. IV, p. 59)
NAVESTOCK. Tithe, 1840: Part of Millmead, almost 1 mile E. by N. of Passingford Bridge Approx. TQ 516980
NAVESTOCK. Curtis Mill. Tithe place name TQ 511972
THEYDON GARNON. Reference to a messuage called Garnesmell, 1500, indicates watermill already gone. Garnish Mill called a farm, 1713, and a farm and mansion house, 1717 (All E.A.T. Vol. VI, p. 120) TQ 477978
LOUGHTON. Mediaeval reference (V.C.H. Vol. IV, p. 116)

RODING (Tributaries)

MORETON. Tithe, 1840: Plot 38, Mill Mead. See also V.C.H. Vol. IV, p. 130 TL530070
STONDON MASSEY. Site near Mill Field Bottom, High Ongar, on 1751 plan (E.R.O. D/DCw P 46) Approx. TL 576018
GREAT ILFORD. Mill Ground on plan c1725 (E.R.O. D/DSa 151) Formerly Barking parish. See also E.R.O. D/A ER 15 p. 122 Approx. TQ 446888

CHELMER

LITTLE DUNMOW. Mill c1600 (E.R.O. D/DYu 1) Approx. TL 643206
HATFIELD PEVEREL. Ancient site marked on 1765 map of proposed navigation (E.R.O. D/DRa 03) TL 792093
ULTING. Old site marked on 1765 navigation plan, as above TL 812085

CHELMER (Tributaries)

FELSTED. Tithe, 1845: Plot 800, Mill Pond Field, near Leighs Priory on river Ter TL 185070
LITTLE EASTON. Tithe, 1839: Mill Field TL 610240
CHIGNALL ST. JAMES. Pengy Mill (Benham p. 34) TL 660090
ROXWELL. Place name on plan, 1666 (E.R.O. D/DXa 21). Mill Pond on N.E. of Tye Hall TL 633082
MARGARETTING. Fristling Mill, rebuilt 1590 (Benham, p. 33) TL 681020
GOOD EASTER. Tithe, 1841: Plot 362, Mill Hoppet TL 641111

BLACKWATER

FINCHINGFIELD. 1295 reference in Ashwell Hall manor (Cal. Inquis. Vol. III. No. 343). Tithe, 1842: Mill Field TL 693311
SHALFORD. Mill on plan, 1603 (E.R.O. D/DSm p. 6). Near Water Hall TL 730291
KELVEDON. Mill in Church Hall manor in 1294 (*Kelvedon and its Antiquities*, B. L. Kentish, 1974, pp. 13-14)

BLACKWATER (Tributaries)

FINCHINGFIELD. Tithe, 1842: Plot 645, 8 Acre Mill Field to N.E. of Mill Farm on Stambourne road Approx. TL 705356
WETHERSFIELD. Tithe, 1843: place name near S. windmill site, E. of the Braintree road TL 717305

BRAIN

RAYNE. Upper or South Mill. Tithe, 1839, place names cover a large area
BRAINTREE. Close to Clapbridge Farm (tithe, 1847), and Clapbridge Mill was derelict in 1684 (E.R.O. D/DCw T22)

COLNE

CASTLE HEDINGHAM. Place name. (Benham, p. 74). Plan,

1592, shows mill. (E.R.O. D/DMh). Approx. TL 779354

HALSTEAD. Ancient site in Hepworth Hall manor (above Hepworth Hall). (Morant, Vol. II, p. 257)

CHAPPEL. Tithe, 1843: place name. Site indicated on 1675 plan by place name (E.R.O. D/DWe 2) TL 906275

COLCHESTER. Ancient site in Colchester (North Mill). (Benham, p. 93). TM 074247

WIVENHOE. Rental, *c*1830, with Salt Mill as place name. (E.R.O. D/DEt M27). Evidently former tide mill

COLNE (Tributaries)

TOPPESFIELD. Tithe, 1841: Plots 119, 99, Gt. & Lt. Mill Field; mill may have stood in what was formerly Finchingfield TL 714358

GOSFIELD. Tithe, 1843: place name on Halstead boundary TL 793291

ELMSTEAD. Ancient site on the Harwich road. (Benham, p. 3) Presumably at TM 074247

ELMSTEAD. Tithe, 1844: place name Mill Field points to site in Frating. Morant gives ancient watermill in Alresford manor, which extended into Frating TM 076221

ROMAN RIVER

GREAT TEY. Agreement re watermill, 1384. (E.R.O. D/DU 646/82). Grant of land called Stancroft near watermill, 1316. (D/DU 656/17, 19)

ROMAN RIVER (Tributary)

LAYER MARNEY. Tithe, 1840: Mill Pond Meadow. TL 929171

MISCELLANEOUS

ROMFORD. Site at S. end of Raphael Park. (V.C.H. Vol. VII, pp. 60, 75) TQ 519895

ROMFORD. Mill in 1670. (E.R.O. D/DMs 036). Site unknown, but lay in the direction towards Hornchurch village

HORNCHURCH. Mill, 1247, in Dovers manor, evidently a tide mill. (V.C.H. Vol. VII, p. 33)

RAINHAM (north). Building and mill pond in 1575 plan. (E.R.O. T/M 145) TQ 535836

RAINHAM (south). In South Hall manor, 1270. Evidently a tide mill. (V.C.H. Vol. VII, p. 135)

WEST HORNDON. Place name; building on plan, 1598. (E.R.O. D/DP P 5). See *Essex Journal*, Vol. I, No. I, Jan., 1966 TQ 627898

NORTH OCKENDON. Tithe, 1843: plot 199, Mill Wood TQ 577827

AVELEY. Mill in 1360. (Cal. Inquis. Vol. X, No. 614). See also V.C.H. Vol. VIII, p. 10

GRAYS THURROCK. Mill, 1228, 'near the bridge towards the Thames'. Perhaps the watermill of 1335. (V.C.H. Vol. VIII, p. 42)

MUCKING. Reference in Morant Vol. I, p. 236, to mill at time of dissolution of the monasteries

HADLEIGH. On Sea Reach, mill in 1577. (E.R.O. D/DU 514/29/21)

PRITTLEWELL. Mill apparently destroyed by the sea *c*1327. (B.M. Add. MS. 6159, 6160)

LITTLE WAKERING. 16*c*. mill. (Benham, p. 107) TQ 954886

SUTTON. Mill in 1313. (Cal. Inquis. Vol. V, No. 1460)

GREAT STAMBRIDGE. In 1659 place name 'Old Mill'. (E.R.O. D/DO 560/2/6). Probably the mill of 1222. (Feet of Fines, Vol. I, p. 61)

GREAT BURSTEAD. Kemp's Mill on Crouch in plan, 1593. E.R.O. D/DP P 3) TQ 685912

BURNHAM. Mill in 1328. (Cal. Inquis. Vol. VII, No. 160)

BRADWELL-ON-SEA. Mill in Down Hall manor under Henry III. (Morant Vol. I, p. 376)

GOLDHANGER. Mill in 1270. (Feet of Fines, Vol. I, p. 275)

TOLLESBURY. Tide mill on Norden's map (1594) on a creek of the estuary

EAST MERSEA. Mill in 1282. (Cal. Inquis. Vol. II, No. 432)

LITTLE BENTLEY. Tithe, 1841: Gt. & Lt. Mill Fields adjoining Holland Brook. Approx. TM 124263

KIRBY-LE-SOKEN. 17c. reference to 'Birchall mills in Kirby'. (Benham, p. 111)

THORPE-LE-SOKEN. Mill at Landermere, 1222. (Wood: *Hist. of Thorpe-le-Soken*, p. 12). New watermill — almost certainly at Landermere — in 1493. (Wood, p. 22)

BEAUMONT. Plan, 1688: Mill Field. (E.R.O. D/DBm P 5) TM 190240

LITTLE OAKLEY. Mill in 1551. (Cal. Patent Rolls, Vol. IV, p. 107). Plan, 1798: Mill Marsh or 19 Acres. (E.R.O. D/DRw P 1).

BRADFIELD. 'Le dam de Bradfield mill' mentioned 1392. (Benham, 2nd edition, 1983, p. 6)

WIX. House called Fresh Mill, alias Pond Hall, 1805. (E.R.O. D/DA T562). Site probably on Bradfield boundary at TM 148297

WRABNESS. Mill in 1263. (Cal. Inquis. Vol. I, No. 583). Place name in 1282. (Cal. Inquis. Vol. II, No 432). Tithe, 1842: Mill Field proves it was a fresh water site TM 165311

ESSEX DOMESDAY MILLS

(A.D. 1086)

From VCH, checked with Darby & Versey, *Domesday Gazetteer*, and using Morant to identify manors within a parish, which VCH vol. 1 seldom does. Domesday order used, except where there is some reason to put entries together. — R. H.

N. BENFLEET. (apparently) ½
S. BENFLEET. now (i.e. 1086) ½
WITHAM
    Newland manor 1
    Powers Hall manor 1
HAVERING. now 1
GT. CHESTERFORD 2 (but then says there was land in that manor in Cambs. inc. 1 mill)
BIRCHANGER. 1 (perhaps Newport N. of bridge)
SHALFORD. 1
FINCHINGFIELD.
    King's manor 1
    Manor held of Count of Boulogne 1

WETHERSFIELD.
  Picot's manor 1066 & afterwards 1 m, now 2
  Stanard's land 1
STANWAY. 1
LEXDEN. now 2
W. BERGHOLT.
  Goding's land 1 m 1066, now none
  Land seized by Richard de Clare ½ m 1066, now none
  W Bergholt manor 1
WRITTLE. (inc. Roxwell) 1 m 1066, now 2
BRIGHTLINGSEA. now 1
LAWFORD. 1 m 1066, now 2
NEWPORT. 2
GT. SAMPFORD. 1
LT. COGGESHALL. (Canterbury cathedral's manor) 1
COGGESHALL. (Count of Boulogne's manor) 1
STISTED. 1
LAWLING. 1 (in Latchingdon)
RAMSDEN BELLHOUSE now 1
WANSTEAD. now 1 (vol. 6 says probably at Lt. Ilford)
BOCKING. 1
LAYER MARNEY. now 1
BRAINTREE. now 1
CHELMSFORD. 1
WICKHAM BISHOPS. 1
CLACTON. now 1
COLCHESTER.
  Bishop of London now 1
  Leflet 1
  St Peter's church 1
CORRINGHAM. 1
LT. BRAXTED. 1
TILLINGHAM. now 1
HEYBRIDGE. 1
THE SOKENS. now 2
KELVEDON.
  Church Hall manor 1
  Felix Hall manor 1
Hugh de Montfort's encroachment 2 ms 1066, now 1 (probably in or near Kelvedon)
W. HAM. 9 ms 1066, now 8 (entered twice because of joint ownership) (Note says inc. Temple Ms, but vol. 6 is inconsistent)
LEYTON.
  Leyton manor 1 m 1066, now none
  Ruckholt manor 1 m 1066, taken away under King Wm
  Ralph Baynard's manor 1 (vol. 6 says m in W Ham, evidently near boundary; perhaps same as Ruckholt). NB. Lasted too long to be Temple Ms.
FEERING. 3
KELVEDON HATCH, now 1
MOULSHAM. (Chelmsford) 1
WALTHAM ABBEY. 1 m 1066, now 3
WOODFORD. 1 m 1066, now none
MUCKING. now 1
BARKING. 2
HOCKLEY.
  Hockley Hall manor 1
  Lower Hockley Hall now 1
  Other holdings 1
TOLLESBURY. (St Mary's manor) now 1
HADSTOCK. 1 m 1066, now none. N.B. Hadstock M (now Linton M) was sometimes said to be in Essex.

LITTLEBURY. 4
STRETHALL. 1
BENTON HALL. now 1 (in Witham)
HARLOW. 1
WRABNESS. now 1
GOOD EASTER. now 1
TAKELEY (Warish Hall manor) 1066 & afterwards 1 m, now ½
LT. CANFIELD. now 1
BIRCHANGER. near Bishop's Stortford 1
FELSTED. 2
GT. BADDOW. 1
VANGE. now 1
GT. STAMBRIDGE. 1
PATCHING HALL. 1 (in Broomfield)
MOULSHAM. (Chelmsford hundred) 1. Note says perhaps in Gt. Leighs (Witham hundred); Darby & Versey say definitely so.
THORRINGTON. now 1
WHITE NOTLEY. (Alvric's manor) now 2
BLACK NOTLEY. (Walter's manor) now 1
(?BLACK) NOTLEY. (Jn, son of Ernuciun's manor) 1
RIVENHALL. 1 m 1066, now ½ of it taken by Gt. Braxted
GT. BRAXTED. now ½
LANGENHOE. 1
LAYER DE LA HAYE. now 1
CLARET HALL. 1 (in Ashen)
BOXTED. 1 m 1066, now none
STANFORD RIVERS. 1
BOREHAM. now 1
LT. BARDFIELD. 1
GT. YELDHAM. 1 m 1066
"GERHAM". (Darby & Versey say Yeldham) now 1
SAFFRON WALDEN. 1 1/3
MANHALL. 2/3 (in Little Chesterford)
QUICKSBURY 1 (in Sheering)
HALSTEAD.
  Hepworth Hall manor 2
  Other holdings 1
POOLEY. (now Hunt's Hall) now 1 (in Pebmarsh)
THAXTED. 1 m 1066, now 2
GT. DUNMOW. manor now 1
LT. DUNMOW. manor now 1
DUNMOW. (land held of Swein) now 1
GESTINGTHORPE. 1 m 1066, now none
ASHEN. now 1
LANGHAM. 1 m 1066, now 2
GT. BARDFIELD.
  Richard de Clare's manor 2
  Land seized by Richard de Clare now 1
LT. SAMPFORD. 1 m 1066, now none
EASTWOOD. now 1
ROCHFORD. 1
PLUMBEROW. now 1 (in Hockley)
PUDSEY. now 1 (in Canewdon)
LT. HALLINGBURY.
  Lt. Hallingbury manor now ½
  Monksbury manor now ½
  Note says evidently new shared m.
CLAVERING 1 m 1066
HORKESLEY. said to be in Swein's demesne, with 1 m, but then says sub-tenant now has 1 m.
STAPLEFORD TAWNEY. 1

ELMSTEAD. 1
LINDSELL. now 1
LEIGHS. (Chelmsford hundred)
   Manor held of Eudo Dapifer now 1
   Manor held of Geoffrey de Mandeville 1
GT. HALLINGBURY. 1
RAYNE.
   Rayne Hall manor 1
   Old Hall manor 1
FAULKBOURNE. 1 m 1066, now none
GREENSTEAD. near Ongar now 1
STEBBING.
   Hy de Ferreriis's manor 1/2 after Conquest, now none
   Ranulf Peverel's manor 1 m 1066, 1 1/2 after Conquest, now 2
WOODHAM FERRERS. now 1
S. OCKENDON. now 1
GT. WALTHAM.
   Geoffrey de Mandeville's demesne 2
   Roger's manor 1
WALTHAM. (Chelmsford hundred) (manor held of Rt, son of Corbutio) 1
BROOMFIELD. 1
CUTON HALL. 1 (in Springfield)
MOZE. 1 m 1066, now none
GT. OAKLEY. now 1
BERNERS RODING. 1
BIGODS. 1 (in Gt. Dunmow)
CHINGFORD.
"LEGA" (Winstree hundred) now 1. VCH suggests "Lega" might be an error for "Legra" (Layer).
STANSTED HALL. (Uttlesford hundred) 1
SHORTGROVE. 1 m 1066, now none (in Newport)
GT WENDEN. 1 m 1066 & after Conquest, now 2
BENTFIELD. 1
WORMINGFORD. now 1
WIVENHOE. now 1
LT. BIRCH. 1
CULVERTS. 1 (in Boreham)
COLD NORTON. now 1
WOODHAM WALTER. 1 m 1066, now 2
"CURLAI". 1 m 1066, now none. Note suggests it was in Woodham Walter, which had annexed its m; Darby & Versey say is Curling Tye Green, Woodham Walter. N.B. "Old m", Ulting, on navigation map, appears to be this site.
PENTLOW. 1
BURNHAM. now 1
LT. BADDOW. (Chelmsford hundred) 1
RAMSEY. now 1
LANGFORD. 1
HATFIELD PEVEREL. (Ranulf Peverel's demesne) 2 ms 1066, now 1, but then says sub-tenant had 1 m throughout.
BLUNTS HALL. 1 (in Witham)
TERLING. 1 m 1066, now 2
FAIRSTEAD. now 1
LT. MALDON. 1
DEBDEN. 1
GT. HENNY. 1
SPRINGFIELD HALL. 1
ST. OSYTH 1 (apparently St Clere's Hall manor)

GT. CANFIELD. 1
CASTLE HEDINGHAM. 1 m in demesne 1066, now none; 1 m tenanted throughout
SIBLE HEDINGHAM. now 1
EARLS COLNE. manor 2
COLNE ENGAINE.
   Colne Engaine manor 1
   Over Hall manor 1
WAKES COLNE. (Wakes Hall manor) 1
COLNE. (land seized by Richard de Clare) now 1
SHEERING 1
LT. PARNDON. 1
LOUGHTON. 1
THEYDON BOIS. (Peter de Valognes's manor) 1
THEYDON. (Wm, son of Constantine's manor) 1. Vol. 4 suggests Theydon Garnon wrm.
ROYDON. 1
NAZEING & EPPING. 1 m between them 1066, now none
BAYTHORN. 1
STEEPLE BUMPSTEAD. 1
STURMER. 1
MESSING. now 1
DEDHAM. 1 m 1066, now 2
LT. MAPLESTEAD. 1
FYFIELD. now 1
LT. EASTON. 1
LT. CHESTERFORD. 1
WESTON. 1 (in Foxearth)
STANSTEAD HALL. (Halstead) 1 m 1066, now 2
MOUNT BURES. 1
LISTON.
   Geoffrey Talbot's manor 1/2
   Ilbodo's manor 1/2
   Note says evidently partition not long before Conquest
ARDLEIGH. (probably Bovills manor) now 2
FORDHAM. 1
BRUNDON. 1
CHIGWELL HALL. 1, & then says in 1066 there was a m on land held by 6 free men, now gone.
GT. EASTON. 1
"SCIDDINCHOU". 1 m 1066, now none. VCH says definitely Manningtree, Darby & Versey say Sheddon or Sharing, now Old Hall (in Mistley).
WALTHAMSTOW. 1
WIGBOROUGH. 1 m 1066, now none
LT. ILFORD. now 1 (manor wholly S of Essex Great Road)
ELSENHAM. 1
PITSEA. 1 m 1066 (& probably means still)
WIGGEPET. (now Rockells) 1 (in Arkesden, Elmdon, & Wenden)
PLESINGHO. 1 m 1066 (in Willingale)
"HASINGHAM". (Lexden hundred) 1
GREENSTEAD. (Colchester) King's land 1 m 1066, now 1/2, 1/4 being held by Count of Boulogne, and 1/4 by Jn. son of Waleram

R. H. states there were very few mills in waterless manors in Essex.
Evidently nearly all the mills listed in Domesday Survey *in Essex* were water-driven and many reappear in later lists.

CORRIGENDA

VOLUME I, p. 28. Rettendon mill destroyed by fire at end of 1872; press report is in 1873.

I, p. 36, col. 1, lines 4, 5; col. 2, lines 15, 16; II, 71, under Stock tower mill, lines 11, 12; II 80, 2nd paragraph, line 17: there is evidence of one drive change only — from over to underdrift.

I, p. 41. In the second mill list, Asheldham should bear the grid letters TL (not TQ).

I, p. 47. 1st paragraph, Beam River Mill, Dagenham, had one projection on the O.S.: 1:2500.

I, p. 58, note 32. For T86 read 786.

I, p. 79, col. 2, line 9. For 'fell' read 'full'.

I, p. 83. 'The History of Mr Polley', 1st paragraph. Polley was, in fact, tenant at the north mill, presumably in conjunction with Royce.

I, p. 96. The 1299 Compotus. The discrepancy between the Latin (vii s. ii d.) and the translation (8s. 2d.) in reference to the enlargement of the mill mound occurs in the 1932 article (see note 29); in fact 8s. 2d. is correct.

I, p. 100, col. 2, 3rd paragraph, line 5. For Vol. IV read Vol. V.

I, p. 102, Note 24 is misprinted 14.

I, p. 103, Arkesden. 6 acres *or* Mill Field. (probably relates to mound listed on p. 92.)

I, p. 103. Aveley. W. R. Powell, V.C.H. *Essex* states (1983): D/DL T1/192 (1341) seems incorrect. That document is in fact dated 1373 and does not mention a mill.

I, p. 104. Danbury. The easting in the grid reference should read 775 (not 765).

I, p. 105. Farnham. R. Hawksley revises his contribution as follows: Enclosure map *c.* 1826 (E.R.O. Q/RDc 24) show Mills Field as including Mill Field Common, so there was evidently a watermill site at *c.* 485241.

I, p. 107 Prittlewell: delete the N.G.R. (871863).

I, p. 107 Stifford, last line: T32 should read T38.

I, p. 107 Takeley: N.G.R. 557223 should read 557233.

I, p. 112 Total of mills, 1st 6 in: 239 (West Bergholt omitted; it did not appear on later maps).

VOLUME II, p. 9 List of Illustrations. No 74: for 'Ramsey' read 'Aythorpe Roding'.

II, p. 9. List of Illustrations. No. 106b: for 'Ockenden' read 'Ockendon'.

II, p. 28, col. 1. Under Sails, for 'pitch' read 'Memel'.

II, p. 34. col. 1. Line 23 of the long paragraph, for 'sheer' read 'shear'.

II, p. 41. Plate 74. For 'Ramsey' read 'Aythorpe Roding' (in reference to the bolter).

II, p. 61. End of 1st paragraph: Fig. 37 subsequently revised to Fig. 39.

II, p. 71. Stock. See under 2nd entry, Volume I Corrigenda, above. Also II, p. 80, 2nd paragraph, line 17.

II, p. 73, Fig. 17B. The worm on the fan spindle and the gear ring engaged should be a pair of bevel gears.

II p. 77, col. 1, line 10: The 2nd Roman numeral should read 'II'.

II, p. 81. Stansted footnotes 1 and 2: D/DEf B5 should read D/DHf B5.

II, p. 84, col. 2, long paragraph, line 9 up: for 'best' read 'better'

II, p. 101, col. 1. Under 'SIGNIFICANT REMAINS' add between Lt. Dunmow and Halstead: P. High Easter. Substructure enclosed in a residence.

II, p. 113. Under Widford, Stone Floor, line 4, for 4″ 6 read 4′ 6″.

II, p. 123, col. 2, lines 3 and 4 under the capacity table: '504 lb, or 4½ cwt.' should read '252 lb, or 2¼ cwt.'

II, p. 126, col. 1, line 15, under April-Sept. 1981, Mountnessing, for 'rabetted' read 'rabbetted'.

VOLUME III, p. 15. Ardleigh, mill (2). The road, formerly the A604, is now the A137.

III, p. 19, Asheldham. The N.G.R. lettered square should read TL, not TQ.

III, p. 38. West Bergholt. In the N.B. under the heading, for Fig. 35 read Fig. 36.

III, p. 45. Bradfield, mill (2). The N.G.R. lettered square should read TM, not TL.

III, p. 47, note 8: 32.8.1833 should read 31.8.1833.

III, p. 73. Add (3) before Rainsford Mill.

III, p. 81. Under mill (3) in the last line of the site description, for 44 a-e read 144 a-e.

III, p. 92. Fifth line up from foot of Col. 1: for 'years' read 'yards'.

III, p. 93. For 1843 (sale particulars) read 1842.

III, p. 100, note 5, under 'Other Colchester windmills': insert E. & H.M. after the first newspaper entry, viz. before 2.9.1834.

VOLUME IV, p. 10. Acknowledgement of photographs to Mr Donald W. Muggeridge: delete a,b,c after 179.

IV, p. 53, Hornchurch: at the end of the site description of mill (3) Fig. 38 should read Fig. 35.

IV, pp. 64, 77, 101. TL should read TQ in the N.G.R.s to the following mills: Latchingdon mill (2), Mayland mill (2), Purleigh mill (3).

IV, p. 111, Col. 2, line 7: for 1943 read 1843.

IV, p. 114. Ridgewell, mills (1) and (2). The bearings given in the site descriptions are from an easterly datum; from a northerly datum through the church they are (1) 195° and (2) 225°.

IV, p. 115. In the caption to Plate 215, for 'water-colour' read 'oil painting'.

IV, p. 128. Note 19. Delete J in front of C.C.

ADDENDA

ARDLEIGH
Deeds re Spring Valley (water) mill and the Harwich road windmill at 038281: Thos. Wright sold 1791 to Bezaliel Angier; John Angier, miller, sold in 1810 to Zachariah Lewsey, miller, of Ardleigh. 1821 bought by Joseph Smith Surridge, miller, who 1824 conveyed to Jn. Webb, who died 1827. Another Jn. Webb sold in 1841 to Jn. Lott Nickalls, etc. (The windmill had gone in 1830). (E.R.O. D/DE1 T303)

ASHDON
Reaney, *Place Names of Essex* (1935) p. 641, lists 'John de molendino, 1288' in Ashdon. Topographically the likelihood is that the mill was wind-powered (see App. A, I, 103), but a watermill did exist in 1794 (III, 18). Reference in 1549 to manor of Over Hall and mill, etc., in Bartlow and Ashdon. Evidently a windmill and possibly that at approximately 567418 (see App. A, I). (*Feet of Fines, Essex*, Vol. V, p. 23)

ASHELDHAM
See reference to Asheldham windmill in the will of Thos. Hardye under LITTLE LAVER.

GREAT BADDOW
Windmill, etc., 1576, also 1579. (*Feet of Fines, Essex*, Vol. V, pp. 345, 389). Upper Windmill. R. Hawksley contributes a note: Court book (E.R.O. D/DWv M65) states that in 1742 Isaac Brazier sen. transferred the windmill to himself and Isaac Brazier jun. as joint tenants, and in 1792 Isaac Brazier jun. by his will left his post mill to John Brazier (admitted 1793) for life. Evidently in 1825 it was sold out of court to Henry Sewell.

GREAT BARDFIELD
R. Hawksley reported that apparently the only Essex windmill casualty of the October, 1987 hurricane which devastated some of S.E. England, was half a sail at this mill, which is to be repaired. A national newspaper item said that in the famed great storm of 1703 some 400 windmills had been destroyed, and it would be interesting to know whether such a figure had a basis in fact.

BARNSTON
Kelly 1866 is the last directory to indicate activity, John Harvey being miller.

BELCHAMP ST PAUL
In July, 1908, after Crisp's decease, the freehold mill property was offered for sale as a 'going concern', the mill having 2 pairs of stones and all in excellent order, but there is no record of a milling successor.

BELCHAMP WALTER
The freehold post mill (Cottonbury M.) was advertised by the late John Firmin's executors for sale by auction in the *Halstead Gazette* of 23.3.1877. Details of the machinery were not given.

LITTLE BENTLEY
Tithe (1841): First and Second Mill Fields at 131242. Remote position for a windmill; stream some distance to south.

BERDEN
Wm. Hills of Berden, miller, examined by magistrates April 21, 1651. Said he had practised astrology for 3 years and had discovered stolen goods by such means. (E.R.O. Q/SBa 2/76). Same day bailed to appear at quarter sessions to answer charge of practising unlawful and deceitful arts. (Q/SR 349/92).

BIRCH
Jas. Carter assigned in 1794 to Jas. Digby his lease from Jas. Round of Birch windmill (at 943206). (E.R.O. D/DR E1).

BOBBINGWORTH

Will, 1567, of John Tydye of Waltham Holy Cross: 'To John Tedye (sic) my son the Windmill at Bobbingworth with the millcote and the appurtenances.' (Guildhall Library, Court of Commissary of Bishop of London, MS. 9171/15 fo. 280 per F. G. Emmison)

BOCKING

Bocking Church Street: the sack-hoist assembly in this post mill is taken as a typical example and is very fully described and evaluated in *Bell Alarms and Sack Hoists in Windmills*, Clark and Wailes, *Trans. Newcomen Soc.*, Vol. XLV, 1972-3, pp. 60, 62. There are drawings in plan and section to illustrate.

BOREHAM

A booklet by the vicar, Rev. W. J. T. Smith, confirms one pair of stones and has a distant sketch of the mill. (Per R. Hawksley.)

BOXTED

Tithe, 1841. Plots 459, 460: Lower and Upper Mill Field, both on a hill. (995340).

BRADWELL-ON-SEA

History of Bradwell-on-Sea, Rev. Herbert Brown, 1929, pp. 126-138, contains references to wind and water mills. P. 127: windmill present in 1306; p. 130: manor of Down Hall in 1502 included windmill decayed and in ruins.

BRIGHTLINGSEA

Jas. Barker, by his will, 1835, proved 1837, left copyhold property including a windmill (at 093166 at Hurst Green) in trust. Deed of arrangement 1845 states lease of mill had been assigned to Daniel George Ransome. Property made freehold 1862 and handed over to Misses Alicia, Emma and Sarah Barker. (E.R.O. D/DDw T208).

BULMER

An account of the February, 1928, fire at the smock mill, following a lightning strike, appears in the *Halstead Gazette*.

HELIONS BUMPSTEAD

A sale notice in the *Halstead Gazette*, 19.6.1890, confirms that the mill was a 'brick built tower windmill', and the issue of 10.7.1890 records that the freehold mill and cottage were purchased by R. Ruffle of Haverhill for £100.

BURNHAM-ON-CROUCH

The 'Town Mill' (post) was erected 1788/9. Jn. Raven, victualler, bought land in February, 1788, and sold it with the windmill to Joseph Newman, victualler, in November, 1789. (E.R.O. D/DGe M172). John Elliott,

miller, who probably left the 'tower windmill' in Burnham after a sale in 1812, was described in a notice of his death in October, 1816, in Chelmsford, as having successfully employed 'medical electricity' to effect cures for a variety of ailments ranging from the more exotic such as St Anthony's Fire, King's Evil and Knots in the Flesh, to the mildly assertive such as wens and chilblains. Elliott may well have retired from milling to follow his medical bent with the support of a wife who in widowhood declared her intention to continue the practice. (C.C. 18.10. & 27.12.1816).

GREAT BURSTEAD (BILLERICAY)

The west post mill on Bell Hill (676939) was described as ruined by P. Lindley in *New Holidays in Essex*, published 1889. (Per H. E. S. Simmons)

CANEWDON

Windmill, 1566. (*Feet of Fines, Essex*, Vol. V, p. 215).

LITTLE CANFIELD

Lease, 1731, by Lord Maynard of farm to Richard Wyatt for 21 years, with windmill interlined as an after-thought. (E.R.O. D/DU 182/8).

CHILDERDITCH

Windmill and watermill in 1295. (V.C.H. *Essex*, Vol. VIII, p. 21).

CHRISHALL

John Pryor of Much Hadham, Herts., miller, admitted 1699 to land (446403) which he sold in 1726, together with a windmill, when still miller at Much Hadham. (E.R.O. D/DHf M2 & D/DU 803/1 respectively). The mill was probably built 1699/1700.

GREAT COGGESHALL

Reference to moiety of Windmill Field, 1538. (E.R.O. D/DHt 71/3).

COLCHESTER

Deeds refer to Wyndmyll Hill, Colchester, in 1507 and 1537, the earlier being a conveyance to John Wilbore jun. of 'Le Stone House and Windmill Hill'. (Printed, unindexed *Catalogue of Essex Arch. Soc. Library*, 1923, pp. 61, 55, respectively). Location unknown. R. Hawksley, on checking, states that the Stone House was in St Runwald, but Windmill Hill obviously elsewhere.

Lexden Road. D/DE1 T356 copy deed of 1698 about land 'between ye two windmills next to ye road leading from Colchester aforesaid towards Lexden'. This shows that the third windmill on Oliver's map of Essex, 1696, had gone.

Parish of St Michael, Mile End. In 1730 John Wallis of Colchester, by his will, left properties in St Michael Mile End, including George Meadow occupied by his son John, and a piece of pasture adjoining, with a wind-mill, occupied by Isaac Polley. (E.R.O. D/A CR 14 p.

355). Despite the stated field name, the location of this mill has not been determined, but it was probably in the area of the symbol shown by Warburton, Bland and Smyth (c1724), approx. at 995260.

Parish of St Botolph. Reference to a windmill (8 Chas. I) 1632-3 on Golden Acre in an article by Alderman J. B. Harvey in *Colchester Chronicle* 4.1.1890. In 1681 a house and 1½ acres with a windmill in St Botolph called Golden Acre was owned by Thos. Talcott and occupied by George Harrington. Site shown by the tithe map and apportionment to be at 002245 (mill 5c under Colchester III, 86). (E.R.O. D/Q 30/1/10).

Scarlett's Mill: the wind oil mill, 1656, listed in Appendix A, I, 104 was in fact later Scarlett's, John Scarlett being first involved as mortgagee. (E.R.O. D/Q 30/1/4).

Parish of St James. Wright's history of Essex, I 287, refers to windmill near St Ann's during siege, 1648

COLNE ENGAINE

Vol. III, 102. Confirmed that (Harcourt) Runnacles, who built the tower of the wind engine, was a local man who erected, *inter alia*, major public buildings in Halstead.

Confirmed also that the mill stood until early 1923. The following was reported in the *Halstead Gazette* for 9.2.1923: 'The question of the demolition of the old windmill at the sewage farm at Langley Mill came up for consideration, the Sewage Farm Committee (of the Halstead U.D.C.) recommending that the building be sold and demolished. Mr G. Nash presumed it was no good for the council to pull down the mill and make use of the bricks? It was considered that this would not be worthwhile. Ultimately it was decided that the building be sold, but the shed adjoining be retained as a tool shed, it being considered that this building would prove useful as it was proposed to erect a cottage nearby.'

(The above notes all contributed by Adrian Corder-Birch of Little Yeldham).

COPFORD

This sketch by John Constable, R.A., on loan to the Tate Gallery, London, is dated 'Aug 9 1817', and is described as 'A Windmill near Colchester (Stanway Mill)'. Kenneth Farries did not see it, but Roland W. Smith has little doubt that it is Copford Mill, described in III, 103, while the tower mill on the right would probably be Colchester (4) Mersea Road Mill, four miles east of Copford Mill, and detailed in III, 90. This is an interesting example of how an unillustrated mill can still be found pictorially recorded! Constable was of course the son of a miller. (C.S.)

CORRINGHAM

One of Mr Farries' last letters mentioned new information about a Corringham Windmill, and Roland W. Smith was kind enough to follow this up, eliciting the

266 *Copford (Post) Mill, by John Constable*

following from Mrs J. K. Payne of Southend-on-Sea: In an indenture of 20th June, 1493, between Thomas Bawde and William Austin, when Thomas let the manor to William for 13 years, the windmill was reserved for himself.[1]

In 1597, Blanche, late wife of Thomas Kent deceased and afterwards of Henry Deare held a cottage and garden 'abutting west on part of the highway called Mylle Strete between a mill which is laid waste on the north and the village of Corringham on the south'.[2] From the situation of the mill being on the south of the village it does not seem as if it could have been the old watermill mentioned in the Domesday Survey.

By 1631 there was definitely no mill as the constables in their report at the quarter sessions stated this.[3]

[1]The Lordships of Corringham and its Lords to 1604, Dr W. E. Corringham, unpublished MS. E.R.O. A5.
[2]E.R.O. D/APM 219. Court roll 1597.
[3]E.R.O. Quarter Sessions Rolls 274-90 (1631).

DEBDEN

Will of John Palmer senior of Debden, miller, 12 June, 1599. To John my son my lease of Radwinter windmill which I hold of Mr Birde of Radwinter gentleman, with the profits. To Joan my wife and Roger my son my lease of the windmill in Debden and my tenement in which I dwell holden of Mr Wiseman esquire, with the profits. (E.R.O. D/ACw 3/320 per F.G. Emmison). See also E.R.O. D/DC 41/324 (1608).

In 1609 Matthew Feltwell of Clavering, labourer, with a confederate, broke into the mill of Roger Palmer at Debden, and stole 1½ bushels of wheat valued at 7s., a sack (1s.), 2 sailcloths (10s.) and 2 scythes (2s.). For this and other offences he was sentenced to hang. (*Calendar of Assize Records: Essex Indictments, James I*, edit. J. S. Cockburn, H.M.S.O. (1982).) Which mill was involved is not known.

Magistrates' examination of Jn. Humpfrey, of Debden Hall windmill, 1648, states that he took and carried away timber from the windmill to repair the mill stable. (E.R.O. Q/SBa 2/68).

The diary of Charles (alias 'Clap' per R. Hawksley) Ennos, of Debden Tower Mill, (III, 112), extracts from which are quoted below thanks to the kind co-operation of Mrs D. M. Walter of Debden, are illustrative of the struggle to maintain a windmill in working order in the face of storm and other damage at a time of overall decline in the windmill's competitiveness with rival forms of milling. Choice of millwrights and the dominance of wind changes in the miller's thoughts are also noteworthy; regrettably the cost of repairs is not stated. In the interests of brevity some diary entries within the period covered, mainly of a non-milling nature, have been omitted:

1881 *14 October* John Holland's mill sails were blown off and . . . by the gale (this refers to the mill in Newport parish at 516357). Heavy gale wind and destruction by fire at Thaxted. 23 houses and barns destroyed. The mill rack was broken by the wind on that day.

1882 *26 March* The winding tackle was blown down on a Sunday morning about six o'clock in a snow storm. Very strong wind. Smashed it to pieces. North west wind.
29 April A very strong wind from the west. Lasted all day and night. Lambson was hanged.
10 May The fantail flyers was put up on a Wednesday 1882. Beautiful day.
23 May Our horse was stolen at a quarter to 12 at night.
24 October A very strong wind vering from South East to West done damage to trees and Henham Mill.

1882 *October* Comet seen.

1884 *19 January* A storm was raging on Saturday January 26 very strong wind and rain Thunder and lightening for some time.
22 April An earthquake at Colchester and Wivenhoe.
27 July The new segments was put on to the spur wheel in Mill and finished on the 31 July by two of Mr Francis men from Cambridge.
The Break wheel was new geared on August 1885 by Joseph Cooper Thaxted.

1887 *30 October* A very strong storm of wind that took our mill sails off, a shaft and brake wheel to the ground on Sunday morning at a quarter to 7 o'clock with wind from the North. Likewise Wimbish Mills, Elsenham Mill, Clavering Mills, Lindsell Mill with lots of damage to Mills about.

1888 *3 January* Gentry begun to repair the Mill pulled the old back out of shaft. The shaft of the mill was pulled up on February 3 in the afternoon.
26 January The two backs come for the mill.
15 February The four sails for the mill come from Braintree on Ash Wednesday.

20 February 1 back was put up. February 21 1 back and 2 Sails was put up. Very cold and windy.
22 February 2 Sails put up and the striking rod put in. Very cold East wind.
15 March 3 sails of shutters was put in. A nice day.

1889 *2 September* A very severe thunderstorm over this neighbourhood in the night done lots of damage in Essex.

1890 *January* The New spindle to wheat stone was put up 24th January by Gentry.
The New Iron Bridge at Chelmsford was opened for traffic on November 1st. New London Road Bridge.

GREAT DUNMOW
(4) R. Hawksley examined the first 1/2,500 map (1875) which shows a projection, indicating that the smock mill had a stage. He was told that the engine was not for corn.

LITTLE DUNMOW
Throws Mill: This post mill was one of those bought up by a building firm for its seasoned oak to be used in a millionaire's mansion in the north of England (*Halstead Gazette* 15.5.1913). It was stated that the mill had often been working 'until lately' day and night. Another source points to Yorkshire as the destination.

HIGH EASTER
Reference to Henry Grove, miller, 1668. (E.R.O. D/DU 295/7-8).

EPPING AND THEYDON GARNON
Vol. I, p. 41. To the list of windmills on Ogilby and Morgan (1678) not appearing on subsequent maps should be added: Theydon Garnon, mill evidently on Stonards Hill (467021). See *Essex Journal*, Summer, 1981.

FELSTED
Felsted Common Mill (site now in Rayne): Despite the mill's appearance on the 3rd O.S. 6in. map (1919) per R. Hawksley, it appears that the body had been removed by May, 1913. It was reported in the *Halstead Gazette* for 15.5.1913 that a new use had been found for old windmills: they were changing hands at good prices for the sale of their seasoned oak, which was being used for a millionaire's mansion in the north of England. In addition to Throws Mill, Lt. Dunmow, the mill at 'Tyes Bridge-road', Felsted, had been lately removed for this purpose. It was said to date from 1751.

FINCHINGFIELD
R. Hawksley reports (autumn, 1987) that restoration is nearly complete, with sails already up on an all-wooden windshaft. A pair of stones is to be fitted.
See under MILLWRIGHTING, below.

FOBBING

Will of Joan Jacksone of Wickford, widow, 21 Sept. 1575. '. . . My executor shall have my lease of the windmill of Fobbing, and the letting thereof, saving that the miller which now has it when his years come forth shall have it again for the rest of my years afore any man and shall not pay above £6 by the year, if he will have it.' Proved 19 Dec. 1575. (From MS of the Essex Wills in E.R.O. series, Vol. 3, ed. F.G. Emmison.)

LITTLE HALLINGBURY

1729 sale particulars mention a windmill apparently rented at 10s. annually. Entry preceded by Jas. Wilson at a cottage near Monkbury *(sic.)* Monksbury lay east of the church, and the mill, if close, must have stood in Little, as opposed to Great, Hallingbury. No other information on this post-1700 windmill (not included in Vol. IV). (E.R.O. D/DB L1/3/20)

HALSTEAD

The conflict in dates for the destruction of Box post mill in a gale in 1882 (IV, 26) is settled in favour of 29th April by a diary entry quoted in *Some Reminiscences of Thomas Francis Adams and Mary Adams and their Family of Halstead, Essex,* (1894).
Greenstead Green Mill: In a move evidently aimed at reviving a declining trade, S. Bigg of Greenstead Green Mill had the following inserted in the *Halstead Gazette* of 27.2.1868: 'Grist-Grinding. All kinds of Corn for Cattle feeding, 2s. 6d. per qr. Wheat ground and Dressed, 4s. per qr. Corn for Grinding collected when inconvenient to Customers to send it, and in all cases delivered when ground. Flour, Barley Meal, &c, at current market rates. S. Bigg, Greenstead Green, Steam and Wind Mill.' Box Mill: A lengthy and harrowing account of the death of the miller, Ruffle, in the watermill (see IV, 26) appears in the *Halstead Gazette,* 26.7.1888. (The above all per Adrian Corder-Birch).

WEST HAM

Pigeons Mill. John Potts sold in 1788 to Thos. Finney 5 messuages and a windmill formerly occupied by Caesar Preston and then by Chas. Stephens & Rt. Theobald (or their respective undertenants). (E.R.O. D/DCh T52).

EAST HANNINGFIELD

Windmill public house occupied 1763 by Samuel Miller; 1713 deed has no mill name on the land. Name of public house probably derived from name of licensee Miller. (E.R.O D/DB T161).

SOUTH HANNINGFIELD

Manor of Prestons, 1561: windmill, etc., in S. & W. Hanningfield & Stock. Evidently at site N.E. of Great Prestons. (See Appendix A, I, 105). (*Feet of Fines, Essex,* Vol. V, p. 152).

HARLOW

F. H. Maud in *The Hockerill Highway* (1957) p. 53, states that a claim of £400 was made for a windmill which succumbed to the laying of a new road under the Turnpike Act of April, 1829. (Site (3) at 473126). Wide-ranging enquiries by Mr E. F. Goatcher, of Sawbridge-worth (1985-6) have revealed a broadly based local tradition that a post-mill body was moved 'between the years 1820 and 1830' to the mill house of the watermill at Sawbridgeworth, there to be incorporated into the structure, an external view of which adds credence to the story. However, recent (1987) examination of the interior by Mr W. J. Wright of the Bishop's Stortford and District Local History Society has shown a more subtle use of the old timbering which indicates that the old mill body lies at right angles to the existing facade and roof line; thus first appearances are deceptive. Details such as the mode of removal and the route taken do not emerge reliably from the informants, though a horse-drawn trolley was the form of transport according to several versions.

HATFIELD BROAD OAK

Town Mill: Barrington settlement, 1676, included windmill, with house and 3 acres of land (E.R.O. D/DB T1471)

CASTLE HEDINGHAM

The west mill (Ruffle's) is stated by Henry Ranger (*Castle Hedingham: Its History and Associations,* publ. 1887) to have been erected in 1797 by Lewis Majendie for £1,300 and to have been demolished in 1877 by L. A. Majendie. The Majendies were the owners of Hedingham Castle. The cost of building appears very high for a post mill, even for a 'substantial' one, as it is described; it was evidently a replacement for that shown by C & A (1777). According to another writer the milling by wind was supplemented by a 6 h.p. engine with a vertical boiler (*Recollections of an Old Woodpecker,* H. T. Ripper, 1948). (Information supplied by A. Corder-Birch, of Lt. Yeldham)

SIBLE HEDINGHAM

(1) Deeds of 1795 (D/DU 1319) conveyed the windmill into a trust for Robert Partridge in consequence of non-payment of a mortgage debt, reciting that it was 'formerly in the occupation of Thomas Hickford late in the occupation of John Stammers deceased and then of Sarah Stammers and William Stammers or one of them. 'It had been in trust for William Stammers, miller and baker, since 1777. (Per R. Hawksley, September 1986, noting a bundle of deeds just become available at E.R.O.)

HEMPSTEAD

Fig. 34 (IV, 49) is extracted from map in E.R.O.

catalogued as D/DB P 42. See also E.R.O. D/DO T869 (1857-76) relating to windmill at 634378.

HENHAM

The extent of the manor, 1363, included a windmill 'in ruins'. (*Cal. Inquis.* Vol. XI, p. 379).
The last mill: after ceasing to work commercially the mill ground for the occupier until eventual demolition. (Miss Winmill, local historian, to R. Hawksley)

HOCKLEY

The Archdeacon of Essex Act Book records at the court held January, 1606/7, in reference to John Harrison of Hockley, miller: 'P(r)s(en)tat for suffering his windmill to grinde corne in the tyme of divine service (bothe in the fore noone and after noone) upon the vij of December last past and hath done the like diverse sabathe daies heretofore.' Defendant alleged 'that in case of necessitie he did grind &c.', whereon the judge dismissed the case. (E.R.O. D/DA EA 24 fo. 79v).

GREAT HOLLAND

Three watermills and three windmills etc. in 1540 in High Roding and Great Holland. From place-name evidence it is likely that 2 of the windmills stood in Great Holland. (*Feet of Fines, Essex*, Vol. IV, p. 234).
The smock-mill remains and outbuildings: On Christmas Eve, 1985, a fire broke out on the premises, believed to have been caused by an electrical fault; the remains of the smock mill and much of the stock of animal feed-stuffs was destroyed. The fire-fighters from Clacton, Frinton and Brightlingsea found difficulty in obtaining adequate supplies of water and their efforts were hampered by a strong wind. Mr Brian Smith, the owner of the business, stated that the firm would continue operation, and it was much regretted that damage to the old mill stump had occurred. (*East Essex Gazette*, 28.12.85)

HORNCHURCH

Marks Mill, 1633: see E.R.O. D/DM T11/8.

INWORTH

Will of John French of Messing, 1598: 'To Robert French my brother's son £3 6s. 8d. and my two houses at Potter Row in Inworth and one windmill, i.e. which I late built with the windmill and the lands belonging which Christopher Steele now holds in lease.' (Per Dr F. G. Emmison, quoting from his *Essex Wills* Vol. 7). The Windmill Hill named by C & A (1777) and O.S. maps on the Braxted road some 7 furlongs S.S.E. of the parish church, probably relates to this mill. Reaney, in *The Place Names of Essex* p. 395, records 'le Wyndmelle hille' in 1515 (court roll).

KEDINGTON

In Vol. IV, 59-60, it is hinted that the name Stone Mill Common in Kedington and the depiction of a tower mill in an ancient stained glass window in Stoke-by-Clare church nearby may be related. A note by the late Denis Sanders states that the glass dates from the second half of the 15c., giving as authority the Rev. Christopher Woodforde, and adds that evidently it gives the earliest known pictorial representation in England of a tower mill. This depiction is illustrated in *Windmills in England*, Rex Wailes (p. 3 in 1975 reprint).

KELVEDON HATCH

A photograph of 1907 in *Kelvedon Hatch Revisited* by Judy Conway and one c1906 in her *Kelvedon Hatch* show shutters in all bays of the sails, but with the canvas in terrible condition, and the mill apparently painted white. This indicates that its absence from directories, 1906-10, is because it was not then working. (Per R. Hawksley).

LATCHINGDON

Lease, 1759. (E.R.O. T/A 264/1,2).

LITTLE LAVER

Will of Thomas Hardye of Fyfield, millwright, 18 July, 1583, includes: 'To Mary my wife my part of each commodity and profits as shall arise from the millhouse in Little Laver and also . . . from a windmill in the same parish until Mary and Joan Hardye my daughters are 14, when they shall be equally divided into three parts and Mary and Joan shall have their parts. To my wife the yearly rent of 50s. until Mary and Joan are 14, when each to have one-third part, from a tenement and windmill in Asheldham. Proved 3 Oct., 1583.' (Per F. G. Emmison in a private communication, extracted from E.R.O. D/A ER 14 p. 251)

LINDSELL

'An extent of the possessions in Essex of the French abbey of St Valery in 1324 . . . records a windmill in Lindsell worth 20 shillings a year.' (Per John McCann, in *Suffolk Mills Group Newsletter* No. 6, July, 1978, citing B.M. Add. MS. 6164 p. 178).
At Chelmsford Bankruptcy Court it emerged in 1895 that Frederick Charles Heath, an insolvent miller at Bocking, had taken over Lindsell Mill from his mother c1892 with a capital of £15, and had left shortly after, stating in court that the business 'which consisted of a shut-up bake-house and an old windmill' was not worth anything. (*Halstead Gazette*, 11.4.1895).

LITTLE MAPLESTEAD

1692: Marriage settlement mentions the 'Windmill House' &c., but no mill, suggesting that the presumed

17c windmill (see Appendix A, I, 106 site 833336) had gone, and that the later Mill Farm of Great Maplestead was unconnected with it. (E.R.O. D/DGd T42)

MARGARETTING
Conveyance of Hoyes Farm, 1666, mentions windmill in occupation of Susan Davidge, alias Dabage, widow. (E.R.O. D/DC 27/595-7)
Will of Robert Hatcheman, of Margaretting, 1584, refers to Great Mill Ridden. (Per F.G. Emmison)
Gt. & Lt. Mill Fields in the parish were part of the manor of Coptfold (alias Cold) Hall, 1654. (E.R.O. D/DC 27/530)

MASHBURY
Thos. Lukin, sen., 1646 sold to Thos. Lukin, jun., windmill lately set up on land called Walkingdon. 1691 Jn. Lukin's jointure to wife. 1727 he was described as miller. Mill on W. B. & S. (c1724), but not on O. & M. (1678). (E.R.O. D/DSu T69).

MOUNTNESSING
Manor of Arnolds, 1578, with two mills, etc., in Mountnessing. Presumably in reference to the modern site and to that indicated in Appendix A, I, 106 (638974). (*Feet of Fines, Essex*, Vol. V, p. 373).
The surviving post mill (1985), believed to date from 1807, may have been (belatedly?) erected in response to an initiative by Lord Petre in 1800: 'Lord Petre, learning that the poor in the central part of his Essex estate found great difficulty in getting wheat ground at the neighbouring mills, has humanely directed a windmill to be erected at Mountnessing, in that county, the possessor of which is to covenant to grind the corn of the necessitous, in preference to that of any other persons whatsoever.' (*Essex Journal*, Winter, 1984, Vol. 19, No. 3, p. 57, quoting *Norfolk Chronicle*, 29.3.1800).

NEWPORT
The suggestion (Vol. IV, pp. 84, 5) that the alleged horizontal windmill east of Duck Street level crossing may have served as a pug (clay) mill at a local brickworks, is reinforced by the existence of such an occurrence at Husborne Crawley, Beds., in the first half of the 19c. (*Bedfordshire Mills*, Hugh Howes, Beds. C.C., 1983, pp. 15-16, text and illustration)

NORTON MANDEVILLE
Wm. Pawn 1569 left to son Wm. 'my lease of the windmill on Norton Heath'. (*Elizabethan Life: Essex Gentry's Wills*, Emmison, p. 151). Statement 1642 re closing and reopening of mill path from Blackmore to the mill on Norton Heath. (E.R.O. Q/SBc 2/31).
The windmill (O. & M. 1678) probably survived until 1706, when John Licoras (*sic*), miller, of Norton, by his will of that date, devised to Wm. Robjent his windmill &c. in High Ongar. (E.R.O. D/A ER 28 p. 231).

COLD NORTON
Elizabethan Life: Wills of Essex Gentry and Yeomen, F.G. Emmison, 1980, pp. 92-3, alludes to the will (1568) of Wm. Clark, yeoman, who lived at the manor house and whose will referred to a mill there, evidently a windmill.

BLACK NOTLEY
Poor rate books (E.R.O. ref. not available) last give it as working in January, 1839 (occupier Saml. Beddall, owned Smiths). In 1835 it was occupied by Aldham (plainly the 'Alderman' of *Pigot's* 1832 directory), owned Shoobridge. This windmill was sometimes called Red Mill, indicating that it was one of the very few painted red. (Per R. Hawksley).

NORTH OCKENDON
Draft leases of windmill, etc., 1758-68. (E.R.O. D/DBe T13).

ORSETT
Reference to Thos. Johnson of Orsett, miller, in 1555. (E.R.O. D/DAc 285). Thomas Jonson (*sic*) of Orsett, by his will made and proved in 1559, bequeathed the lease of his mill to his wife Agnes. (*Essex Wills*, 1558-1565, ed. F. G. Emmison, National Genealogical Soc., Washington D.C., U.S.A., 1982, p. 75, No. 239).
Will of Thos. Johnson of Orsett, miller, in 1580. (E.R.O. D/A BW 29, p. 149).
In *The Prints of Samuel Chamberlain* (published by Boston Public Library, 1984) will be found among many other reproductions of brilliant etchings a drypoint of Baker Street Mill, by this modern American master of the medium. The subject of only slight artistic licence, it is a dramatic depiction of the mill *c* 1928 and was much liked by Kenneth Farries. (C.S.)
The mill cap was removed in 1986, but it is hoped to replace it. (Per R. Hawksley).

PEBMARSH
The *Halstead Gazette*, 8.5.1890, reported that Pebmarsh Mill, offered for sale by auction at Halstead on 6th May by the Saffron Walden Building Society, was withdrawn at £130.

PRITTLEWELL
Hamlet Mill. 1767: Moss Jarvis committed to quarter sessions for breaking open the windmill of Mary Womack and stealing about $\frac{1}{2}$ bushel of flour. (E.R.O. Q/SBb 248).

RADWINTER
1599 (relating to the Grange Mill, (605367) Lease of Radwinter windmill held of Mr Birde, gent., by John Palmer senior of Debden, miller (see ref. under

267   *A windmill (identified as Baker Street Mill, Orsett), c1928,*
etching by Samuel Chamberlain, N.A.

Addenda: DEBDEN). Miller indicted 1604 for stealing windmill sailcloths. (E.R.O. Q/SR 166/70, Vol. XVIII).

Although it is just circumstantial evidence, Roland W. Smith believes this postcard, reproduced by courtesy of the owner, Mrs Caroline Mackly, Wickhambrook, is of the East Mill, Plough End, Radwinter (IV, 105).

R. Hawksley, however, is of opinion that it is perhaps Fordham Heath.

268   *East Mill, Plough End, Radwinter (conjectural)*

RAWRETH

Windmill, 1574. (*Feet of Fines, Essex*, Vol. V, p. 314). See also Appendix A I, 107 for further 1574 references.

RAYLEIGH

Will of John Marten of Rayleigh, 24 Jan., 1584/5. 'To Frances my wife my houses in Rayleigh with my windmill for her life; after her decease to Stephen my son; if he die without issue, to my brother Nicholas Marten's children [not named]; if Stephen live to 18, he shall have with my wife one half of the profit of the wind-mill; if he marry before my wife's decease, he shall have my dwelling house at the mill.' (Per F. G. Emmison in a private communication).
See also will dated 1624 of John Marten of Rayleigh, miller. (E.R.O. D/A EW 17 p. 196)

RETTENDON

By his will dated 11 Oct., 1587, and proved on 3 Nov., John Gates of Rettendon, miller, directed *inter alia* (and further to the references in Vol. I, pp. 100, 102): 'To 20 of the poor of Rettendon 6s. 8d. among them by the discretion of my executrix. To Mr Seredge, parson of East Hanningfield, 13s. 4d. to preach 2 sermons for the benefit of the people on the day of my burial, 1 at Rettendon, the other at East Hanningfield'. (E.R.O. D/A ER 15 p. 156)

RIDGEWELL

In writing the parish section for Vol. IV (see p. 114) I had conflicting information about Mill Road mill from D. W. Muggeridge and from a local informant. As Mr

Muggeridge's information was gathered much earlier than mine I chose to quote his, in the third paragraph. (In similar terms Mr Muggeridge referred to this mill in his written contribution to Rex Wailes' Newcomen Society paper on Essex Windmills — see offprint, page 178.)

I visited Ridgewell on 1st Nov., 1969 and recorded the following note about the south mill: 'Mr Pannell, aged about 87, remembered both mills working, the second being the one to the south on the east side of the Yeldham road. Joe Chaplin worked the Stambourne road mill and Jack Chaplin the southerly one. The south one was a post mill, was painted white and had a fantail on the steps, according to Mr Pannell.'

The statement that the mill was painted white and had a fantail on the steps adds strength to the Ridgewell identification of the photograph now reproduced. The fantail, incidentally, was perhaps added very late on: note trimmers on rear ladder where tail pole formerly passed through. The album containing the photo was purchased in Chelmsford's street market by Roland W. Smith.

The *Halstead Times*, 4.5.1893, contained an advertisement for the sale of the Moat Farm estate (sale by mortgagees with the concurrence of the mortgagor) in which, *inter alia*, appears: 'The Round House Wind Corn Mill, near the Moat Farm, with all the going gear therein, and fitted with auxiliary steam power.'

The contributor who sent the above (Adrian Corder-Birch, of Little Yeldham) stated in his covering letter:

269   *Ridgewell Moat Farm (conjectural)*

'The *Gazette* of 1st June, 1893, reported that at the sale held on 26th May, 1893, the windmill had been withdrawn. Unfortunately no other details were given. As much of the other property was sold I assume the windmill did not reach the reserve price. The windmill was then advertised for sale again and I enclose a copy of the sale notice from the *Gazette* of 3rd August, 1893. I could not find any reference to the sale thereafter.'

The sale notice is relevant to the mill merely as follows: 'Messrs Balls will sell by auction at an early date the steam and wind corn mills, dwelling house and outbuildings, with 9a. 2r. 15p. of land, at Ridgewell.' Also: see under STAMBOURNE.

AYTHORPE RODING
Windmill included in Barrington estate deeds 1676-1778. (E.R.O. D/DB T1471).

HIGH RODING
See under GREAT HOLLAND

WHITE RODING
References to mill in 1652 (E.R.O. Q/SR 352/26 (Vol. XXI)) and in 1729 (E.R.O. D/DK T195).

RUNWELL
'Matthew Brete, the miller of Ronnell [Runwell] Mill, in 1600 has stopped up, hedged and ditched two stiles, in Ramsden Bellhouse in 'a market and church way'.' (*Essex Journal*, Vol. 8, 1973, p. 120. Article by Dr F. G. Emmison). Indeterminate as to milling site: three in Runwell existed before 1700.

GREAT SALING
It is stated that in 1564 Wm Brodbelt of Gt Saling windmill took one quarter of a customer's wheatmeal as toll. (*Elizabethan Life: Home, Work and Land*, F. G. Emmison, 1976, p. 191)

MISCELLANEOUS
Karl Wood (1888-1958) painted a little short of 1400 windmills and windmill remains in Great Britain, mainly during the 1930s. These include over 60 Essex subjects, more than half of which were executed in 1932. They are listed on pp. 14-15 of *A Check List of Windmill Paintings by Karl Wood*, edited by Catherine Wilson, published by Lincolnshire C.C. (1982). The collection is held in the Usher Art Gallery, Lindum Road, Lincoln.

MILLWRIGHTING
Among the major tasks undertaken by Vincent Pargeter, the Essex County Millwright, since the publication in 1982 of Volume II (see pp. 125-6) is the preparation of a new all-wooden windshaft for Finchingfield post mill; this must be the only such shaft constructed in Essex for well over a century. Mr Pargeter details (Sept., 1985) the procedure as follows:

Making a New Wooden Windshaft
Finchingfield Mill was one of the last English windmills with an all-wooden windshaft, mortised to carry the sail stocks. Cast iron in the form of entire shafts or canisters attached to old wooden shafts had proved its worth, and became almost universally used.

When Finchingfield Mill was restored in 1958, the old wooden shaft was found to be very rotten, and was taken down and stored in the roundhouse as an exhibit. A second-hand cast-iron shaft was taken from Toppesfield tower mill nearby, but not before 5ft. of the tail end had been broken off in hurling it 50ft. from the cap to the ground. This deficiency was "made good" by jamming the reduced end of a length of timber into the bore of the iron shaft and clamping it in place. A piece of 1¼in. diameter iron rod was driven into the other end, forming a new tail journal.

The marriage of the Toppesfield shaft to Finchingfield Mill was never a happy one. The canister was greatly oversize for the small post mill's modest stocks, necessitating the use of many wedges all round, which tended to work loose. After some years, rainwater trickling down the bore of the shaft rotted the wooden extension, causing an enormous sag at the junction.

When consideration was given to restoring Finchingfield Mill, it seemed appropriate to make a new wooden shaft rather than use the defective iron one. The original shaft was available to copy, and modern wood preservatives could be used to extend the life of the timber.

The timber 'blank' for the shaft was an oak trunk 18ft. long and sawn to taper from 22in. sq. at one end to 15in. sq. at the other. This had to be fetched from a timber merchant near Norwich, who had felled the tree specially. The piece of oak, weighing well over a ton, was moved into the workshop on rollers and jacked up on to timber bearers.

The old shaft had squares for brake and tail wheels (the latter never used), the length between them being made 16-sided with decorative chamfer stops adjacent to the brakewheel. The neck journal was, of course, round, with iron 'parcels' let in flush and secured by two hoops. The tail end was also round where the wing gudgeon entered with two hoops driven on to a slight taper.

As a first step, the round and 16-sided areas were cut to octagonal using chainsaw and adze. This made turning the shaft over much easier. In the square state, turning through 90 degrees involved jacking under one side until the shaft rested on one corner, after which it would teeter over and fall on to the next flat with a bang that shook the workshop to its foundations.

The next step was to cut the mortises for the sail stocks. These were 15in. x 9in. and represented days of chopping with a large chisel. It was decided to use a chainsaw to speed up the process and the job was carried out using specially made guides to control the saw and make it cut straight and true. Cuts were made from both sides, and when these met all round it was possible to push out the block of wood so released. It just remained to clean up the corners and remove any humps and roughness with a plane.

New 'follow-round' cramp irons were provided before and behind the mortises to prevent splitting. The originals had disappeared, and replacements were welded up from 1in. square mild steel bar, and provided with large square nuts. The new work was galvanised to prevent rusting.

The original cast-iron tail gudgeon was removed from the old shaft and was skimmed on a lathe to remove rust pitting. It had four wings to locate in deep housings in the end of the shaft. After the new housings had been cut, a central hole was gouged out to fit the diameter of the gudgeon, and the casting was driven in using a wooden block to avoid damage. The wings were tapered towards the journal end, and wedges were driven into saw kerfs made $\frac{1}{2}$in. either side of the housings in order to close the sides of the housings on to the wings. This locked the casting into the wood with a dovetail effect. The two original iron bands were driven on, but were provided with flanges welded on and bolts to tighten them in view of the 'greenness' of the timber used.

At the head of the shaft excess timber was cut away leaving a spigot of 6in. diameter and about a foot long. The purpose of this was to carry the end of the shaft on a bearing so that the surface of the neck journal could be turned up true, lathe-wise. Sometimes these spigots can be seen on photographs of old shafts, that at Galleywood Common Upper Mill, Great Baddow, having been particularly prominent.

Once mounted on the tail brass, and with a wooden bearing under the spigot, the shaft could be rotated without too much difficulty. The neck had been reduced to a 32-sided shape by measurement, and this was further improved by setting up a fixed bar, measuring to each flat in turn by revolving the shaft, and making corrections as necessary. Next, a crank handle was fixed to the spigot and a gouge applied to the neck in several places with the shaft spinning as fast as the handle and human power would allow. These cuts represented a true circle, and were used as a guide to further planing. Finally the shaft was spun again and glass-papered true.

The wearing surface of the neck journal was formed by letting 20 iron 'parcels' in flush. These are $2\frac{1}{8}$in. wide and $\frac{3}{8}$in. thick, the ends being cut off at an angle so that the forward end of the corresponding rebate is under-squinted, and the rear end over-squinted to fit. This strategy helps to retain the parcels at the forward end, near which they will bear on the brass. With all the parcels rebated in, the wearing surfaces are radiused to form a truly cylindrical surface, together with the remaining $\frac{3}{4}$in. wide strips of wood. The parcels were held firmly in place by two hoops equipped with flanges and set-screws to tighten them.

The new shaft has been 'fed' with a mixture of linseed oil and wood preservative to extend its life, and currently adorns one side of the workshop (at Weald Park, near Brentwood). The situation of Finchingfield Mill precludes the use of a crane to raise it, so it appears that more traditional means will have to be used when the time comes.

(V. G. PARGETER, Sept, 1985)

DISCURSIVE BIBLIOGRAPHY

Reference to the sectional notes will suggest sources for further reading, but a short list of related and parallel studies is appended below to suit a variety of tastes:

I Works on Essex Windmills

Works wholly or substantially devoted to Essex windmills are: MS notes (about 90 pages) made *c* 1920 by Dr J. Turner, of Rochford, held in Southend R. L. Mainly historical, but contain reports of personal interviews with millers and others. An album of photographs is included.

Donald Smith. *English Windmills*. Vol. 2. The Architectural Press, 1932. 152 pp., of which 88 relate to Essex. Contains historical and technical data, and is a fascinating record of the windmills then standing in Essex.

Rex Wailes. *Essex Windmills*. Trans. Newcomen Soc. Vol. XXXI, 1958. Spans pages 153-180. A timely, detailed and authoritative technical record.

B. J. & J. M. Turpin. *Windmills in Essex*. Published in Thaxted, 1977. 28 pp. A contemporary guide in the form of a simple introduction for the general public.

P. R. Gifford (editor). *The Maize, the Wheat and the Rye*. Published by Essex County Library, Local Studies Dept., 1979. 31 pp. Brief notes on 26 Essex windmills, past and present, with illustrations drawn largely from the Turner Collection, and described as 'a nostalgic look at Essex Windmills'.

II Introductory and Explanatory Works of a General Nature

R. J. De Little. *The Windmill yesterday and today*. John Baker, 1972. 101 pp.

Rex Wailes. *Windmills in England*. The Architectural Press, 1948. 47 pp. Reprinted by Charles Skilton, 1973.

Rex Wailes. *A Source Book of Windmills and Watermills*. Ward Lock, 1979. 128 pp.

These books offer a clear and accurate explanation of the basic essentials, and are well illustrated photographically.

III Standard Works on Windmills with Different Emphases

Two books of a general nature which provide absorbing and instructive reading and were the first in English to explore in depth the technical aspects of windmills:

Stanley Freese. *Windmills and Millwrighting*. Cambridge University Press, 1957. 168 pp. Reprinted by David & Charles, 1971. (Trans. Newcomen Soc. Vol. XXXII. 1959-60, pages 93-109 may be read in conjunction with profit).

Rex Wailes. *The English Windmill*. Routledge & Kegan Paul, 1954. 246 pp. Reprinted.

IV Publications for the Specialist

Richard Bennett and John Elton. *The History of Corn Milling* (in four volumes). Simpkin, Marshall & Co., 1899. Facsimile edition of Vol. 2: *Watermills and Windmills*, and Vol. 4: *Some Feudal Mills*, published by EP Publishing, East Ardsley, Wakefield, Yorks., 1973, 1975. 343 pp., 242 pp.

This monumental work is primarily historical, but includes some technical observations. The scope of the research and the sober and scholarly style of presentation make compelling reading, and the four volumes remain the definitive work in English on the history of corn milling in all its forms.

The *Transactions* of the Symposia I-VI held by the International Molinological Society in 1965, 1969, 1973, 1977, 1982 and 1985. These contain the texts of papers read to the Symposia on a wide variety of topics, and are accompanied by numerous maps, drawings and photographs. They are valuable also for the reported discussions.

Also of comparable merit for the specialist are the papers on windmills, mostly by Rex Wailes, published in the *Transactions* of the Newcomen Society, extending over many years.

V Windmills in the Context of Industrial Progress in Essex

John Booker. *Essex and the Industrial Revolution*. Published by Essex County Council, 1974. 244 pp. (Essex Record Office Publications No. 66).

This work, by a professional historian specialising in industrial archaeology, reviews the whole of that field in the mid-18th century, drawing on Essex sources and devoting some 15 pages to mills and milling. The text invites the narrow specialist to discard his blinkers and observe the changes which took a more or less parallel course through most basic industrial processes. The spread of iron foundries and the gradual adoption of steam power are two of a number of trends which profoundly affected milling, and these and other important examples are discussed in detail in this compendium of technical change.

VI   WINDMILLS BY COUNTIES

Having followed the fortunes of the windmill in Essex, some readers may look to neighbouring counties for comparable information. For the South and East the following books are available:

William Coles Finch. *Watermills and Windmills*. C. W. Daniel, 1933. 336 pp. Reprinted 1976 by Arthur J. Cassell, Sheerness, Kent. Despite its title, deals almost exclusively with the windmills of Kent. The most intimately miller-derived county history of milling by wind that one can hope to acquire, tapping memories rooted well back in the 19th century.

Jenny West. *The Windmills of Kent*. Charles Skilton, 1973. 126 pp. 2nd (revised and enlarged) edition 1979. Deals with the surviving mills of Kent and implants the urge to be up and away to view them. Gives a valuable summary of approaches to mill preservation.

The Rev. Peter Hemming. *Windmills in Sussex*. C. W. Daniel, 1936. 138 pp. A broad survey of the windmills then in existence, aimed to satisfy the general reader.

Martin Brunnarius. *The Windmills of Sussex*. Phillimore, 1979. 211 pp. A detailed survey in which human, historical and technical aspects are covered and receive strong photographic support.

Richard and Richard McDermott. *The Standing Windmills of East Sussex/West Sussex*. Two small illustrated books, Betford Publications, 1978, each 48 pp.

K. G. Farries and M. T. Mason. *The Windmills of Surrey and Inner London*. Charles Skilton, 1966. 276 pp. This exhaustive work was the first uninhibitedly to present detailed technical and dimensioned surveys of selected mills. It devotes space to related topics such as the manufacture of bolting cloth, and presents an ample bibliography of windmill publications up to 1965.

Arthur C. Smith, *Windmills in Surrey and Greater London: a Contemporary Survey*. Stevenage Museum, 1976, 18 pp, illustrated.

Brian Flint. *Suffolk Windmills*. The Boydell Press, 1979. 164 pp. Competently written by an author who has devoted much time and energy to mill restoration. A general survey of late surviving Suffolk windmills taken collectively — the alluring tip of a massive iceberg — is followed *inter alia* by a close look at 'Marshmills and Pumps' and 'Preservation and the Future'.

Peter C. J. Dolman. *Windmills in Suffolk: a Contemporary Survey*. Suffolk Mills group, 1978, 56 pp, illustrated.

VII   BIBLIOGRAPHICAL

Windmills: A Bibliographical Guide. Compiled by C. F. Lindsey, 1974, of 15 Bournemouth Road, London, SW19. Contains 237 references to large and small books and articles against authors' names, and lists institutions such as museums and societies possessing windmill data. The updating of this to the present time would be a formidable task.

VIII   ESSEX WATERMILLS. A major 'sister' work on former Essex milling should not be overlooked:

Hervey Benham. *Some Essex Watermills*. Essex County Newspapers, Colchester, 1976. 120 pp.; 2nd edition with revision, 1983.

ILLUSTRATED GLOSSARY

Apart from the windmill-associated terms, this glossary includes general expressions of a technical nature, freely used in the text, which may not be readily intelligible to some readers, e.g. breaking joint, hogging (of timber), soffit, strakes. Many Suffolk terms have been included on the assumption that there would have been an overlap into north Essex, given that certain prominent millwrights operated in both counties. Nor was the opportunity to be missed to draw upon the great fund of milling lore possessed by Jesse Wightman, former Suffolk millwright, who absorbed and locked into his memory seemingly all that the last generation of Suffolk windmillers could tell him.

As stated under *Appendix D* (Vol. II), what may be called the standard terminology relating to windmills has been used throughout these volumes in preference to terms local to Essex. This vocabulary was largely established by Rex Wailes in the 1950s in his many papers on windmills read to the Newcomen Society and in his published books. All known terms of importance relevant to Essex windmills are included in the glossary, and doubts in interpretation are stated where they exist.

The reader should refer to the plates and figures quoted as illustrative if the verbal description proves inadequate. The Roman numerals give the volume in which they are to be found. Some listed items may appear as incidentals in drawings in the glossary under other headings.

ANNULAR SAIL (Wind Wheel)
A circular sail consisting of a ring of radially-disposed vanes which can be either remotely controlled and pivoted on an iron frame or permanently fixed to an iron frame.

ANTI-CLOCKWISE SAILS (□ 133a III)
Sails which revolve anti-clockwise when viewed from the front, as for most mills. Also named right-handed (sails) from the direction of movement as seen from the rear.

ARRIS
The edge formed by the intersection of two surfaces.

AXLETREE: *see* Windshaft

BACK STAY (Fig. 13 II)
Wooden pieces secured to the middlings to give support at the rear of the sail frame and to help maintain the 'weather' of the sail.

BACKLASH
'Kick-back': an uneven and sometimes violent resistance to the normal motion of the mill machinery.

BALANCE BOX (Fig. 1 I)
A small iron box or receptacle let into the back of some runner stones for the insertion of (lead) weights for maintaining balance.

BALANCE DISH
An automatic device for regulating the flow of grain to the hopper. It consists of an inner hopper, preferably of metal, with a wide opening in the bottom, suspended by 2 cords or chains which are fastened to a slide in the wheat spout and have a counterweight. When the inner hopper is filled it closes the slide, shutting off the spout. When the hopper empties the counterweight opens the slide, allowing more grain to enter.

BATTER
In reference to tower-type mills the inclination of the tower walls from the vertical.

BAY (Sail Bay) (Fig. 13 II shows 12 bays in the sail)
The interval between sail bars on shuttered sails, usually accommodating three shutters.

BEDSTONE (Fig. 1 I)
The fixed lower or nether millstone.

BELL ALARM
The system whereby the miller is warned when a feed hopper to the stones is running short of grain &c., a small bell being activated automatically.

BELT PULLEY (Fig. 6 II)
A wheel with a broad and flat or convex rim, sometimes flanged, either driving machinery &c. by belt friction, or itself driven by belt. With a convex rim the belt is less likely to slip off in the absence of a flange.

BILL: *see* Mill Bill

BIN FLOOR (Fig. 39 IV)
The floor containing the material for grinding; in tower-type mills usually next below the top or 'dust' floor, and in post mills under the roof — there termed the 'stage floor' in Essex.

BIRDSMOUTH JOINT Also (Suffolk): Frog's Foot (Fig. 4E II)
A joint designed to resist the outward thrust from an inclined timber over a supporting horizontal member.

BIST Also (Suffolk): Doss
A cushion, often of an improvised nature, used in stone dressing for the stone dresser's comfort.

BLUE STONE: *see* Cullin Stone

BOLLARD (Fig. 6 II)
In mills normally a wooden drum for raising sacks, stones, &c.

BOLTER (□ 74 II; Fig. 6 II)
A machine for dressing (sifting and grading) flour from the ground meal by means of a cylindrical cloth bag which is beaten automatically.

BOLTING CLOTH
Cloth of finer or coarser weave, according to requirement, fixed to the reel of a dressing machine (the bolter) for separating flour from the meal.

BOTTOM SIDE RAILS (Lower Side Girts) (Fig. 5 II)
The lowest fore-aft timbers running between the front and rear corner posts in the side framing of a post mill.

BRACE (in mill framing)
A term applied especially to timbers enhancing the rigidity of a mill frame, e.g. triangulating members, ties.

BRAKE (□ 93 II; Figs. 6, 17B, C II)
The nearly complete ring of heavy wooden segments which can be applied to the rim of the brake (or head) wheel. A few brakes were of iron.

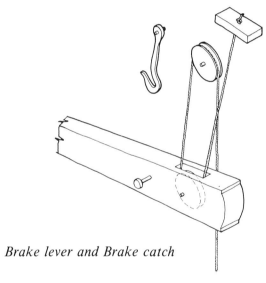

Brake lever and Brake catch

BRAKE CATCH (Fig. 6 II)
A pivoted wooden or iron contrivance designed to hold or release the brake lever in response to remote control by rope, e.g. from the mill base.

BRAKE LEVER (Figs. 6, 17B II)
A heavy pivoted timber by which the brake is operated.

BRAKE ROPE (Fig. 6 II)
Used for remote control of the brake lever, and hence of the brake.

BRAKE STAFF: *see* Brake Lever

BRAKE WHEEL (□ 93, 64 II; Fig. 6 II)
Mounted on the windshaft: the first gear wheel, and one of large diameter whose rim offers a convenient braking surface.

BRAY, BRAYER Also (Suffolk): **Breel** (□ 144c III; Fig. 1 I)
A horizontal wooden or iron member pivoted at one end and controlled by a steelyard at the other. Intermediately carries one end of the bridgetree. Part of the tentering system.

Breaking joint

BREAKING JOINT
A term indicating the 'staggering' of joints to preserve overall strength, e.g. in the case of two wooden curb rings one of which overlaps the other.

BREAST (of post mill)
That part of the mill body forward of the crowntree. Hence breast stones, breast beam.

BREAST BEAM: *see* Weatherbeam
Suffolk: the central horizontal member in the breast (or front frame) of a post mill.

BRICK PIER (Fig. 5 II)
In windmills indicates especially the brick-built supports on which rest the crosstrees of a post mill.

BRIDGING BOX (Fig. 1 I)
The iron box accommodating the footstep or thrust bearing of a vertical shaft (spindle) and having provision for adjustment of the spindle.

BRIDGETREE (Fig. 1 I)
A heavy horizontal wooden or iron member carrying a vertical shaft or spindle.

BRIDLE IRONS: *see* Rein Irons

BUCK (Suffolk)
The body of a post mill.

BUSK (Suffolk)
A loop or strap to secure the top bearing of a quant when moved out of gear.

CANISTER (Poll End, Sail Box) (□ 109 III; Figs. 5, 17B II)
The external head of the windshaft designed to receive and secure the middlings.

CANTS (of a wheel) (□ 63, 88; Fig. 16B II)
The basic rim-forming segments of a wooden wheel to which the felloes and arms are attached.

CANT POSTS (Fig. 11B II)
In a smock mill: the inclined corner posts running from the sills on the mill base to the curb.

CAP CIRCLE

In some caps the bearing surface which enables the cap structure to ride over the rollers of shot curbs, or over the skid plates of dead curbs.

CAP FLOOR

Term used (probably widely) in Essex for the 'dust-trap' floor beneath tower-type mill caps.

CAP RAFTER CIRCLE (Figs. 17B, 19A, B, C II)

In caps having an approximately circular base a horizontal timber ring built over the base members of the cap frame for rafter support.

CAP SHAPES: Boat, Domed, Ogee, Pent, Waggon.

Refer to illustrations and descriptions, Vol. II, pp. 92-4.

CAP SPARS (Rafters) (Fig. 5 II)

The supports for the weatherboarding of a mill cap.

CAPSTAN (□ 94 II)

Sometimes used for stone raising, when may be fixed horizontally beneath the flooring above the stones.

CARRIAGES, CARRIAGE PIECES

Supports, usually in iron, for bearings to shafts.

CATCH MILL

Dressing machine used to catch anything missed by previous dressings.

CENTRING WHEELS (for cap) (□ 96 II; Figs. 12, 16A II)

Generally flat-rimmed wheels rotating horizontally when in contact with the inside face of a curb in tower-type mills, and positioned to prevent cap drift.

CHUTE

In mills normally an enclosed wooden or canvas slide or drop for meal, etc.

CLAMPS (Sail Clamps) (□ 196a IV; Fig. 13 II)

In windmills often conspicuous as pairs of reinforcing timbers strapped together on either side of a middling and rebated at the canister as necessary.

CLASP ARMS Also (Suffolk): Grip or Gripe Arms (□ 133b III; Fig. 6 II)

A set of four single or double wooden arms attached to the cants of a wheel and forming a square at the centre, by which the wheel is secured to its shaft by wedges.

CLOCKWISE SAILS (□ 144a, 156 III)

Sails which revolve clockwise when viewed from the front. Also named left-handed (sails) from the direction of movement as seen from the rear.

CLOTH SAILS ('Commons') (□ 107, 133a, III, 31 I)

Sails consisting of canvas which may be spread on wooden frames.

CLOTHING TROLLEY (Suffolk): see Moving Stage

CLUTCH BOX

Term used in Essex especially for couplings in two or three-part upright shafts.

COCK HEAD

The top of the stone spindle.

COLLAR (Dead Collar) (□ 2 I, 106(d) II; Figs. 4G, 5 II)

In a post mill, the built-up square of stout timbers encircling the main post and resting on the quarterbars. It is static (or 'dead') but may act as a bearing surface for the sheers in movement above.

COLLAR (Live Collar)

A term sometimes applied to the timbers on the spout floor of a post mill which abut the main post and circle round it when the mill is winded. Often lined with 'wood-wears' and forms a steady bearing.

COMMON SAILS (Commons): see Cloth Sails

COMPASS-ARM WHEEL (□ 83 II; Fig. 16B II)

A wheel whose arms are mortised through the shaft which carries it.

COMPOSITE MILL (□ 161a, 210 IV)

One of hybrid character, having a post-mill type body turning on rollers over a substantial fixed base.

COMPOSITION STONES

Composed of a manufactured bond of cement with a granulated material, such as burr chips or emery, to form a milling surface. Rarely used, if at all, in Essex windmills.

CORBEL ('Corbelled out'): see also Jowled Timber

A projection (in mills usually of timber) designed to support an overhang or a heavy weight-bearing beam (e.g. weatherbeam, floor beam).

COREBOX (Stone Box) (see illustration on next page)

Term used by Jesse Wightman for the iron box set in the eye of the bedstone to receive the spindle for the runner stone.

CORNER POSTS ('true', 'false' of a post mill) (Fig. 5 II)

The post-mill body has 4 corner posts into which the side girts (normally present) are tenoned. At the rear such corner posts are often described as 'true', but in an extension of the body the additional and normally slighter corner posts are called 'false'.

CORSET (□ 2 I)

An iron framework set round a timber of large section by way of reinforcement; commonly applied to post-mill main posts.

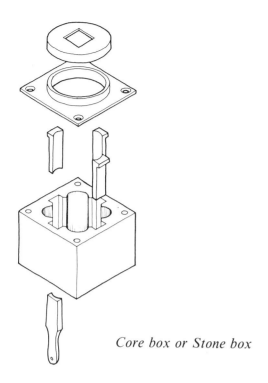

Core box or Stone box

COUNTERSHAFT (Lay Shaft) (Fig. 14c II)
A shaft driven from another shaft or from a gear; in mills used to set auxiliary machines in motion.

COWPOP GEAR (Trundle Gear) (□ 196b IV)
A primitive wooden face gear usually with rounded pegs or cogs secured in a single wooden plate.

CRACKS, CRACKING (Drills, Stitches)
Narrow, parallel grooves cut into the lands of a millstone for the grinding process. Jesse Wightman (Suffolk/Essex) allowed $\frac{1}{8}$in. intervals between cracks for grist and $\frac{1}{16}$in. for flour.

CROOK STRING (□ 40 I)
A cord running from the region of the hopper and shoe to the spout floor below, by means of which a gate in the hopper or shoe or the angle of the shoe can be controlled from a twist peg situated where the miller checks the quality of the meal.

CROSS (Iron, for sail attachment, also the casting connected to the forward end of the striking rod)
1. A substitute for the canister at the windshaft head: a large iron cross to which the sail whips are bolted and strapped. Rare in Essex.
2. The casting in the form of a cross which links the forward end of the striking rod to the couplings at the triangles. (□ 106(c) II)

CROSSTREES (□ 227 V, 77 II)
Stout-sectioned horizontal members acting as ties and steadying timbers resting on brick piers at the base of a post-mill substructure.

CROSS-TAILED GUDGEON: *see* Gudgeon

CROTCH SPINDLE: *see* Quant

CROWNTREE (□ 62 II; Figs. 4H, 5, 7 II)
The large-sectioned horizontal timber bearing on the main post in a post mill, from whose ends the body framing is suspended.

CROWN WHEEL (□ 85 II on stone floor; Fig. 14 II driving item 14)
In tower-type mills a gear mounted on the upright shaft and normally used to drive auxiliary machinery.

CULLIN (CULLEN) STONES
Millstones cut in one block from a blue or purple basalt quarried in the Eifel mountain range to the south of Cologne. There were shipped out down the Rhine from Andernach and through Cologne (hence the use of 'Cullen'). Also known as Blue Stones.

CURB (Figs. 11B, C, 12, 16A, 17B II)
In tower-type mills the circular wooden capping at the top of the tower over which, with appropriate ironwork, the cap runs.
1. Dead curb. One over which the cap turns without rollers, but by means of greased blocks or skid plates.
2. Live curb. One on which the cap runs on rollers attached to the cap frame.
3. Shot curb. One where the cap and curb are separated by rollers set into an iron ring, itself free to move round the curb but restrained from lateral drift.

DAGGER POINT: *see* Sail Cloth Settings

DAMSEL *(see illustration on page 137)*
A ribbed iron forging or iron casting footed on the rynd or other centre irons over underdrift stones; its purpose is to vibrate the shoe and so maintain the flow of grain.

DEAD CURB: *see* Curb

DOG CLUTCH (□ 144d III)
Iron coupling uniting two parts of an upright shaft, as most commonly seen in mills.

DOG IRON
Iron strap shaped as required to hold timbers together; it usually has one or both ends turned at right angles for an inch or so to enter mortises in the timbers to prevent spreading.

DOUBLE-SHUTTERED SAILS (□ 206, 219a IV; Fig. 13 II)
Sails with two rows of shutters or vanes, one either side of the whip.

DRESSER: *see also* Bolter, Wire Dresser
A machine for separating and grading flour from the coarser content of the meal.

DRESS, DRESSING (of millstones)
The disposition of grooves, furrows &c. on a millstone for grinding purposes, and the operation by which this is effected. For a pair of stones each has the same direction of dress.
Left-handed dress: one in which the master furrows, seen as roughly tangential to the eye of the stone, follow clockwise around it. The runner, so dressed, when turning and seen from above, moves anti-clockwise (sometimes described as 'against the sun').
Right-handed dress: the reverse of the above.

DRESSING (of flour)
The process of extracting the higher grades of flour from the ground grain (meal).

DRIFT (in stone dressing)
The amount by which the furrows diverge from the line of radius.

DRIVING SIDE (of a sail)
The main part of the sail to receive the wind pressure: the 'trailing' or rear side of the whip in relation to the direction of rotation.

DUST FLOOR (Cap Floor) (Fig. 39 IV)
In a tower-type mill the top floor, largely protecting the bin floor below from dust, grit, etc.

EDGE-RUNNER (stone)
A millstone rolling on its edge round a circular bed of stone. These occur in oil mills or gunpowder mills in Britain.

EYE (of the wind)
Direction of frontal wind pressure.

EYE (of stone)
Circular hole at the stone centre for driving irons and the passage of grain in the runner stone, and for the stone box, spindle, &c. in the bedstone.

EYE BOLT
In mills commonly set into heavy timbers above the stones for use in stone raising. A bolt having a ring-shaped head.

EYE STAFF
A short staff for identifying high spots near the eye of the stone; these must be dressed down.

EYE TIN
A tin or light metal casing sometimes used to line the eye or centre of the runner stone; this was found to prevent 'hoarding', i.e. the accumulation of grain in the eye, and it ensured that all the grain entered the eye of the stone from the shoe.

FACE (of cog)
The cog surface presented to engaging cogs, its height

(i.e. the longer dimension of the cog head) being often quoted in technical accounts in addition to the cog pitch.

FACE GEAR
A gear in which the pitch circle of the cogs lies within the wheel diameter; i.e. the cogs or teeth are set at right angles to the plane of the wheel.

FAN, FANTAIL (□ 84 II; Fig. 17B II)
A device consisting usually of 6 or 8 blades or vanes so angled as to be rotated if not edge-on to the wind, thereby turning, through gearing, the mill head automatically into the eye of the wind.

FANG (GRIPE) STAFF
Terms used in Suffolk for brake lever (q.v.).

FANSTAGE (□ 59 II, 202 IV)
A staging at the rear of the cap of a tower-type mill giving access to the fan for greasing, etc.

FAST AND LOOSE PULLEYS
A pair of adjacent pulleys of equal diameter on the same shaft, one fixed to the shaft, the other loose. A belt in motion over the fast pulley may be switched to the loose pulley and thereby made inoperative without halting any other drive in progress from the same shaft.

FEATHER (on a shaft)
A longitudinal rib cast on a shaft which may be provided as a guide for a movable mating part (see IV, 82: disengagement of stone nuts).

FELLOE (Fig. 16B II)
A segmented wooden rim attached to the cants of a wheel providing extra strength at the circumference and the required depth to secure the cog shanks.

FINIAL (□ 43 I, 131b III)
A decorative wooden block in the form of a ball, acorn, or other shape surmounting the cap of a tower-type mill.

FIRST REEF (of common sail): *see under* Sail Cloth Settings

FLOCK (RAG) MILL
A mill used for shredding old cloth, etc.

FLOORING, FACING (a millstone)
Taking off the high surfaces when dressing a millstone.

FLOUR CLOTH
Cloth with mesh ranging from fine to coarse, as required, used in bolters for flour dressing.

FLOUR MILL: *see* Bolter, Wire Dresser
General term for machines used to extract flour of various grades from meal.

FLY, FLYER (Suffolk): *see* Fan, Fantail
Also flyposts, meaning fantail supports.

FOLDING WEDGES (Fig. 4N II)
Pairs of two-way angled wedges driven in opposition

into housings or rebates to position timbers and prevent movement, e.g. between spindle beams and the side framing in post mills.

FOOTSTEP BEARING (□ 71 II)
The bearing receiving the thrust at the foot of a vertical spindle or shaft.

FORK IRON (□ 34 I, 106a II; Fig. 13 II, where not listed)
The iron couplings between the triangle and the shutter bars of double-shuttered patent sails.

FOUR-POST MILL
Term occasionally used in Essex to denote a post mill.

FORWARD SILL (CILL): *see* Sill

FRENCH BURR
Can signify a complete French millstone, but also a single shaped segment thereof. French burrs were built up into millstones.

FRENCH STONE
A millstone composed of segments of very hard fresh-water quartz formerly quarried in the Paris region of France, especially at La Ferté-sous-Jouarre on the Marne 60 km. east of Paris.

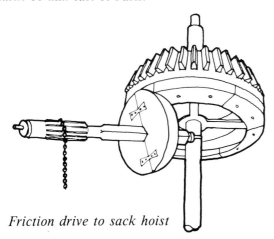

Friction drive to sack hoist

FRICTION RING, FRICTION DRIVE (□ 97 II)
An arrangement of wood blocks ('planks') usually fixed to the back of an existing gear wheel (e.g. the wallower in tower-type mills). The ring ('cone clutch') drives by friction, when pressure is applied, a built-up rim at the end of a bollard for sack hoisting, etc.

FULL SAIL
The final setting of a cloth sail, giving maximum coverage of the sail frame.

FURROWS (of millstones) (Fig. 1 I)
Channels cut in the working face of a millstone, usually in a series of groupings known as 'harps' or 'quarters'. In Suffolk named (in decreasing order of length): master

(furrow), journeyman, apprentice, butterfly (per Jesse Wightman).

GALLERY (□ 59 II)
Term usually reserved for the staging or 'cat-walk' around the cap of a tower-type mill.

GATE (grain feed)
A slide or hatch set to control the flow of grain from hopper to shoe, or the passage of grain through the shoe.

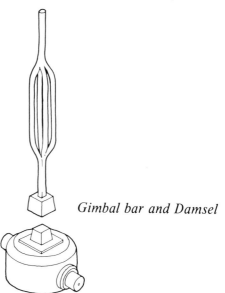

Gimbal bar and Damsel

GIMBAL BAR OR RING (Fig. 1 I)
Iron bar or ring set into bearings in the runner stone about which the stone is balanced; it also conveys the drive to the stone.

GIRDER
Term often used in Essex and elsewhere for a heavy horizontal timber, especially a floor beam. Noteworthy in smock mills as a tie or locking beam in the main frame.

GIRDLE
An East Anglian term for the (dead) collar (q.v.) in post mills.

GIRTS
Term used to describe transoms in Little Totham smock-mill frame. (Mecklenburgh, millwright, 1832.) *See also* Side Girts.

GLUT BOX (□ 15 I) *(see illustration on next page)*
An earlier form of plummer block (q.v.) with provision for holding the top bearing of a shaft (especially a quant) out of gear. Per Wailes (*Trans. Newcomen Soc.*, Vol. XXXI, p.294): 'consists of a top bearing with an extended cap; by removing a wedge or packing piece, the top of the quant can be moved out of bearing and sideways and the wedge replaced to hold it out of

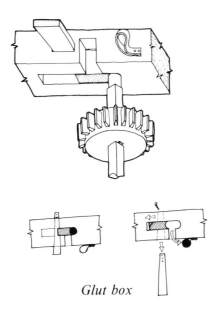

Glut box

position'. In cruder examples, a recess in the spindle beam with a removable block, the shaft being held out of gear by a strap.

GOVERNOR (Regulator) (□ 81 II; Figs. 1 I, 6 II)
Device for maintaining a constant gap between the mill-stones irrespective of the speed of rotation of the runner stone. Based on the movement of pivoted arms carrying (lead) weights which raise a collar on the governor spindle and hence a steelyard when accelerating. Variants: centrifugal governor, lag governor.

GRAFT SHAFT
Term used by several authorities for an upright shaft having coupled iron and wooden sections.

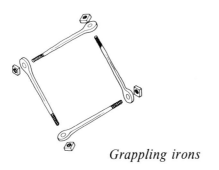

Grappling irons

GRAPPLING IRONS, GRAPPLES
Irons, normally consisting of sets of four 'follow-round' eye bolts designed to grip or bind a large-section timber where under strain, e.g. fore and aft of the sail mortises in the head of a wooden windshaft.

GREASE WEDGE
Detachable wedge for grease insertion in a bearing box, e.g. in the stone box central to a bedstone.

GREAT SPUR WHEEL (Fig. 1 I)
The gear wheel usually near the foot of the upright shaft which drives the stone nuts (pinions) and hence the runner stones.

GRINDING FLOOR (Suffolk): *see* Spout Floor

GRIPE (Suffolk): *see* Brake

GRIPE (GRIP) ARMS (of a wheel). (Suffolk): *see* Clasp Arms

GRIST
Corn for grinding: 'all grist to the mill'; also feed for animals.

Cross-tailed or winged gudgeon

GUDGEON (Winged —, Cross-tailed —)
An iron casting having arms or wings let into a wooden shaft, to which it is secured by iron hoops or by grappling irons (q.v.), and having a pintle or journal at its extremity.

HACKLE PLATE
A metal plate fixed to the stone box in the eye of the bed-stone, and intended to exclude grit, &c.

HAND WINDING
Turning a post mill or a tower-type mill cap into the wind by manual means.

HANGER
A relatively short and vertical 'pendant' timber or iron fitting commonly serving to carry heavy components such as bridgetrees and brays.

HARP (on millstone)
A master furrow together with the shorter furrows grouped parallel to it; can refer also to a stencil for marking out the furrow edges prior to stone dressing.

HEAD (TAIL) SICK
Of post mills: an inclination of the body forwards (head sick) or rearwards (tail sick) resulting from poor design, destabilising modifications, joint failure, &c.

HEAD WHEEL: *see* Brake Wheel

HEADSTOCK (Fig. 17B, item 5 II)
Term applied by some to the transverse beam in mill caps between weatherbeam and brake wheel acting as a tie between the sheers and in some mills also as a seating for stub members passing forwards under the weather-beam for the latter's support.

HEEL (of sail)
The innermost part of the sail near the canister.

HEMLATH (Fig. 13 II)
The lath along the outer (longitudinal) edge of a sail frame. ('Hem-lath'.)

HOGGING (of a timber)
Deformation resulting from the sagging of the ends of a timber below its central support, e.g. of a post-mill side girt on either side of the crowntree.

HOLLOW POST MILL
A post mill in which the drive is taken down by a vertical shaft through a hollowed main post to the machinery in a fixed chamber or roundhouse below.

HOPPER
Particularly applies to the container from which grain is fed via the shoe into the eye of the runner stone.

HORIZONTAL WINDMILL
One in which the sails or vanes rotate in a horizontal plane, thus turning directly the vertical shaft. Note that the conventional windmill is sometimes named the 'vertical mill'.

HORNS
1. In post mills: projections downwards from the corners of the centre post into the angles made by the crosstrees, therefore helping to stabilise the mill body. (□ 147 III; Fig. 4c II)
2. Short, horizontal, large-section timbers ('puncheons') radiating from the cap sheers in tower-type mills, and forming part of the cap construction. (Figs. 19B, C, F II)

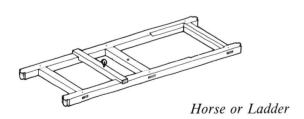

Horse or Ladder

HORSE (□ 40 I)
Light framework over the stones carrying the hopper and shoe. In some Essex inventories apparently named the 'ladder'.

HUFFER (Suffolk): *see* Paddle

HURST, HURST FRAME
A massive wooden framework footed on a mill floor on which the stones are mounted and within which the underdrift gearing is accommodated. Was present in some tower-type mills and (rarely in Essex) in post mills in the breast on the lower floor.

IDLER GEAR
A gear wheel intermediate between a driving and a driven gear. (See IV, 28, for a milling application.)

IMPROVER
An employee who has served his apprenticeship and seeks experience to improve his knowledge and skill in the trade by agreeing to work for a lower wage than a journeyman would command (see IV, 127: Chopping *v.* Ling).

INTERMEDIATE UPRIGHTS (**Window Posts, King Posts**)
1. In most Essex post mills two vertical timbers, one on either side of the crowntree, which strengthen the side framing near centre. Often pass either side of a window on the stone floor, hence 'window posts'. (□ 200d IV; Fig. 5 II)
2. In a smock mill set into the transoms centrally in each panel formed by the cant posts. In this position named 'king posts' or 'kings' by Essex millwrights. (Fig. 11B II)

IRON MORTISE WHEEL (□ 123c III, 219c IV)
A gear wheel cast with mortises shaped to receive the shanks of a wooden cog ring.

IRON SEGMENT TEETH (□ 63 II)
Arcuate castings of iron teeth for bolting in a ring on a wooden wheel, often serving as replacements for wooden cogs.

JACK (**Slip Jack and Cord**)
A cord-tightening device such as that frequently used when pitching tents.

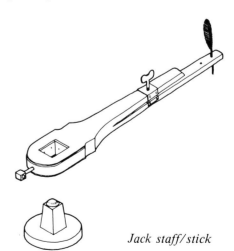

Jack staff/stick

JACK STAFF (STICK)
Usually wooden; is placed on the stone spindle in the absence of the runner stone and rotated over the bed-stone to test the verticality of the spindle by the miller's checking the passage of a quill barely touching the stone's surface.

JIGGER: *see* Jumper

JOCKEY PULLEY
A movable pulley which can be made to tighten a slack belt, so initiating a drive, e.g. of a sack hoist.

JOGGIN(S)
A term found in some Essex mill inventories. May denote a jumper or a posser (q.v.).

JOG-SCRY
A shaking or jogging device for sifting purposes.

JOURNEYMAN
An assistant who has served his apprenticeship and is qualified to practise his trade as an employee of a master for the prevailing level of remuneration.

JOWLED TIMBER (Figs. 4ĸ, 7 II)
A timber, such as a corner post in post mills, thickened towards the top to give adequate support to framing members: the 'gunstock head' effect.

JUMPER
General term in Essex for an agitated sieve or screen used for sifting and separating.

KEEP FLANGE Also (Suffolk): **Check Flange** (Fig. 12ᴀ II)
In tower-type mills a horizontal projection from the inside of the rack, beneath which run the horizontal centring wheels or wooden rubbing blocks. The flange would resist the overturning of the mill cap.

KEY, KEY WAY
Usually takes the form of an iron wedge driven tight along a channel (key way) cast in an iron shaft or fitting. Particularly associated with the fixing ('hanging') of gear wheels.

KIBBLE
To kibble: to grind coarsely.

KING POST (Fig. 11ʙ II)
Intermediate post in the panels formed by cant posts and transoms (sills) in smock-mill frames. Is footed on the lower transom and is off-vertical, following the batter of the frame.

LADDER
Term used in Essex inventories evidently denoting the frame or horse (q.v.) over the stones for carrying the hopper, shoe, &c.

LAMINATED SPRING CROSS (□ 101 II)
Present in a few Essex mills: a laminated assembly resembling cart springs forming a cross in the place of the normal unsprung cross attached to the forward end of the striking rod.

LANDS (of millstones)
The surface between the furrows to which the dress is applied for grinding.

LANTERN PINION (Trundle Gear)
An old-style gear consisting of staves set between two circular wooden plates. None survives in Essex windmills, but still seen in Holland and elsewhere.

LATHS (on common sails) (□ 125a, 133a III)
Intermediate longitudinal bars of light section in a 'common' sail frame to stiffen the construction and resist the wind pressure on the spread canvas.

LAY SHAFT: *see* Countershaft

LEADING BOARD (sails) (□ 202 IV: top right sail)
Board(s) covering part or all of the leading side of the sail; the outer section(s) often being easily detachable.

LEDGER (Suffolk)
Bottom side rail (lower side girt).

LEFT-HAND DRESS (of millstones): *see* Dress

LEFT-HANDED MILL, FANTAIL MILL: (□ 144a, 156 III); Fantail: (□ 107 III)
Mill: A mill having sails rotating clockwise when viewed from the front (hence clockwise mill), or with the sails descending to the left seen from the rear (hence left-handed).
Fantail: May be described as left-handed if the blades are so angled that they turn to the left (anti-clockwise) under wind pressure; this will be apparent to a viewer on either side of the fantail, provided that he has his back to the wind.

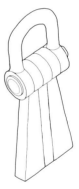

Lewis

LEWIS BOLT, — CLAMP, — CLAW
A device for use in lifting stones. Two half-splayed wedges are spread by a straight wedge inserted between them to be held captive in an iron socket let into the side of the stone. From the ends of the sheer pin carrying the wedges an iron ring is provided for hoisting by lifting tackle.

LIGHTER IRONS: *see* Steelyards
The various steelyards and linkages employed in tentering (q.v.) the stones.

LIGHTER SCREW: *see* Tentering Screw

LINE SHAFT: *see* Countershaft

LINK CHAIN (to tail pole) (□ 48 I)
A chain with long single-bar links for the support of the tail pole of a post mill from the mill body.

LIVE CURB
A curb on which the mill cap rotates on rollers fixed under the main members of the cap-base frame. The curb — built on to the top of the mill tower — normally consists of a double ring of heavy wooden segments 'breaking joint' (q.v.).

LOOP, WEATHER LOOP (□ 129 III, 214 IV: just discernible; □ 198 IV: clearly seen)
A small shuttered port-hole usually present in the breast on the lower floor of a post mill, to which the miller could apply a 'weather eye'.

MACE (Fig. 1 I)
The iron fitting socketed on the square section at the top of the stone spindle at the cock head. The recesses in the upper part of the mace carry the rynd, or a gimbal bar, on which the runner stone is balanced, and which also turns the runner stone.

MACHINE DRIVE (Fig. 11D II)
Any means by which auxiliary machines are activated. Machine drives differ in post and tower-type mills.

MAIN POST, POST, CENTRE POST (□ 61, 76 II, 216a, IV; Fig. 4B II)
The principal and static post in a post mill, from which the mill body is suspended and about which it can be turned into the wind.

MANYHEIGHT: *see* Notch Block

MEAL BEAM (Fig. 5 II)
The central horizontal beam in the breast framing of a post mill. In Suffolk the term denoted the lowest cross member (resting on the sheers): viz. the forward sill.

MEAL BIN (□ 144e III)
Wooden receptacle into which the meal (the ground product) is delivered, and especially present on the 'spout' or 'meal' floor.

MEAL FLOOR: *see* Spout Floor

MEALMAN
Entrepreneur or employee concerned with flour dressing and the distribution of the product, particularly before *c*1820, when bolting (dressing) was still frequently carried out in premises detached from the mill.

MEAL SPOUT
The spout at the end of the chute below the stones from which the meal (ground material) falls into bins or sacks.

MIDDLING (Sail Back, Stock) (□ 106(a) II; Fig. 13 II)
The main heavy-sectioned but tapered timber passing through the sail canister to which are attached the whips carrying the sail frames.

MIDDLINGS (flour)
Second-grade flour.

MILL BILL
Instrument of very hard steel, tapering to a chisel-edge at both ends, held in a thrift for stone dressing.

MILL HILL
Apart from referring to a commanding natural feature topped by a mill, and to a mound raised deliberately as a mill site, this term was sometimes used loosely in Essex to denote a (level) mill site.

MILL MOUND (Mill Hill)
Term applied to a (generally) artificially raised eminence on which a mill stands.

MILL PICK (Pritchel(l))
A mill bill of pointed form employed for pitting or roughening the surface (lands) of a millstone, especially for grinding animal feed.

MILLER'S SCALES: *see* Scale Beam and Scales

MORTISE GEAR: *see* Iron Mortise Wheel

MOVING STAGE (□ 227 V)
A mobile platform on wheels giving access to the sails from the ground.

NECK BEARING (□ 219b IV; Fig. 5 II)
The support of the front or neck journal of a windshaft, usually of brass, sometimes of stone or timber.

NECK BRASS
The brass in direct contact with the neck journal of a windshaft.

NECK JOURNAL
The circular section of a windshaft behind the sail box or canister which revolves upon a bearing.

NOGGIN(G)S
Horizontal wood pieces set between studding or roof rafters, e.g. in a post-mill roof framing (Ramsey) for stiffening the framework (see II, 35).

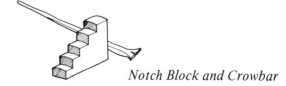

Notch Block and Crowbar

NOTCH BLOCK (Manyheight). Also (Suffolk): **Snotch Block**
A narrow, stepped wooden block giving a range of heights on which to pivot a crowbar when stone raising.

NUT (Stone Nut) (□ 71 II, 180c IV)
A driven gear or pinion such as is found on a stone spindle or a quant.

OFFAL
Low quality meal, &c. used for animal feed.

ONION HEAD (Suffolk): *see* Pintle

OPEN TRESTLE (□ 227 V)
The unenclosed substructure of a post mill.

OVERDRIFT STONES (□ 15 I, 123b III; Fig. 11D II)
Stones driven from above.

PADDLE
A small metal or wooden tag fixed to the side of the runner stone, which pushes the ground meal into the chute to the floor beneath.

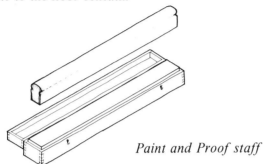

Paint and Proof staff

PAINT AND PROOF STAFF
A flat iron plate about equal in length to the diameter of a millstone and used for testing the accuracy of the paint or wooden staff (q.v.).

PARCELS (on neck of windshaft)
Iron or brass strips let into a wooden neck bearing to take the wear (see Widford, 1804, II, 113).

PARISH MILL
A mill owned and run by the parish, especially *c*1800, for the benefit of the poor.

PASTRY
In Essex: a meal store, sometimes a boarded-off section of a windmill. Also a term used by some millers in reference to a flour-dressing machine.

PATENT SAIL (□ 59, 106(a) II; Fig. 13 II)
A sail whose shutters could be regulated from the rear of, and sometimes within, the mill whether or not the sail was turning.

PEAK STONE (Grey Stone)
A millstone made from a single block of millstone grit from Derbyshire (hence Peak stone).

PETTICOAT (□ 131b III, 181 IV)
A boarded skirt around the base of a mill cap or of a post-mill body giving protection against the weather.

PICK: *see* Mill Pick

PIERS (Brick Piers) (□ 227 V; Fig. 4B II)
Supports for the substructure of a post mill.

PILLOW BLOCKS (□ 219b IV; Fig. 5 II)
Timber supports, especially those carrying the neck bearing of a windshaft.

PINION (e.g. Stone Nut) (□ 15 I; Figs. 14C, 11D II; 180c IV)
A small gear or cog wheel driven by a larger gear.

PINTLE (Fig. 4B II)
A pin or journal projecting from the end of a shaft, as from the top of the main post of a post mill into the crowntree above.

PITCH CIRCLE
Of a cog wheel: the circle around which the contact with meshing cogs is made.

PITCH (Cog Pitch)
The distance between two cogs on the pitch circle.

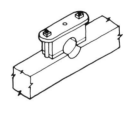

Plummer blocks

PLUMMER BLOCK (□ 5, 15 I)
An iron box or case with bearings for the support of a rotating shaft.

POINTING LINES
Cords used in securing common sails to the sail frame as required.

POLL END (□ 109 III; Figs. 5, 17B II)
The canister or sail box at the head of a windshaft through which pass the middlings.

POLLARDS ('Thirds')
Low-grade flour.

POPPET
Fitting or bracket for the carriage and support of bearings for a shaft.

POSSER (*see illustration on next page*)
A device used when filling sacks, consisting of a suspended lever having a wood ring with sack hooks at one end for sack attachment and sufficient leverage for the sack to be shaken manually.

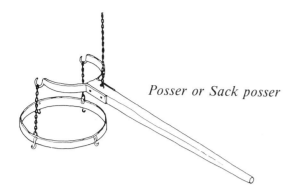

Posser or Sack posser

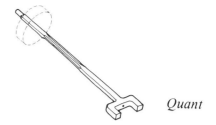

Quant

POST MILL (□ 66, 67 II; Figs. 5, 6 II)
A mill in which the body containing the driving and grinding machinery can be turned round a fixed centre post to face the wind.

PRICK (PROW) POST (Fig. 5 II)
The intermediate upright post in the front (breast) frame of a post mill, serving to support the weatherbeam and windshaft and to stiffen the framing.

PRITCHEL(L)
A sharp-pointed instrument resembling a cold chisel for punching holes, deepening furrows, &c.

PROW POST: *see* Prick Post

PULL-ROD STRIKING GEAR (□ 29 I; Fig. 20 II)
The mechanism by which the shutters on patent sails are closed to the working position by a rearward movement of the striking rod.

PUNCHEONS (Horns) (Figs. 17B, 19B, C, F II)
Stub timbers projecting from the sheers and other heavy members at the cap base in tower-type mills to serve as supports for the cap rafters and, if present, a gallery.

PURCHASE WHEEL (□ 32 I; Fig. 17A II)
A pulley wheel, part of a system for remote control: e.g. a 4-armed wheel with a grooved rim to carry the striking chain or rope, which might be fixed to an eye on the rim, or might operate effectively by friction.

PURLIN (Fig. 7 II)
A horizontal and intermediate member securing the rafters in a roof frame.

PUSH-ROD STRIKING GEAR (□ 34 I; Fig. 20 II)
The mechanism by which the shutters on patent sails are closed to the working position by a forward movement of the striking rod.

QUANT (Crotch Spindle in Essex) (□ 144d III)
In overdriven mills: the spindle carrying the stone nut, having a fork or crotch at the foot for location over the rynd or bridge bar (gimbal).

QUARTER THE MILL
To turn the sails edge on to the wind.

QUARTERING: *see* Studding

QUARTERBARS (Spars, Spurs) (□ 2 I; Fig. 4B II)
The large-sectioned inclined members in a post-mill substructure which carry the weight of the mill body to the crosstrees where they rest on the brick piers.

RACK (□ 87 II; Figs. 12, 17B II)
In a tower-type mill the toothed or cogged ring around the top of the tower against which the winding gear operates to turn the cap. Also present in composite mills at the top of the fixed base.

RACKING OUT (Suffolk)
Suffolk term for taking underdriven stones out of gear.

RADDLE (Reddle, Ruddle, Tiver)
Diluted red oxide (red ochre) brushed over the surface of the staff prior to testing for high spots on the stone surface.

RAISING SCREWS: *see* Screw Jacks

RAP
A piece of hard wood (sometimes bone) secured to the side of the shoe to take the repeated impact of the damsel or quant.

REAR SILL (or Cill): *see* Sill

REEL
The wooden frame in a bolter (flour-dressing machine) over which a dressing cloth is fixed.

REGULATOR: *see* Governor

REIN IRON (□ 106(a) II; Figs. 13, 20 II)
The coupling in the striking gear for patent sails linking the spider (or cross) at the forward end of the striking rod to the triangle, whence the shutter bars are operated.

RIBS (in dresser) (□ 74 II)
Inclined wooden bars forming the frame of a cylinder which could be rotated, and over which a bolting cloth or sleeve was passed. Also, in a wire dresser, the framework supporting the wire mesh against which the meal was brushed.

RIGGER (□ 180c IV)
Generally indicates a pulley. Also a term for a lever with chains or straps for lifting gears out of mesh.

RIGHT-HANDED DRESS (of millstones): *see* Dress

RIGHT-HANDED MILL, FANTAIL MILL: (□ 143 III); Fantail: (□ 84 II)

A mill having sails rotating anti-clockwise when viewed from the front (hence anti-clockwise mill), or with the sails descending to the right seen from the rear (hence right-handed).

A fantail may be described as right-handed if the blades are so angled that they turn to the right under wind pressure; this will be apparent to a viewer on either side of the fantail, provided that he has his back to the wind.

ROCKING LEVER

A pivoted lever at the rear of the windshaft controlling the striking mechanism. Rare in Essex, where a rack and pinion controlled by a purchase wheel were normal.

ROLLER (Curb Roller, etc.) (Figs. 12, 16A II)

Substantially cast weight-bearing iron wheels in mills, as employed in a ring beneath the tower-type mill cap, or beneath the rotating body of a composite mill; in both these cases the wide rims may have a slight taper towards the mill centre to prevent skidding.

ROOL

Term for Roller often appearing in inventories.

ROUNDHOUSE (□ 30 I, 201b IV)

An enclosure, usually of brick, sometimes of timber, around the substructure of a post mill. Sometimes denotes a lean-to enclosure around the base of a tower-type mill, and also, in some instances, the brick base itself, whether circular or polygonal.

ROUND-HOUSE MILL

A description occasionally used in north-west Essex in sale notices to denote a post mill.

RUB STONES (Rubbing Burrs)

Pieces of (hard) French burr stones with flat surfaces which are rubbed over the grinding surface of a millstone for the preliminary reduction of high spots before dressing.

RUBBLINGS

See II, 114 (Ardleigh, 1882): 'Rubling bag'. Possibly corrupt form of 'Ruddle bag' since listed with stone-dressing equipment, but more probably a bag containing a mixture of bran, pollards and middlings (see III, 91, last para.), possibly for elbow-support in stone dressing. Rubblings: the whole of the offal.

RULE OF THUMB

Instant and informative subjective judgment: the miller's test for the quality of the meal passing down from the stones above — a pinch between thumb and forefinger, with twist pegs within reach for any adjustment deemed necessary.

RUNNER STONE (Fig. 1 I)

The upper of a pair of stones — the stone that rotates.

RUNNING BALANCE (of millstones)

The required balance of a stone when in motion for even grinding.

RYND

The iron bar, cross or circle with trunnions by which the runner stone is hung from the stone spindle. Broadly evolved from the fixed rynd to the balance rynd to the gimbal rynd ('universals').

SACK BRAND

Used for putting the miller's name &c. on to sacks, which were prone to loss and theft. (Bicknacre Mill, Woodham Ferrers, inventory, 1822: 'A Sack Brand, pitch pen & two Kittels'.) Not evident whether used as a stencil or as a stamp, though melted pitch clearly the marking material.

SACK CHAIN, ROPE

In association with the sack hoist, the chain or rope descending through the mill for sack raising.

SACK HOIST (□ 72, 73 II; Figs. 9, 17A II)

The (often complicated) system of pulleys and drums to secure mechanical advantage for sack raising.

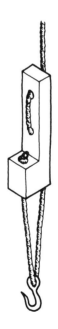

Sack jack

SACK JACK

A suspended wooden bar with hooks to hold a sack open beneath a chute.

SACK POSSER: *see* Posser

SACK SLIDE (□ 3 I)

A wooden slide for sack movement. Commonly found on the left side of the rear ladder of Essex post mills (as seen from the ground).

SACK TRAPS

On succeeding mill floors: vertically disposed paired flaps which are free to open and close automatically as sacks of grain are hoisted up.

SADDLE TREES (□ 111 III: just visible)

A pair of wooden guides on the ridge of a post-mill roof for the suspension of a cradle for repairs, painting, &c.

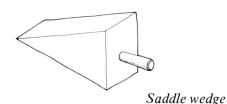

Saddle wedge

SADDLE WEDGE

Probably a wedge for insertion under a partly raised stone pending change in the crowbar position on a notch block (q.v.) or the passing of a rope for hoisting through the stone eye. Such wedges consisted of a heavy, tapered wooden block with a projecting handle at the rear.

SAILS: *see* under Annular, Common, Patent, Spring, Spring-Patent

SAIL BACK

In general denotes a substantial sail whip used on mills (especially notable in Lincs.) where an iron cross was employed in place of a canister, a middling not being used. At Stansted (1860) 'sail back' was used in reference to a middling (I, 76).

SAIL BAR (Fig. 13 II)

Lateral wooden sail-frame support, so mortised through the whip as to contribute — in conjunction with other sail bars — to the progressive increase in 'weather' or angle from the plane of rotation from sail tip to heel.

SAIL CLOTH SETTINGS

Much variation in the setting terms used, and those for Essex not reliably recorded.
Jesse Wightman (Suffolk) knows only 3 settings: full sail, stock, heel.
Stanley Freeese (*Windmills and Millwrighting*) gives 4; in decreasing order of cover: full sail, first reef, dagger point, sword point.
F. G. Clarke, son of the last miller of Takeley Old Mill, Essex, in a diagram, recorded: driver (evidently full sail), short point (i.e. dagger point), long point (i.e. sword point).

SAIL CROME

A long-handled crook to bring down the sails for reefing, etc.

TO SAIL IN/OUT

To close or open the sail shutters.

SAIL ROD

Latterly appears to have denoted wooden shutter bars to open or close the shutters. At Thaxted (14c) used evidently for windshaft (I, 97).

SAIL SHUTTER (□ 106(a) II; Fig. 13 II)

A pivoted vane used on spring or patent sails or on spring-patents.

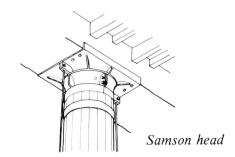

Samson head

SAMSON HEAD (□ 216a IV)

An iron casting used in some post mills to strengthen or replace the top section of the centre post.

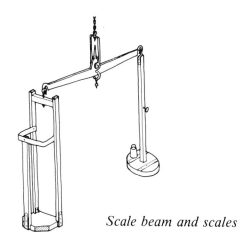

Scale beam and scales

SCALE BEAM AND SCALES

Beam suspended at centre and carrying a wooden framework (scale) at each end large enough to accommodate filled sacks.

SCARF JOINT (Fig. 4A II)

In mills commonly employed to replace part of a defective timber so as to preserve the original length and cross section.

SCREW JACK(S) (□ 27 I)

1. Used in heavy lifting operations: formerly large wooden screws threaded in pairs into stout wooden blocks, the jacks being turned by an inserted lever.
2. May refer to hand screw for lifting a stone nut out of gear off a taper on its spindle by means of a ring. Variousiy contrived, and the system is confined to mills with underdriven stones.

SCREW PINS (□ 71 II)
The adjusting screws in a bridging box.

SCUPPIT (Suffolk)
A wooden shovel, as used by millers.

SCUTTLE CANISTER (Figs. 7, 17B II)
A sail box or canister with extended rear walls, thereby presenting a larger surface for the reaction of the middlings to wind pressure.

SHAKE
A split or crack in timber.

SHANK (Cog Shank)
The tail of a wooden cog, by which it is held rigid in a mortise in the wheel.

SHARPS
Grinding product intermediate in quality between flour and bran.

SHEERS (Figs. 5, 10A, 17B, 19 II)
In mills sheers (in pairs) are large-sectioned horizontal timbers acting as the main base members for a post-mill body and for a tower-type mill cap.

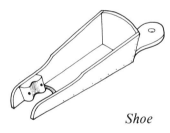

Shoe

SHOE
A gently-inclined open wooden chute between the grain hopper and the eye of the runner stone.

SHOT CURB: *see* Curb

SHUTTER BARS (Sail Rods; also (Suffolk): **Slides**
(□ 106(a) II; Fig. 13 II)
Wooden bars connecting the shutter cranks on the sails to the striking gear.

SHUTTLETREES (Sheers: Suffolk)

SIDE GIRTS (□ 200d IV; Figs. 5, 7 II)
The pair of heavy-sectioned timbers in a post-mill framing passing fore-aft intermediately between the corner posts and resting on the ends of the crowntree.

SILL (CILL) (Forward, Rear Sill) (Figs. 5, 7 II)
The heavy timbers at the base of a post-mill body passing over the sheers and supporting the front corner posts (forward sill) and the rear (true) corner posts. Also used to describe the wall-plates of a smock mill.

SINGLE-SHUTTERED SAILS (□ 217 IV)
Sails with one row of shutters only, on the trailing side of the whip.

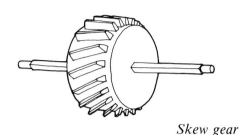

Skew gear

SKEW GEAR
A bevel gear with cogs set obliquely to the wheel radius. Sometimes seen in post mills working off the brake wheel for machine drive, the 'skew' position necessitated by space shortage, and by the presence of the windshaft, above or below which the drive shaft had to pass.

SKID PLATE
In tower-type mills with dead or near-dead curbs: greased wooden blocks or iron plates fixed to the curb or to the cap circle to enable the cap to turn.

SKIRT (Stone Skirt)
The outer section of the grinding face of a millstone.

SLACK BELT (Figs, 9, 11D II)
This is a belt running between two pulleys, one on a shaft and the other one a machine. A lever tightens the belt so that enough friction is imparted for the drive to be transmitted through the belt to the machine.

SLIP COGS
Cogs with provision for easy removal (e.g. by extracting pins from the rear) to put a wheel out of gear.

SMOCK MILL (□ 59 II)
A popular description of the wooden-bodied tower-type mill. But see the note headed 'Tower-type mills' under *Explanatory Notes* in any of Volumes I-V.

SMUT MACHINE, SMUTTER
A machine designed to remove smut (black fungus) from wheat, &c.

SNAP ROPE (Snap Line, Cord) (Fig. 6 II)
Evidently refers to ropes giving the miller remote control from below of the sack hoist, brake catch (by a jerk on the rope), machine drives, &c. (see Widford, 1804, II, 113).

SOFFIT
The underside of a framing member.

SOKE (Rights of Soke: milling)

Mediaeval customs and manorial jurisdiction relative to milling.

SPIDER (Iron Spider)

1. Term sometimes applied to the couplings from the forward end of the striking rod to the triangles from their superficial resemblance to spiders' legs. (□ 34 I; Fig. 13 II)

2. Term descriptive of the iron arms of a wood-rimmed wheel. (□ 88 II)

SPILLING THE WIND

Reduction of the effective sail area by the partial opening of the shutters under strong wind pressure against the springs of spring sails, and the weights tensioning patent sails.

SPINDLE BEAM (Sprattle Beam) (Fig. 17B II)

Term commonly used for a horizontal beam carrying the top bearing of a vertical shaft; also described as a sprattle beam by some writers.

SPLINES (Land and Furrow Splines)

Flat strips of wood, the wider used for marking out the lands on the millstone, the narrower for the furrows.

SPLIT SHEERS (Figs. 15, 19A II)

A term indicating the use of several unaligned heavy fore-aft timbers in conjunction with lateral beams for the base of a cap framing: an alternative to 'all-through' sheers.

SPLIT WHEEL

An iron wheel cast in two halves and bolted along a diameter.

SPOUT FLOOR (Meal Floor); also (Suffolk): Grinding Floor (Fig. 39 IV)

The floor to which the meal descends from the stones.

SPRATTLE BEAM (Figs. 11E, 17B II)

Term used by some writers (and in the present work, consistent with the policy of following the 'standard' glossary in Wailes: *The English Windmill* (1954)) to indicate a bridging beam e.g. at the foot of an upright shaft. Other writers limit the term to a top bearing beam (spindle beam). In this they are supported by the authority of John Russell, former miller of Cranbrook Mill, Kent. (Paper read to the Inst. of Mech. Engineers, 8.3.1944.) The term 'sprattle' has not been noted in Essex. Wailes, op. cit., 1954, gives both connotations; p. 133, Fig. 63 and p. 218, glossary.

SPRING SAIL (□ 100 II, 133a III)

A sail in which shutters are closed by the manual setting of the shutter bar at the tip against the tension in a spring usually fixed at the heel. The shutters open to 'spill the wind' if the wind strength exceeds the tensional pull of the spring.

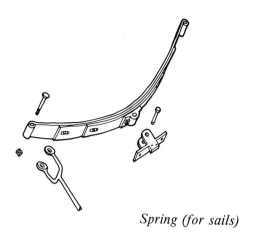

Spring (for sails)

SPRINGS (for sails)

The springs by which the shutter bars are tensioned, normally fitted at the heels of the sails. In form: elliptic, half-elliptic, quarter-elliptic, single leaf or laminated. Fully elliptic springs not observed in Essex; coil springs noted at Tolleshunt Major.

SPRING-PATENT SAIL (□ 101 II)

A combination of spring and patent sails in which springs are introduced between the head of the striking rod and the couplings (rein irons) to the triangles.

SPUR WHEEL, GEAR (□ 79 II; Figs. 14C, 16B II)

One in which the cogs or teeth project radially from the rim.

STAFF (wooden, for stone dressing)

A single or composite (laminated) piece of wood (mahogany, oak, etc.) used for testing the surface of a millstone prior to dressing. It should be perfectly flat and of size approximately 4ft. x 3in. wide x 4in. thick. *See also* Paint and Proof Staff.

STAGE FLOOR (□ 80 II: underside)

A term used in Essex to describe the part-floor in post mills at windshaft level to accommodate the bins.

STANCHIONS (Storey Posts) (Figs. 11B, 17A II)

Iron or wooden supports commonly found in tower-type mills up to stone-floor level to support weight-bearing, horizontal members ('girders') from the ground floor.

STANDING BALANCE (of millstones)

The condition sought for a runner stone at rest and effected by the addition of weights as needed.

STEADY PIECES (□ 158 III)

Evidently braces (in relation to the fantail assembly, Dunmow, 1822: see II, 116).

STEELYARD (□ 70 II; Fig. 1 I)

An iron lever pivoted at one end and controlled by a governor at the other, forming the first link in the tentering system. Sometimes made to operate through a secondary steelyard. In Essex: 'lighter iron'.

STEP BRASS (Footstep or Toe Brass)(□ 71 II; Fig. 1 I for bridging box containing brasses)
A brass-lined bearing or pot at the bottom of a vertical shaft or stone spindle.

STITCHING: *see* Cracks, Cracking

STIVES
Husks, dust, &c., removed from grain by a fan.

STOCKS (□ 106(a) II; Fig. 13 II)
The timbers of heavy section passing through the sail canister to which the whips are fixed. Almost invariably named 'middlings' in Essex, but generally stocks in Suffolk.

STONE BOX
The iron box with bearing brasses in the eye of a bed-stone through which the stone spindle passes.

STONEMAN
An assistant specialising in stone dressing. Might be itinerant or employed at one location.

STONES, MILLSTONES (□ 38 I; Fig. 1 I)
The seat of the grinding process, comprising the c. 4ft-diameter runner stone above and the fixed bedstone below, between whose working surfaces a very narrow gap, sometimes called the 'nip', is maintained.

STONE BEARERS (Fig. 6 II)
Large-sectioned beams or trimmers, part of a strong framework on which the bedstones rest.

STONE CASING (Tun, Vat) (□ 38, 40 I)
The vertical octagonal or circular wooden casing around the stones. Iron examples rare in Essex.

STONE DRESSING: *see* Dress, Dressing of Mill-stones

STONE FLOOR (Fig. 39 IV)
The floor on which the stones are situated.

STONE NUT (□ 15 I; Fig. 1 I)
The pinion on the stone spindle or the quant taking the final drive to the runner stone.

STONE SADDLE (and bolts)
A device to prevent slippage of the runner stone during lifting and replacement. Made of two pieces of wood spiked together with an overlap, the upper block being perhaps 2ft. x 1ft. x 5in. thick and having a narrow curved waist to accommodate the side of the stone and withstand its lateral pressure when under leverage. The saddle is temporarily secured to the stone curbing by bolts placed vertically through it into prepared holes. (e.g. Woodham Mortimer, 1844, lease: 'stone saddle

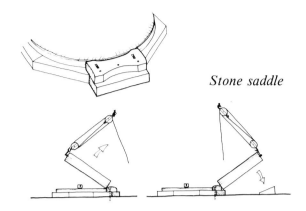

Stone saddle

and two bearers. Six bolts to ditto'.) Bearers would support the stone while on its back.

STONE SPINDLE (□ 70, 71, 99 II)
The spindle carrying the runner stone above and footed on the bridgetree. A stone nut or governor may be fixed to it.

STONE STAFF: *see* Staff

STONE WEDGE
A wooden block for insertion under a stone during lifting.

STOP CHAMFER (Figs. 4B, C II)
A bevelled junction between two faces of a timber with a 'stop' or graduated end.

STORM HATCH (□ 28 I: open for reception of replacement windshaft)
A detachable wood panel above the neck bearing of the windshaft giving ready access to the sails.

STRAKES (□ 72 II; Fig. 9 II)
In mills commonly occur as iron strips along the length of rotating bollards or drums to minimise wear from chains or ropes.

STRIKE
A convenient straight-edged piece of wood used to strike off level the grain, &c. in a measure or container.

STRIKING THE SAILS
Operating the control by which the shutters of patent or spring-patent sails are opened or closed.

STRIKING CHAIN
The chain (sometimes rope) by which the striking gear for setting the sail shutters is operated manually by remote control, e.g. from a stage or from the ground.

STRIKING GEAR(□ 321: purchase wheel, pinion and rack at rear; Figs. 13, 20 II; front mechanism) *(see illustration overleaf)*
The elaborate mechanism by which the sail shutters of

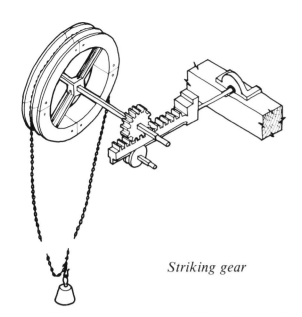

Striking gear

patent sails may be opened or closed whether the mill is or is not at work. The term was probably also used for spring sails.

STRIKING ROD (Fig. 13 II; rod shown, but not listed)
The iron rod running through a hollow core in the windshaft, part of the mechanism for operating the sail shutters.

STUDDING (□ 200d IV; Fig. 5 II)
The smaller members in timber framework to which the weatherboarding is intermediately secured.

STUMP IRONS (Figs. 13, 20 II)
Short brackets footed on the whips or middlings providing pivots for the triangles in the striking gear.

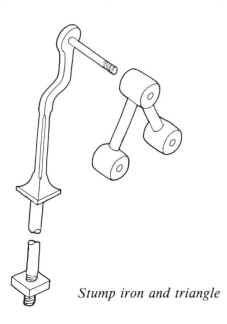

Stump iron and triangle

SUBSTRUCTURE, TRESTLE (of a post mill) (□ 227 V, 2 I; Fig. 4B II)
Refers to the piers, crosstrees, quarterbars and centre post supporting a post-mill body.

SUNK POST MILL
Term loosely applied to a post mill having the lower part of its substructure (the crosstrees and parts of the quarterbars and centre post) entrenched; a common feature in mediaeval mills.

SWAKE (Suffolk)
Lever for operating the striking gear, but very few found in Suffolk or Essex.

SWALLOW (of millstones)
In bed and runner stones: a reduction or slight hollow around the eye below the grinding surface to ease the inflow of grain.

SWAN NECK IRON (Suffolk) (Figs. 6, 17C II)
The iron tie which anchors the lower end of the brake band to the mill frame (post mill) or cap frame (tower-type mill).

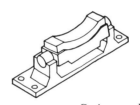

Swingpot bearing

SWINGPOT BEARING (□ 109 III, 219b IV)
Carried the neck bearing of the windshaft in some Essex mills. A self-aligning bearing which, in certain examples having trunnions at the ends pivoted in strong brackets, and rarely by other means, adopts the angle of slope of the shaft.

SWORD IRONS
1. The iron at the 'live' end of the brake band which passes through the brake (gripe) lever and has a series of holes for adjustment. (Figs. 6, 17C II)
2. Term evidently used by some millers for a lever in the governor linkages having a knife-edge to engage a series of notches on the governor fork lever. (Fig. 1 I, item 14) (*See* Barking, 1883, II, 114.)

SWORD POINT: *see* Sail Cloth Settings

TAIL (of a post mill)
The rear part of a post mill, behind the crowntree. Hence tail stones, tail tree, etc.

TAIL BEAM (□ 63 II; Figs. 5, 6, 7, 17B II)
The horizontal transverse beam carrying the tail or rear bearing of the windshaft. Term sometimes used for tail pole.

TAIL BEARING (□ 230b V)
The iron box or 'carriage piece' with brasses in which the rear journal of the windshaft is carried.

TAIL LADDER (of a post mill) (□ 48 I; Fig. 5 II)
The external ladder giving access to a post-mill body from the ground.

TAIL POLE (Tail Tree) (□ 48 I; Fig. 5 II)
The long wooden lever extending well to the rear of a post mill for manual winding; braced tail poles were also used on some Essex tower-type mills, but were comparatively rare after 1800.

TAIL SICK: *see* Head Sick

TAIL TREE: *see* Tail Pole
Also used in Suffolk for the rearmost tie beam between the upper side girts in a post mill.

TAIL WHEEL (□ 63 II; Fig. 6 II)
In a post mill the rear of a pair of driving wheels on the windshaft.

TAIL WIND, TAIL WINDING (□ 11 I, 127 III)
A wind blowing from the rear of the mill, in some circumstances leading to the destruction of the sails and mill components (tail winding).

TAT: *see* Rap
Term (tatts) used at Widford Mill in 1804 (II, 113) evidently referring to raps.

TEMPLATE (Fig. 4B II)
In post mills play an important part as wood plates spreading the load of the crosstrees and hence of the mill on the supporting brick piers.

TENTERING GEAR (Fig. 1 I)
The complex system for regulating the gap between the stones as changes in the speed of rotation occur: see under Governor, Steelyard, Bray, Bridgetree.

TENTERING SCREW (□ 99 II, 144c III; Fig. 1 I)
A provision at the controlled end of the bray for fine manual adjustment of the gap between the stones.

THIMBLES, THIMBLE BAR (Fig. 13 II)
The small iron or brass pots or sockets into which the trunnions or pins at either end of a sail shutter are pivoted. Thimble bar: a wooden bar, with thimbles, bolted to the sail bars, the gap between it and the whip being filled by a shaped board.

THRESHOLD (*Rear Sill*)
The sill or cross member below the rear door in a post mill.

THRIFT
A wooden instrument with a mortise in the head for temporarily securing a mill bill or pick when dressing stones.

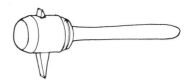

Thrift and Mill bill

THROAT WEDGES (Suffolk); *see* Folding Wedges (Fig. 4N II)

THROUGH ARMS (Suffolk): *see* Compass Arms

THRUST BEARING
A bearing receiving the thrust or pressure longitudinally from the end of a shaft, e.g. the tail bearing (q.v.) of a windshaft, the footstep bearing (q.v.) of an upright shaft.

TIE BEAM (Fig. 17B II)
Commonly a framing member of heavy section tenoned into and secured to two parallel members to prevent drift or divergence, e.g. ties between cap sheers.

TIE ROD (□ 125b III: tie rods either side of post; Fig. 5 II)
An iron rod performing the same function as a tie beam (q.v.), and also employed to counter sagging: e.g. in post mills of the extremity of the tail pole and of the sheers at centre.

TILLER (□ 48 I)
A pivoted lever on the tail pole of a post mill by which to raise the ladder prior to winding the mill.

TIVER: *see* Raddle

TOE BRASSES
Brass bearings at the foot of the upright shaft or spindle.

TOLL
By ancient custom the retention by the miller of part of the milling product for services rendered.

TOP PLATES, TOP GIRTS (Suffolk): *see* Top Side Rails

TOP SIDE RAILS (Upper Side Girts) (Figs. 5, 7 II)
The uppermost fore-aft timbers running between the front and rear corner posts in the side framing of a post mill.

TOPPINGS
Poorer quality constituents of the ground product fed to animals.

TOWER MILL (□ 92 II)
A mill built of brick or stone in the form of a tower, and surmounted by a rotating cap.

TRAIL (Stone Trail)
Included in the Ardleigh inventory, 1882 (II, 114). Evidently the stone tracer or jack stick used to check that the stone spindle is vertical. The tracer is a wooden or iron arm placed over the spindle and carrying a quill at its end barely touching the dressed and levelled bedstone; rotation of the spindle from the floor beneath will record any variations in the gap between quill point and stone surface, which can be corrected at the bridging box.

TRAILING SIDE (of a sail): *see* Driving Side of ditto.

TRAMMEL, TRAMMEL STICK
In milling references a wooden or iron arm made to rotate about a vertical axis for tracing out a circle, e.g. when constructing a mill tower or building a burrstone.

TRAMWAY
The circular track round a post mill for the carriage wheels (if present) at the foot of the external ladder; the wheels run on the track when the mill is winded.

TRANSOM
A horizontal member in a timber framework acting as a tie and also a support for studding, &c.

TRAVELLERS (Suffolk) (□ 4 I)
Carriage wheels at the base of a post-mill rear ladder.

TREENAIL, TRENAIL (Fig. 4J II)
Wooden pins or dowels for securing wooden joints.

TRESTLE: *see* Substructure (□ 227 V, 2 I; Fig. 4B II)
The substructure of a post mill

TRIANGLE (in sail striking gear) (Figs. 13, 20 II)
Pivoted triangular crank supported over a middling or a whip by means of which the push-pull movement of the striking tackle is conveyed to the shutter bars.

TRIMMERS (stone)
In mills can indicate the horizontal members forming a hollow square over which the bedstone rests; timber framing a void.

TRUCK WHEELS (cap) (Fig. 16 II)
Term commonly used for wheels or rollers in a 'live' curb, i.e. a curb over which the cap rotates on rollers.

TRUNDLE GEAR (Lantern Pinion)
A term of ancient usage for a wooden gear consisting either of two discs with round staves between, comprising a pinion, or a single disc with rounded cogs: *see* cowpop gear. Some writers restrict 'trundle' to the single-disc wheel. No example with two discs noted in Essex windmills.

TRUNNIONS
Cylindrical projections on either side of a casting for support in carriages (bearings), e.g. the extremities of a swingpot bearing (q.v.) for the neck of a windshaft.

TUMP
A mound; a term sometimes applied to mill mounds.

TUN, VAT: *see* Stone Casing

TURNBUCKLE (Bottle Screw)
A connector of hollow cylindrical form with reversed threads inside at either end. The threaded buckle or connector, on being turned, will draw two opposed tie rods together to the required degree of tension.

Twist peg

TWIST PEG
A control near the meal spout for adjustment of the cord (crook string) regulating the flow of grain to the stones. Usually takes the form of a wooden knob with an iron pin set through diametrically for turning.

TWO-PART, THREE-PART (upright) SHAFT
(□ 85 II: two-part; Fig. 17A II: three-part)
Indicates that the shaft comprises 2 or 3 lengths of timber or iron coupled longitudinally.

UNDERDRIFT STONES (Fig. 14 II)
Millstones having the runner driven from below. An underdrift mill: a mill having such an arrangement.

UNIVERSAL (CENTRE) IRON: *see* Gimbal Ring

UPLONG (□ 133a III)
A longitudinal member of the common sail frame.

UPPER SIDE GIRTS: *see* Top Side Rails

UPRIGHT SHAFT (□ 38 I, 85 II; Fig. 39 IV)
The shaft taking the drive in tower-type mills from the brake wheel (via the wallower) to the great spur gear. Also present in the breast of some post mills, and — very rarely — in the tail.

VAT: *see* Stone Casing

WALLOWER (□ 5 I; Fig. 1 I)
The bevel gear mounted on the upright shaft and driven directly by the brake wheel.

WEATHER (of sails) (□ 29 I; Fig. 13 II)
The angle by which the sails are offset from the plane of rotation to give an effective driving surface. The angle decreases from heel to tip.

WEATHER (BREAST) BEAM (□ 37 I; Figs. 5, 17B II)
The large-sectioned transverse member in the breast of a mill or a mill cap taking the weight of the windshaft, sails and brake wheel.

WEATHER HATCH: *see* Storm Hatch

WEATHER STUDS (Fig. 7 II)
The pair of studs or rafters footed in the weather beam on either side of the windshaft.

WHEAT SCREEN
1. A cleaning machine (e.g. two on stone floor, Woodham Mortimer, 1844: 7ft. x 1ft. 2in. and 6½ft. x 10in.).
2. A heavy wire screen placed in a spout with an outlet for rubbish.

WHEEL AND CHAIN GEAR (for winding)
A 'purchase' wheel (q.v.) of large diameter with an endless chain for winding a tower-type mill cap from the ground or from a stage. None survives in Essex.

WHEEL SAIL: *see* Annular Sail

WHIP (□ 19 I; Fig. 13 II)
The main longitudinal (tapered) member of a sail frame which is itself fixed to the middling or stock.

WINDING (pronounce with short i as in *wit*)
Turning the mill into the wind.

WIND ENGINE (□ 149, 150 III)
This term is used in Britain to describe the annular-sailed iron-framed windmill tower known in the U.S.A. as the 'windmill'. Commonly used for pumping water and for generating electricity, though examples exist which drove farm machinery.

WIND PUMP: *see* Wind Engine

WINDING WORM (□ 87 II; Fig. 14 II)
A wooden or iron worm gear in mesh with the rack for winding purposes.

WINDOW POSTS: *see* Intermediate Uprights

WINDSHAFT (□ 28 I; Figs. 6, 7, 17B II)
The inclined shaft on which the sails and the first driving wheels are mounted.

WIND WHEEL: *see* Annular Sail

WIRE MACHINE
A machine consisting of an inclined cylinder in a wooden casing used for dressing (or grading) flour by the rotation of brushes against wire meshes of varying gauge.

WOOD-WEARS (□ 61 II)
A term sometimes applied to wooden rubbing pieces, notably those forming part of the steady bearing around the centre post at the base of a post-mill body (i.e. at the level of the sheers).

WORM GEAR (□ 68, 87 II, 219b IV)
A wooden or iron gear in the form of a cylindrical block with a spiral thread or ridge, engaging, therefore, with a worm wheel or rack whose cogs are offset from those of a normal spur gear.

WORM RING (□ 68 II)
A gear ring having offset spur teeth or cogs in mesh with a worm gear.

YOKE (□ 48 I)
Commonly employed in the tail-pole winding of a post mill, and may consist simply of two vertically disposed pieces of wood against which the miller could apply shoulder pressure.

Y-WHEEL (□ 205 IV)
A purchase wheel with Y-shaped forks around the rim to contain the rope or chain. Often used in association with the striking gear.

INDEX

The index is divided as follows:
    I Personal Names
    II Place Names
    III Technical and General
    It does not in general list persons giving information on the mills who were not themselves involved in milling, which means that a number who have made the greatest contributions to the work have not been indexed.
    The index does not include road names or places etc. given in location details at the parish headings, nor does it list mill fields or minor topographical references in the text.
    Mill components, technical details, etc. are not listed unless especially noteworthy.

PART 1

PERSONAL NAMES

A

Butcher, Thomas, Manuden 1850 IV 74

Butcher, William, Finchingfield 1757 V 97

Butcher, William, Boxted 1841 III 45

Butler, Firefighter, Chelmsford 1873 IV 114

Butler, James, Sieves, Saffron St., London 1805 II 120

Buttrum, Robert, Little Bentley 1818 III 37

Buttrum, Martha, Little Bentley 1824 III 37

Byatt, Henry, Bocking III 53

Byford, John, Chelmsford 1866 III 74

Byford, Pharaoh, Chelmsford 1874 III 74

C

CAMP, Edward and Ann, Great Canfield 1745 III 70

Camp, James, Quendon 1771 IV 104

Camp, James, Saffron Walden 1806 V 78

Camp, James and Kezia, Thaxted 1821 V 48

Camp, John, Great Easton 1848 III 121

Camp, Robert, Standted Mountfitchet 1732 V 33

Camp, Thomas Harvey, Saffron Walden 1806 V 78

Camp, William, Saffron Walden 1819 V 79

Cane, Saffron Walden 1821 V 78

Cannon, Simon, Epping 1800 III 123

Cardinall, John, Tendring 1843 V 44

Cardnell, George, Mayland 1863 IV 77

Carrick, Earl of, Hatfield Broad Oak c1295 I 105

Carrington, Colchester 1805 III 93

Carter, Alexander and Stowers, Colchester post 1752 III 88

Carter, C., Birch 1819 III 39

Carter, James, Birch 1794 V 119

Carter, James and John, Colchester 1801 III 88

Carter, John, Little Bardfield ante-1827 III 27

Carter, Thomas, Great Coggeshall 1827 III 84

Carter, Turpin, Colchester 1818 III 88

Carter, William, Belchamp St Paul 1840 III 34

Cary, George, Epping 1752 III 123

Cassel, Little Canfield 1837 III 71

Cassell, Joseph, Birchanger 1807 III 42

Cassell, Thomas, Matching 1804 IV 41

Castlemaine, Viscount, Halstead 1727 IV 25

Catchpool and Thompson, Messrs., Ironmongers, Colchester 1871 III 96

Cater, A., Terling 1970 V 46

Catlin, T. A., Saffron Walden 1826 V 79

Caton, A. E., Clavering 1935 III 82

Caton, William, Clavering 1906 III 82

Cattermole, Henry, Tolleshunt Knights 1898 V 64

Cavill, William Balls, Great Horkesley 1834 IV 53

Chalk, John, Southminster 1705 V 24

Challis, Henry, Gt. Waltham 1886 V 81

Challis, Stephen, South Ockendon 1877 IV 89

Challis, William, Felsted 1822 IV 14

Chamberlain, Samuel, The Prints of 1984 V 125

Chambers, Esq., West Ham 1702 IV 34

Chambers, Thomas, West Ham 1730 IV 34

Chandler, James, Foulness 1824 IV 21

Chandler, John, Halstead 1701 IV 25

Chandler, John, Foulness 1802 IV 20

Chandler, Sarah, Foulness 1804 IV 21

Chaplin, Abraham, Belchamp Otten 1822 III 33

Chaplin, Cleer, Wakes Colne 1821 III 103

Chaplin, D., Great Coggeshall 1823 III 85

Chaplin, Henry, Epping 1787 III 123

Chaplin, John, Stanford Rivers 1797 V 30

Chaplin, John, Ridgewell ante-1835 IV 114

Chaplin, John Abraham, Navestock 1835 V 30

Chaplin, John Richard, Ridgewell 1855 IV 114; V 127

Chaplin, Joseph, Ridgewell 1841 IV 114

Chaplin, Joseph, Toppesfield 1902 V 68

Chaplin, Joseph C., Ridgewell 1910 IV 115; V 127

Chaplin, Richard, Epping 1800 III 123

Chaplin, Thomas, Harlow 1818 IV 41

Chaplin, William, Ridgewell 1848 IV 114

Chaplin, William Merrington, Ridgewell 1874 IV 114

Chapman, George, Radwinter late 19c IV 105

Chapman, John, Blackmore 1847 III 43

Chapman, William, South Weald 1795 IV 112

Chapman, William, Rettendon 1797 IV 113

Chapman, William, Willingale Doe late 19c V 97

Chappel, John, Rayleigh 1757 IV 112

Chappell, Millwright, Witham 1818 V 45

Chappell, Thomas, Millwright, Terling 1733 V 45

Chauncy, Henry, Farnham 1574 IV 13

Cheverton, Charles, Good Easter 1840 III 119

Child, Richard, Halstead 1701 IV 25

Child, Thomas, Great Waltham 1833 V 80

Childs, William, Wakes Colne 1841 III 103

Chipperfield, George, Quendon 1811 IV 104

Chisnall, William, Ardleigh 1891 III 16

Chisshull, Giles, Little Bardfield 1572 I 103

Chiswell, Richard, Esq., Debden 1721 III 111

Chiswell Arms, Debden 1796 III 111

Chiswick, Joseph, Colchester 1693 III 88

Chiverton, Thomas, Chelmsford 1823 III 73

Choat, Barnston 1765 V 85

Choat, Little Bardfield 1827 III 27

Choat, Widow, Little Bardfield 1840 III 27

Choat, Ann (child killed by sails) Little Sampford 1801 V 20

Choat, Charles, Little Bardfield 1833 III 27

Choat, Edmund, Great Canfield 1783 III 70

Choat, Henry, Sen., Little Sampford 1796 V 20

Choat, Henry, Toppesfield 1833 III 27

Choat, John, Finchingfield 1771 IV 17

Chopping, Mashbury 1868 IV 76

Chopping, Davy, Stebbing 1840 V 39

Chopping, Fred, Millwright employee, Takeley 1880s V 43

Chopping, Henry, Matching c1830 IV 42

Chopping, H., Little Canfield 1847 III 72

Chopping, Henry, Roxwell 1852 IV 127

Chopping, Henry, Roxwell c1860 II 98; V 110

Chopping, Henry, Thorrington 1866 V 53

Chopping, Henry, Black Notley 1878 IV 85

Chopping, Henry, Black Notley 1881 III 116

Chopping, Henry, Pebmarsh 1890 IV 96

Chopping, Isaac, Great Bromley 1850 III 57

Chopping, Isaac, Colchester 1855 III 39

Chopping, John, Finchingfield 1810 III 17

Chopping, John, Little Canfield 1828 III 71

Chopping, John, Matching 1830 IV 42

Chopping, John, Little Canfield 1850 III 71

Chopping, John, Great Bromley 1853 III 57

Chopping, Joseph, Stansted Mountfitchet 1866 V 34

Chopping, Samuel, Great Easton 1830 III 121

Chopping, Samuel, Jun., Stebbing 1821 V 38

Chopping, T., Little Canfield 1824 III 72

Chopping, Thomas, Manuden 1855 IV 74

Chopping, William, Stebbing 1894 V 39

Christy, Miller, Foulness IV 20, 21

Christy, Fell, Millwright, Ingatestone late 19c IV 59

Christy, James, Jun., Roxwell 1860 IV 128

E

I

J

M

Y

PART 2

PLACE NAMES

A

PART 3

TECHNICAL AND GENERAL

Literally on the day this Volume was sent to press was unearthed this curious and amusing copperplate of *"Prior approaching Down Hall"*, and it is hastily included as an interesting tailpiece and artistic riddle. Matthew Prior, the poet, acquired Down Hall (5½ miles S.S.E. of Bishop's Stortford) but died fairly soon thereafter, so the engraving may confidently be dated to around 1720. — C.S.

"The Windmills of Surrey & Inner London"
By K. G. Farries and M. T. Mason
Published in 1966 by Charles Skilton

Addenda and Corrigenda

The following text was prepared by K. G. Farries

I MUST with sorrow record the death in December, 1969, of my co-author, Martin T. Mason. He would have been pleased to collaborate in the compilation of the following list and to have joined with me in expressing regret for any inaccuracies and misinterpretations, whether since recognised or not, which may have found their way into the text. No field work of the area covered has been done by the authors since publication, and the Addenda below are therefore largely derived from information sent by correspondents.

Printing and other minor errors:

Page 18, line 1, 6th word: meal.
P. 30, 1.7: for 'fig. 11' read 'fig. 12'.
P. 43, 1.5, 13th word: for 'patents' read 'commons'.
P. 48. In the introductory list, item 4, line 2: for 'N.E.' read 'N.W.'
P. 49, 1.21, 6th word: for 'it' read 'its'.
P. 52, last line: for 'p. 68' read 'pl. 70'.
P. 59, 1.7 up, 1st word: the.
P. 64, 1.5: for 'p. 28' read 'pl. 28'.
P. 111 Introductory item 2 line 2: NGR 5348158 should be 53481518
P. 103, lines 27-8: delete 'resembling a clockwise set'.
P. 142, last verse (All the Millers), 1.2, 1st word: What.
P. 143, 1.25: for 'p. 64' read 'pl. 64'.
P. 186, 1.4 up, 3rd word: for 'that' read 'the', referring to Reigate Heath mill.
P. 187 1.24, 13th word 'true' should be 'false'.
Fig. 12, opp. p. 188: for '40' read '41' over roof of front and end elevations.
P. 209, 1.16: delete 'patent'.
P. 212. Introductory list, item 2, line 1: 13th & 14th words: correct to 'which stood'.
P. 240, 1.2: for note No. '17' read '18'.
P. 246, 9th line up: 6th word is 'Outwood'.
P. 249, 1.7 at end: for 'p. 54' read 'pl. 54'.

I am indebted to R. Hawksley for the following notes:

Pp. 56-7. The windmill in the view of the remains of Bermondsey Abbey was Poupart's. Mill (5), the tower mill, stood in Rotherhithe.

P. 77. Cheam mill was evidently on a building seen on the first O.S. 1:2500 map, but gone by the 2nd edition.
P. 78. The map by Senex (1729) proves a windmill site in Chertsey.
P. 93. Croydon: White Mill is shown on the revised first O.S. 1in. map.
P. 107. Frimley: land tax returns refer to York Town watermill.
P. 203. 'Newington windmill' was in Southwark; Widflete mill was a tide mill.
P. 226. Wimbledon: site (1) was in Putney parish.
P. 268. Addenda: for Oxted read Tandridge. Windlesham windmill is shown on a map of the Surrey Hills on a scale of 6in. to 1 mile made in the 1860s.

Michael Short, in his *Windmills in Lambeth: an historical survey*, published by the London Borough of Lambeth, 1971, put on record the fruits of intensive research. With the help of new source-material he was able, with caution, to propose the re-allocation of the 'Drug' mill and the two neighbouring smock mills between the three closely-grouped sites near Lambeth Palace, and to discount as fictitious the representation of the Thames in the water-colour by Paul Sandby (*c* 1780), which features the 'Drug' mill. It was this view especially which led Martin Mason and myself to our particular conclusions. Short assigns the 'Drug' mill to the S.E. position, having decided that the tall smock mill stood at the N. site, off Juxon Street (formerly Mill Street), and that the third mill — Orchard's, 1828, revealed as of smock type in the re-discovered sepia drawing by John Buckler — was at the S. site near Whitgift Street.

Since publication of *The Windmills of Surrey and Inner London* in 1966, the following items of information have emerged from correspondence:

An undated water-colour by John Linnell (1792-1882) entitled 'A View in Surrey', in the possession of J. C. Wolton, of Little Saxham, near Bury St Edmunds, Suffolk (1969), shows two post mills standing as a pair. These must represent one of the three pairs which stood at Tadworth, Coulsdon Common, and Cockshot Hill (Reigate). The scene, as drawn, suggests the Reigate district, but there is some difficulty in reconciling the likely date of the painting with the uncertain date of disappearance of one of the mills, presumed to have been before 1845.

In printing some old negatives in 1969 held by Carshalton library, M. J. Wilks, of the Carshalton Society, discovered one made of a painting depicting a post mill labelled Short's Windmill. This mill has not been identified, but there remains the possibility that it once stood in Carshalton, for the other views were of local subjects. Mr Wilks also noted references to Carshalton Windmill in rate books during the years 1803-12.

In a letter dated 24.8.1968 from D. W. Muggeridge to M. T. Mason, Mr Muggeridge wrote: 'You make no mention, I notice, of the third mill at Chiddingfold . . . the one just of Pockford Road. It stood on a rise at the back of the house where George Curtis, for many years Parish Clerk, lived, and a good many years ago, he once walked with me to point out the precise site, although there was no trace to be seen'.

In a letter to the authors, dated 3.1.1969, Roland W. Smith stated that there was a complete Blackmore bolting cloth in the Science Museum, London. (See p. 218, lines 5, 30.)

In a letter dated 3.4.1967, Frank Gregory, referring to the quotation regarding an alleged mill move from Blechingley to Ifield, Sussex (p. 268, Addenda), stated that H. E. S. Simmons, from whom the information was derived, wished to correct 'Cox Hill' to 'Cucksey's Farm'. R. Hawksley considers the allegation of a move to be false.

In a letter dated 29.8.1969, Robert White, of Upper Gatton, drew my attention to Windmill Field — so named locally — at N.G.R. 52611525, whose crest lies a few yards east of the Reigate-Sutton road (A217), and between the M25 and Gatton Bottom Lane. Mr White reports that ploughing turned up the remains of a flint path from the field entrance to the south, and also flints at the summit. An independent letter of 5th August, 1973, from D. J. Turner, of Reigate, secretary of the Surrey Archaeological Society, requested information regarding the site. Mr Turner referred to the same Windmill Field, which was cited in a Justices' Order of 1756 (Surrey Arch. Coll. XLI (1933) 32) and also mentioned an aerial photograph taken in 1970 by the R.C.H.M. showing a large circular crop-mark about 60ft. in diameter with no sign of markings within. It seems likely that the crop-mark and the presumed windmill site are coincident, and this point may have since been clarified.

Jeremy Greenwood, of Reigate, sent information in December, 1974, on the windmill marked by Aubrey (c 1700) on his map as standing a little east of the stream flowing south across what is now the centre of Redhill: 'A description of the manor of Frenches, when it was sold in 1610, includes "woodland of 19 acres called Combers Charte with the windmill thereon". This field is shown by a 1623 survey of the manor of Reigate and an 18th-century estate map, to be on the south side of the Redhill — Nutfield road, about where Chanctonbury Chase is today. There is unfortunately no further reference to it. (Document in Surrey Record Office ACC 212/87/3)'. The site described is at N.G.R. 52851500 on Redstone Hill, and admirably positioned for wind.

The publisher, Charles Skilton, sent the following:

In the *Wimbledon and Merton Annual No. 3* (1905) pp. 148-9, the origins of the existing windmill on Wimbledon Common are outlined, and it is stated that the use of the mill for corn grinding ceased some time before 1866.

In 1975 the *Wimbledon News* printed a photograph of the grand-daughters of the miller Anthony Hallaway (confirmed as the correct spelling) stated to have been at Wimbledon Common windmill from 1825 to 1830. These descendants, who were on a visit to the windmill, were Mrs Bertha Bridgland, aged 96, and her 94-year-old sister, Miss Amy Hallaway, both of Horsham. A £20,000 appeal by the Commons Conservators for renovation of the mill was also mentioned.

Enquiries of the Hallaway family by Charles Skilton elicited no new facts regarding the windmill, which now houses a mill museum.

Surrey Archaeological Society, Castle Arch Museum, Guildford, is understood to have 16 photographs of Surrey windmills taken by K. W. E. Gravett between 1930 and 1939.

An exhibition of works by the artist Thomas Girtin (1775-1802) was held at the Victoria and Albert Museum in April, 1975. It included views of windmills, also illustrated in the catalogue, listed as: No. 25 Westminster and Lambeth; No. 60 The White House, Chelsea.

Holmwood Common: In Sotheby's (Belgravia) sale of paintings on July 7th, 1975, there was a good picture of Holmwood Common with windmill by Alexander Fraser, F.S.A. (1786-1865). It was illustrated in the catalogue.

In searching files of the *Chelmsford Chronicle* for information on Essex windmills, I chanced upon the items below, which are probably recorded in other local newspapers, and for which I give the references only:

14.5.1819 p. 1, col. 2. Lease: appears to refer to Brixton Hill mill.

31.5.1822. p. 2, col. 3. Reports a fatality at a Battersea windmill, evidently the smock mill at the Red House.

17.4.1818. p. 1, col. 3 and 3.8.1827. p. 1, col. 2: sale notices referring to Lambeth windmills.

K. G. FARRIES

Norman G. Brett-James' volume, *The Growth of Stuart London*, depicts the Mount Mill Fort copperplate of 1643, noted in Farries & Mason, p. 234, and locates a number of central London 17th-century windmills in the various maps. The book was published in 1935 by George Allen & Unwin for the London & Middlesex Archaeological Society.

The first Girtin picture mentioned in Mr Farries' notes above, which was taken from the south end of Blackfriars Bridge, is illustrated also in Lindsay Stainton's *British Landscape Watercolours 1600-1860*, and dates from near the end of the artist's life in 1802. The volume was published by the British Museum.

Scott Wilcox's book, published in New York (Hudson Hills Press, 1985), entitled *British Watercolors, Drawings of the 18th and 19th Centuries from the Yale Collection*, also depicts a distant London windmill. Since Westminster Abbey appears both in this and the Girtin picture it is possible to decide that here is a different mill from those in the other painting.

This water-colour is by Samuel Hieronymous Grimm, and is of Kennington Common, 1776.

Mills were popular subjects with 18th- and 19th-century artists, but research among such pictures, often privately held, is difficult and has still been little done. There was of course a chapter on the subject in Farries & Mason, and I had a contribution in the 40th Volume of the Old Water-Colour Society's Club, 1965, on 'Windmills and Watermills in Water-colour' which illustrated *inter alia* the smock mill at Battersea by David Cox (1783-1859), the original of which is in the National Museum of Wales at Cardiff, and the impressive Randall's Mill, Nine Elms in the Brighton Art Gallery, by John Varley (1778-1842). A recent discovery of mine was an unnamed Surrey Mill, dated

1873, by Harry Hine, at Norwich Castle Museum, and this is here illustrated.

Likewise there is scope for research into old picture postcards, though the first British ones were not published until 1894. The next twenty years were the "Golden Age", when very many thousands of local views were issued, providing nowadays opportunity for local history pictorial discovery. The Post Office did not allow until 1902 the address side to be divided to allow for a written message as well.

In response to my enquiry, Mr Farries mentioned to me, incidentally, that he had not investigated the records of the former Greater London Council in respect of any mill matters.

CHARLES SKILTON

'Finis coronat opus'